AN INTRODUCTION TO
COMPUTER-AIDED DESIGN

PRENTICE-HALL SERIES IN ENGINEERING DESIGN

JAMES B. RESWICK, *editor*

FUNDAMENTALS OF ENGINEERING DESIGN

Introduction to Design—*Asimow*
An Introduction to Computer-Aided Design—*Mischke*
Engineering Communications—*Rosenstein, Rathbone, and Schneerer*

STUDIES IN ENGINEERING DESIGN

Shock and Vibration Concepts in Engineering Design—*Crede*
Wear Considerations in Design—*Lipson*

SERIES IN ENGINEERING DESIGN—BOOKS NOW IN PREPARATION

Fundamentals of Engineering Design   *Studies in Engineering Design*

Systems Engineering in Design   Appliance Design—*Woodson*
—*Besserer and Burnett*   Gears—*Richardson*

PRENTICE-HALL INTERNATIONAL, INC. *London*
PRENTICE-HALL OF AUSTRALIA, PTY. LTD. *Sydney*
PRENTICE-HALL OF CANADA, LTD. *Toronto*
PRENTICE-HALL OF INDIA PRIVATE LTD. *New Delhi*
PRENTICE-HALL OF JAPAN, INC. *Tokyo.*

AN INTRODUCTION TO

COMPUTER-AIDED DESIGN

CHARLES R. MISCHKE

Professor of Mechanical Engineering

Iowa State University

PRENTICE-HALL, INC., Englewood Cliffs, N.J.

Library of Congress Catalog Card Number 68-15843

Printed in the United States of America

Current Printing (last digit):

10 9 8 7 6 5 4 3 2 1

to Margaret, Thomas, and James

PREFACE

The computer can be an engineer's very capable apprentice, which, once instructed, can display recall, speed, accuracy, and endurance superior to human capabilities in these areas. The time-shared mode of computer operation greatly telescopes the delay between the time of the understanding of a problem and the event of obtaining an answer. The development of time-sharing invites engineers to utilize the rapid turnaround and the apparent conversational form of man-computer interaction, neither of which are feasible with the batch mode of computer operation. As the hardware and software bases of the limited utilization of the computer by engineers slowly diminish, we find ourselves moving from a time when some engineers *can* use the computer to the time when most engineers *must* use it.

The utilization of the computer in engineering design requires more than a knowledge of FORTRAN. It requires an understanding of the design process itself as well as its computer adaptation. It does not require a knowledge of machine coding or exotic algorithms for implementing numerical methods. A basic approach to the problem of engineering use of the computer for engineering design purposes is contained in this volume. The approach employed is *independent* of the language used, although FORTRAN is the language of this volume. The approach employed is also *independent* of the particular computer utilized, although examples were processed on the IBM 360.

The purpose of the first chapter of the book is to examine what the computer and the engineering design process have in common. The need to simulate the marketplace is the mother of the notion of the figure of merit. The second chapter discusses the figure of merit in its simplest terms. Then, less simple candidates for the figure of merit, such as cost, design factors, reliability, and time, are examined. Finally trade-off functions and the influence of qualitative factors on the location of the extreme of the figure of merit function are considered.

The third chapter examines the computer requirements in engineering design. The choice of language, control of format, subroutines, documentation, and error messages are discussed. The fourth chapter examines the problem of the pursuit of the extreme of the figure of merit function. Some simple linear sequential searching schemes suitable to one-dimensional functions are examined. The multidimensional space problem is discussed from gradient, pattern, and grid search viewpoints.

At this point the reader can appreciate the problems associated with computer implementation of engineering design problems. Chapter 5 introduces the reader to the IOWA CADET algorithm, displays its anatomy, and applies its stratagem to the solution of some example problems. The fundamentals learned in the first four chapters are applied in a step-by-step fashion to a sequence of problems of increasing dimensional complexity.

After reading the book the reader should have a clearer conception of how to approach his engineering problems so that he will be able to enlist the aid of the computer much more effectively than he can at present. The strategy of IOWA CADET can be used to develop one's own capability for coping with engineering design problems by using the digital computer.

The book was developed from notes written to supplement lectures in a course entitled "Introduction to Computer-Aided Design" offered in the Mechanical Engineering Department of Iowa State University. The illustrations were kept simple so as to avoid having engineering complications obscure computer consideration or the methodology that facilitates computer-aided design work. Simplicity of example also encourages use of the material by any engineering discipline.

If this book is used as a companion text in a first course in computer programming for engineering students, it is recommended that reading assignments in the first three chapters be woven into the sequence of programming assignments. If course time permits a look at linear search and examination of a linear search example from Chapter 5, so much the better. If this book is used as a supplementary text in a sequence of design courses, background assignments will help the student appreciate the methods used by the instructor in the part of his exposition that incorporates the computer.

The book is specifically written to be used as a text in a course that constitutes an introduction to computer-aided design. Excursions into the fascinating world of design can be made in many directions, and the only limitation on experience is imposed by considerations of time and instructional initiative. The emphasis can be varied to meet a wide variety of educational objectives. The examples chosen for illustration are sufficiently simple that any engineering discipline can be served.

The author appreciates both the opportunity to experiment in this facet of engineering education and the latitude in this work extended to him by Prof. Henry M. Black, chairman of the Mechanical Engineering Department at Iowa State University. He is also mindful of the assistance of Mrs. Sandra Emmert, who typed, duplicated, and collated the notes for student use. The cooperation of the Computation Center of Iowa State University in processing the programs presented herein and supporting their development is gratefully acknowledged.

C.R.M.

Ames, Iowa

CONTENTS

Appendix, 161

chapter

1

ENGINEERING DESIGN
AND THE DIGITAL COMPUTER

1.1 INTRODUCTION

The word *design* has several meanings in general English usage and therefore is open to many interpretations. Among these meanings are (as a verb):

1. to designate;
2. to assign or set apart as for a purpose or end;
3. to plan mentally, to conceive of as a whole, completely or in outline;
4. to fashion according to plan, to draw, to picture, to delineate, to model;
5. to proportion and plan, as in the parts of a machine or structure so that all requirements are satisfied.

Since *design* is a common word and not all possible meanings are apropos in engineering, it is common to prefix the adjective *engineering* and speak of *engineering design*.

Since the principal purpose of the engineer is to design, a definition of *engineer* is also germane. An engineer plans or controls (i.e., designs) the interaction between energy, matter, men, and money in order to accomplish a specified purpose optimally. The usual product of an engineering effort is a *service*. Although this service is not usually performed to produce a single economic object, there are examples of this. Plans for a singular structure, a single petroleum refinery, a unique ship, or an urban mass-transport system fall into this category. More commonly the service provides a plan for duplicating objects which meet a specified need. Such mass-produced objects as millions of barrels of detergent or gasoline, thousands of locomotives, airplanes, tractors, or radios, millions of yards of cloth,

1

or millions of kilowatt-hours of electrical energy, delivered where needed and at the demand of the user, are examples of the second or more common service—i.e., products replicated from the implemented plans of engineers.

Engineering design, because it requires accurate prediction and some attempt at optimization, therefore becomes a complicated synthesis of technological, social, and economic factors. When needs are slow to appear and demands for change are modest, designs are marked by a slow, steady improvement that may be characterized as *evolution*. The development of the steam turbine, telephonic communication, and the electric-power utility are examples. When needs are more urgent the thread of development is not along a single (or perhaps not even dual) line, but along a multiplicity of avenues. Computers, data recorders, satellites, and school buildings are examples. Development under these circumstances might be characterized as *innovation* or *revolution*.

In the first set of circumstances the path toward optimality is slow and deliberate, but steady. In the second situation later solutions may be further from optimality than previous ones, but in the urgency of the associated market, these "false steps" are skillfully shrouded in fads, new styles, and glamour to distract the customer besieged by a multiplicity of alternatives,

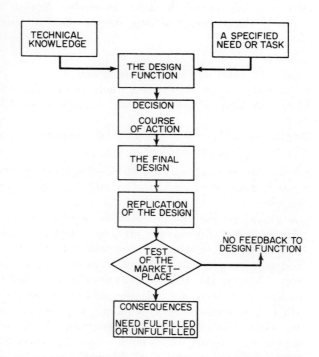

FIG. 1. A macroscopic view of the design process in the absence of feedback from the marketplace.

inadequate time to evaluate, and the pressure to make a quick decision.

The engineering designer is called upon to function in both of these environments. How should he proceed?

1.2 MORPHOLOGY OF DESIGN

There is no more *a* philosophy of engineering design than there is *a* philosophy of science, *a* philosophy of architecture, or *a* philosophy of art. Successful designers adapt their skills and attitudes to the problem at hand and, over a long period of time, outperform their competitors in meeting the test of the marketplace.

An "open-loop" design pattern may appear as depicted in Fig. 1. If no information concerning performance in the marketplace can be returned to the designer, then shortcomings cannot be corrected and triumphs cannot be related to judgments. A designer operating in such an environment can too easily encounter disaster.

Suppose a feedback loop is added as depicted in Fig. 2. In an evaluatory

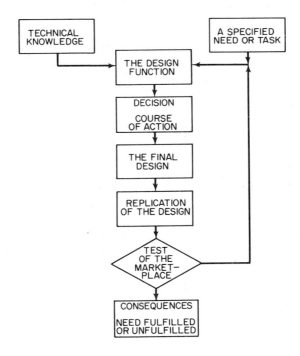

FIG. 2. A macroscopic view of the design process in the presence of feedback from the marketplace.

3

design situation such a feedback might be all that is required to make small modifications that will improve the marketplace performance. The efficiency of a pump, turbine, or compressor might be slowly upgraded over the years as competitors expend resources in order to improve their market potential. Feedback from declining sales can spur the improvements in design.

Because the marketplace exists only for a short span of time, as needs become more pressing, rewards go to those with the best design delivered to the marketplace before the expiration of the time span. In such a situation marketplace feedback might involve only two signals: *yes* (success) and *no* (failure). There is often no opportunity to use this feedback.

When great amounts of capital and other resources must be committed before any information from the marketplace is available, then other feedbacks must be sought and utilized. The marketplace must be simulated as realistically as possible by a testing and evaluation procedure.

Figure 3 shows a magnification of the DECISION block of Fig. 2. A magnification of the DECISION block might reveal that tentative decisions are made which result in preliminary design, construction of pilot models and/or subassemblies, test of prototypes and/or subassemblies by actual construction or modeling (simulation). The results modify the decision and the preliminary design until tests are passed and the "successful" tentative decision becomes the final decision.

Close scrutiny of every step in the design process reveals feedbacks and interactions, indicating the hopelessness of attempting a *fine* view of the design process. The important point, however, is that evaluative procedures *can* occur at *all* steps of the design process. They may or may not be necessary at a particular step, depending upon the problem.

The engineer faced with competition in a marketplace that will not, or cannot, give him meaningful feedback in time to avert disaster or improve his competitive position is not faced with a hopeless task. A

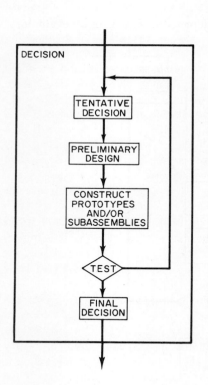

FIG. 3. A magnification of the DECISION block of the design process.

4

stratagem is available to him, although the specific tactics used to attain his goal are up to him, inasmuch as no formalism with universal validity is known.

The stratagem is to produce the design that excels all others. But is that not the goal of all his competitors? And if so, how can he compete? If the design is one that *cannot* be improved upon, then his competitors have a real problem (this is the optimum problem to hand a competitor). What design cannot be improved upon? An optimal design. How does one find an optimal design? If your understanding of the problem is complete, you simply come up with it the first time. If your understanding is less than complete, you generate many alternatives and select the best as approximating optimality. Alternatives do not grow on trees. They require creative imagination at best and much work and drudgery at worst. The first takes time and talent (and therefore money), and the second takes time and staffing (and therefore money). Proceeding along the road toward optimality is a journey of continuously increasing cost.

Where does one stop? Ahead of all competitors. Where is that? This is a very good question, one which haunts all men in positions of corporate responsibility.

The advent of the computer was a development with far-reaching consequences in design. Computers are used, and have been used since their inception, for analysis, since they calculate with speed and accuracy and without fatigue. The impact of the computer on engineering design has so far been small. The exploitation of its potential in this field is only beginning. The development of the time-sharing mode of operation and remote access to large computers will eventually lead to the growth of a *computer utility* (not unlike the electric-power utility) and will provide even small engineering offices with remote access to the largest computers available. The use of these computers by some to improve their competitive position will result in their use by all. Large computers simply attract large problems.

The engineering graduate of today will function in a professional world in which the computer is an integral part of the design process. It is important for the new engineer to be aware of what is known to be possible, for he will be called upon to use his knowledge, imagination, and creativity to make even more possible.

The employment of the computer in engineering design is and will remain an art for some time to come. If an experienced designer can look at a required wing-airfoil body and, on the basis of his experience, make decisions concerning structural patterns and design a wing that is nearly optimal (against some criterion such as weight), then what is the economic worth of knowing precisely the optimal structural configuration? When that question is answered, then we know what amount of additional resources can be committed in discovering optimal parameters. If the original design

5

effort is measured in man-years and a redesign effort (to vary parameters in a search for optimality) is measured in man-months, how many redesigns may be attempted? A half-dozen might double design costs without finding the optimum. Can a computer do the redesigns quickly and at less cost than manual redesigns? If it can, then *whatever* the allowable expense in the pursuit of optimality, the computer will win an economic position in the design process.

To design is to specify precisely how a task is be accomplished. *To specify* requires creativeness and understanding. *Understanding* is based upon experience and codified in analysis, using mathematical deductive and empirical techniques. If a designer proceeds as follows, i.e.,

1. defines his problem in quantitative terms;
2. decides how he will recognize a suitable solution;
3. decides how he will recognize solution merit and order his solutions accordingly;
4. generates alternatives (solutions);
5. through analysis discards unsuitable alternatives and retains suitable alternatives;
6. chooses the solution with highest merit from those found;
7. and makes a decision and implements it;

then he is proceeding in a manner completely compatible with the capabilities of the digital computer.

The box labeled TENTATIVE DECISION in Fig. 3 might be enlarged to reveal an anatomy as depicted in Fig. 4. The black boxes in the figures relate to things that should be done and indicate the sequential logic; but, alas, they say nothing about how to accomplish the functions. They display a design stratagem only. The tactics must be supplied by the designer to accommodate the stratagem to the problem immediately at hand.

1.3 DIGITAL COMPUTER CAPABILITY

What can a computer do? It can add, subtract, multiply, divide, and perform a host of other concerted actions which we can simply call *calculation*. Calculations may be performed with great speed, with great accuracy, and without the slightest indication of fatigue.

Is this capability useful to the designer? Certainly in the analysis phase of design, when programming and service costs can be economically justified.

But the fundamental and critical activity in design is *decision-making*. Can the computer make decisions? The computer can take a direction and make logical decisions of the following kinds:

6

1. It can take a direction to the extent of transferring control to a given location in the logic flow diagram of the program, regardless of the circumstances (the unconditional GO TO statement).
2. It can make a quantitative comparison and—depending upon whether a mathematical expession is positive, negative, or zero—will branch in its logic and undertake a different course of action for each possibility (the IF statement).
3. It can make a quantitative determination and undertake a number of different courses of action depending upon the value of a mathematical quantity (the computed GO TO statement).

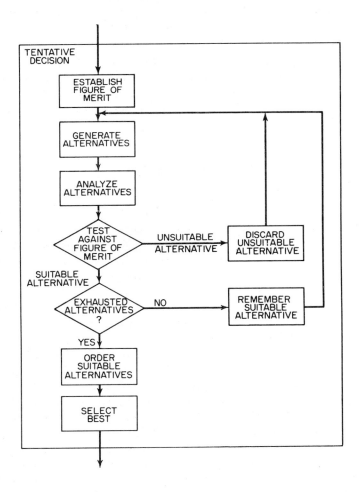

FIG. 4. A magnification of the TENTATIVE DECISION block within the DECISION block of the design process.

4. It can perform a calculation or a routine of calculation iteratively any specified number of times (the DO statement).
5. It can read and write alphanumeric information.
6. It can make decisions based on the truth or falsity of a statement and proceed on a logic path dependent upon that determination (the Boolean algebraic capability).
7. It will remember (store in memory and recall) quantitative and alphabetic information, and it will seem to remember how to do a specific task in which it has had prior experience (the SUBROUTINE capability).
8. It can draw—i.e., plot two-dimensional graphs—and, in the case of some computers, draw on a cathode ray tube to communicate with the designer (the graphical output capability).
9. It will start and stop on command, and also pause.

The computer has some decision-making capabilities. To the extent that the designer can reduce his decisions to combinations of the computer's decision capabilities, the computer can be "trained" to function as a capable "apprentice." In some respects, such as speed and consistency, it will excel its "master."

1.4 THE COMPUTER IN ENGINEERING DESIGN

Decision as a human endeavor is constantly occurring, even in individuals. Some decisions border on unconscious action—such as the placement of feet in walking or judging where to look next—but they are nonetheless decisions because alternatives are present; one is chosen, and the course of events is altered. Decisions may have a negligible or a profound impact on the course of events, depending on many factors; and the effect of a decision may be widespread or local. A decision to commit (and successful implementation of) suicide has enormous effect upon the principal, great effect on next of kin, witnesses, and friends; it may have no effect in a neighboring country or state. Whether a decision is good or bad is relative. A quarterback's decision to run around right end may be good for the team in terms of yardage gained, bad for the opposing team if it was a critical gain, and even worse for the right halfback who was injured running interference.

A decision is evaluated by the decision-maker and/or others who assess its contribution toward the attainment of the immediate and long-term objectives of the designer and his social system.

Implicit in the meaning of *decision* is the ability and opportunity to choose between, or among, alternatives: in order to have decisions there must be alternatives. Each alternative implies a variety of consequences. The advantages and disadvantages may be patently predictable, or they may be clouded with uncertainty, or they may never be observable. The ability to quantitatively assess the relative merits of alternatives is important to the use of the computer in design; indeed, it is essential to competitive design. Yet although it is necessary, it is not sufficient.

Creativeness—or call it inventiveness, or the uncanny knack of conceiving ways to do things—is the other ingredient essential to good competitive design. So far, creativeness has defied tutelage. We seek its presence or note its absence in a person, and provide what we think is an environment in which it will be nourished to fruitfulness. We can also caution against blocks to innovation, providing numerous examples, but we do not know how to teach creativeness as yet.

Can engineering design requirements, the capabilities of the digital computer, individual creative abilities, and decision-making skills be blended into a coherent and effective whole? Efforts in this direction are underway. A suitable one at the individual engineer's or project engineer's level is known as IOWA CADET (*Computer Augmented Design Engineering Technique*). Some elements of this algorithm constitute the subject matter of this book. The IOWA CADET algorithm is predicated on the following notions:

1. Meaningful competitive design is best accomplished when timely feedback is available from the marketplace. There are many situations in which the time available or the enormity of resources committed will not allow meaningful feedback from the marketplace to properly influence design decisions. Under these circumstances the influence of the marketplace upon design must be *simulated*. The vehicle of this simulation is the *figure of merit*.

2. A *figure of merit* is simply a number whose magnitude constitutes an index to the merit or desirability of a solution to a problem. (This is discussed in detail in Chapter 2.)

3. The figure of merit function is what the designer seeks to maximize, subject to many constraints placed upon him by nature; by law; by social, economic, and political factors; and by geometric and material considerations. (Chapter 4 is devoted to the optimization problem.)

4. If a designer proceeds as follows:
   (a) defines his problem in quantitative terms;
   (b) decides how he will recognize a suitable solution;
   (c) decides how he will recognize solution merit, and orders his solution accordingly;
   (d) generates alternatives (solutions);
   (e) through analysis discards unsuitable alternatives and retains suitable alternatives;
   (f) chooses the solution with highest merit from among those found to be suitable;

(g) makes his decision and implements it;

then he is proceeding in a manner completely compatible with the capabilities of the digital computer and the CADET algorithm.

5. Computer time and the engineering and programming time associated with a problem must be charged to design costs. If programming is carried out in the usual fashion of solving only the specific problem at hand, the number of projects in which computer assistance can be economically justified will be few. However, if programming is carried out in such a way as to be useful in other problems, then the unit costs decline and the number of applications of computer assistance will increase.

6. At the project engineering level it will be generally fruitless to wait for proprietary programs to be developed by talented organizations (such as computer manufacturers) because the number of general problems that can be solved by canned proprietary programs is, at best, limited to a small fraction of existing problems. It will be necessary for the individual engineer or engineering group to develop, in terms of their own knowledge of common and recurring problems, their own computer capabilities (programs).

7. Documentation of any capability of any size to be used by many different persons must be carefully structured so as to invite use— rather than deter it by erecting a structure bogged down in red tape.

Any engineering graduate should have a working knowledge of at least one algorithm suitable for implementing computer-aided design. He then will have a basis for deciding if computer assistance is feasible in a given situation.

The remainder of this book is devoted to helping the reader assimilate the pertinent background.

FIGURES OF MERIT

2.1 INTRODUCTION TO FIGURES OF MERIT

A *figure of merit* is simply a number whose magnitude is an index to the merit or desirability of a solution to a problem. It can range from a precise (accurate) one-to-one correspondence with merit to a Boolean (yes or no) index to satisfaction. When a single factor dominates a solution (say, weight), the construction of a *figure of merit function* (sometimes called a *utility function* or *object function* or simply a *merit function*) is simple. When a multiplicity of nonindependent factors vie for dominance, the fabrication of a valid and meaningful figure of merit may be difficult or, in terms of one's current knowledge, "impossible."

The fact that a figure of merit function is elusive is itself sometimes instructive of the vagueness present in the design situation. The need for competitive solutions to engineering problems is still imposed upon the designer and he must perform creditably in the face of many uncertainties, substituting skillful judgments for unavailable rigor.

The merit function is what the designer desires to maximize, subject to many constraints placed upon him by nature; by law; by social, economic and political factors; and by geometric and material considerations. Thus we take a set of parameters $x_1, x_2, \ldots, x_n$ which are in the final analysis variables in the merit function $M(x_1, x_2, \ldots, x_n)$ and by variation strive to maximize the merit function M. In this variation there are not n degrees of freedom, for there are functional relationships among parameters dictated by nature, economics, law, taste, available materials, and shapes. These functions may be m in number where $m < n$, which are written as

$$g_1(x_1, x_2, \ldots, x_n) = 0$$
$$g_2(x_1, x_2, \ldots, x_n) = 0$$
$$\cdot$$
$$\cdot$$
$$\cdot$$
$$g_m(x_1, x_2, \ldots, x_n) = 0$$

Some of the constraints upon the solution are such that a function can have a limited range or region of values. These, λ in number, are written

$$z_1 \leq f_1(x_1, x_2, \ldots, x_n) \leq Z_1$$
$$z_2 \leq f_2(x_1, x_2, \ldots, x_n) \leq Z_2$$
$$\cdot$$
$$\cdot$$
$$\cdot$$
$$z_\lambda \leq f_\lambda(x_1, x_2, \ldots, x_n) \leq Z_\lambda$$

The geometry of this problem is $(n + 1)$-dimensional, and is best visualized in a three- or less dimensional situation. Consider the following three-dimensional problem:

$$M = x_1 + x_2 \qquad \text{(merit function)}$$
$$x_2 = 2x_1 \qquad \text{(functional constraint)}$$
$$1 \leq x_1 \leq 10 \qquad \text{(regional constraint)}$$
$$2 \leq x_2 \leq 10 \qquad \text{(regional constraint)}$$

In this problem M is the merit surface, $x_1 = 2x_1$ is the functional constraint, and $1 \leq x_1 \leq 10$ and $2 \leq x_2 \leq 10$ are the regional constraints. In Fig. 5 the functional constraint appears as a line in the x_1x_2 plane and the two regional constraints define an area which is traversed by the functional constraint locus. The ordinates to the merit surface which can be examined for magnitude must be erected on the line $x_2 = 2x_1$ and within the rectangular region. The largest ordinate to the merit sufrace is erected at position (5, 10) in the x_1x_2 plane, and the magnitude of this ordinate is 15. Despite the three-dimensional geometry we had only one degree of freedom in optimizing M.

We can combine the merit function and the functional constraint and state the problem as

$$M = 3x_1 \qquad \text{(merit function)}$$
$$1 \leq x_1 \leq 5 \qquad \text{(regional constraint)}$$

The merit of a solution outside the allowable region is manifestly zero, so

12

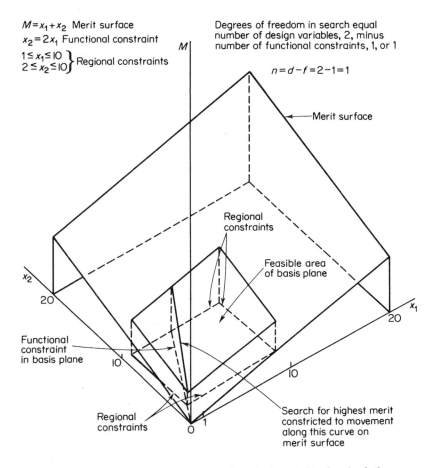

FIG. 5. The geometry of a merit surface in the neighborhood of the feasible region.

by introducing the unit step function $u(x)$ we can write

$$M = [u(x_1 - 1) - u(x_1 - 5)]3x_1$$

and we have geometrically the situation depicted in Fig. 6. This situation is ideal. A single function is to be evaluated. The merit is zero everywhere outside of the allowable domain. This equation, in which free variables may be inserted and appropriate merit calculated, is called a *formal figure of merit function*. If any one of the prior forms—i.e., $M = x_1 + x_2$ or $M = 3x_1$—is evaluated, a nonzero merit is obtained in forbidden regions. These expressions evaluated with a knowing hand are just as useful as

13

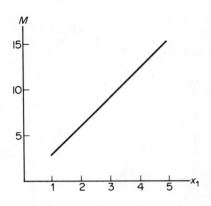

FIG. 6. The merit function with one design variable.

formal figure of merit functions, but they do not tell the entire story. They are therefore distinguished by being called *tactical figure of merit functions*.

Consider a fuse link that must be provided in an electrical circuit. Two constraints are imposed on the solution:

1. Ten amperes must be carried indefinitely.

2. The circuit must be broken by currents of eleven or more amperes.

A fuse link is either acceptable or unacceptable under these conditions.

A Boolean figure of merit is useful, i.e.,

$$M = [u(I - 10) - u(I - 11)]$$

where I is the lowest steady-state current ending in a broken circuit. The seven available alternatives are given in Table 2.1.

TABLE 2.1

Fuse Link	Lowest Steady-State Current Ending in a Broken Circuit, amp	Cost, dollars
A	9.7	0.0194
B	10.0	0.0200
C	10.3	0.0206
D	10.6	0.0212
E	10.9	0.0218
F	11.2	0.0224
G	11.5	0.0230

Fuse links B, C, D, and E have merit of unity and are admitted to the status of suitable alternatives. These alternatives *cannot be ordered* by a figure of merit M, sensitive to the two given constraints. However, if a third constraint is added, that the chosen link must be that of smallest cost, a merit function can be constructed which will order the alternatives. Since figures of merit are to be maximized and the cost minimized, cost has to be introduced into the merit function either as a negative quantity or as a reciprocal, i.e.,

$$M_1 = -[u(I - 10) - u(I - 11)] \text{ cost } (I)$$

14

or

$$M_2 = \frac{[u(I-10) - u(I-11)]}{\text{cost}\,(I)}$$

Table 2.2 displays the figures of merit.

TABLE 2.2

Fuse Link	M_1	M_2
A	0	0
B	−0.0200	50.0
C	−0.0206	48.5
D	−0.0212	47.3
E	−0.0218	45.9
F	0	0
G	0	0

Clearly, link B meets the requirements, but in the case of merit function M_1 adjustment is necessary to make zero merit appear as a large negative quantity lest the computer select alternative links A, F, and G as having the highest merit.

The advantage of M_1 (after repair) is that the difference in figures of merit for links B and C is the increase in cost of selecting link C in preference to link B—i.e., the incremental cost of violating merit ordering. The advantage of M_2 as a figure of merit is that it is positive and geometric thinking comes easier.

If the approach to a problem is to consider every possible solution, evaluate each solution's figure of merit, and order such figures of merit (as in Table 2.2), then the formal figure of merit has to be used. If the approach is to screen out unsuitable alternatives before evaluating figures of merit, then a tactical figure of merit may be utilized. The decision on which approach to use in a particular circumstance is influenced by the difficulty in evaluating the formal figure of merit for every case.

The concept of an abrupt "chop" to zero merit whenever a regional constraint is violated is helpful in understanding the geometric interpretation of a formal figure of merit function. For reasons associated with economy of search to be discussed in greater detail in Chapter 4, it is not always prudent to reduce the figure of merit to zero throughout the domain of violation of regional constraints.

In order to find, efficiently, the locale of the extreme of the figure of merit function, it will be desirable to assess the direction in which search should continue from the slope of the merit function in the neighborhood of a function evaluation. If in Fig. 6 the merit function were evaluated at $x_1 = 2$, then $M = 6$. One way to determine in which direction higher merit lies is to evaluate M at a neighboring position, say $x_1 = 2 + 0.001$.

In this circumstance the neighboring merit ordinate is 6.003. Figure 7 implies that it is probable that the search for increasing merit should proceed to higher values than $x_1 = 2$. In a sense, a geometric property of the merit function "points the way."

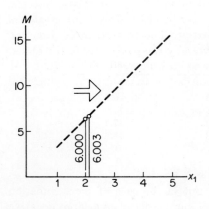

FIG. 7. The implied direction of search for superior merit is to the right of $x_1 = 2$.

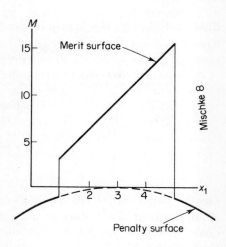

FIG. 8. Merit and penalty surfaces.

Suppose a regional constraint has been violated and a function evaluation is carried out at $x_1 = 6$ and $x_1 = 6 + 0.001$. The corresponding values of merit are $M = 0$ and $M = 0$. Which way should one proceed to find merit values exceeding zero? To avoid such confusion in situations wherein all regional constraints cannot be explicitly expressed, the Boolean "chop" is replaced by incorporating a penalty function which changes the formal figure of merit function from the geometry of Fig. 6 to one suggested by Fig. 8. Under these conditions the evaluation of the merit function outside the regional constraint at $x_1 = 6$ and $x_1 = 6 + 0.001$ will provide small negative values of merit with the direction to large values of merit clearly implied by the function geometry. More detailed consideration of this facet of construction of figure of merit functions occurs in Chapters 4 and 5.

2.2 SIMPLE PARAMETERS AS FIGURES OF MERIT

Perhaps the simplest merit function to compose occurs in cases that are stated, in part " ... provide a system to meet performance specifications $S_1, S_2, \ldots, S_n$ that is smallest in _____ ...." One can substitute for the blank such parameters as weight, mass, length, center-to-center dimensions, or inertia, to name a few. As long as the parameter displayed in the blank is a definite, deterministic quantity (no statistical variation) the procedure to be followed in composing a merit function is intuitively straightforward.

If the specifications are either passed or failed by candidate systems, then the remaining suitable alternatives may be ordered by finding tactical figures of merit for each suitable alternative. The tactical merit function need not supply a figure of merit that is literally the parameter in the blank. A quantity proportional to that parameter may be used. For instance, in the problem of discovering the dimensions of a right circular cylindrical can of volume V, made of a particular gauge steel and using the least metal, the *area* of the sheet metal blanks used to fabricate the can can be used in lieu of the mass or weight.

Figure 65 (p. 97) displays the can problem.

2.3 DESIGN FACTOR AS A FIGURE OF MERIT

Factors of safety under various names and definitions appear in many of the equations used in engineering design. Design factors, a generic term for this family of parameters, are possible candidates for tactical figures of merit, and are useful in ordering alternative solutions.

Disenchantment with the factor of safety actually provided by a design (sometimes being less than the number would imply) has led to the factor of safety being designated as a *design factor*, thereby eliminating the implied one-to-one correspondence with safety.

In a static situation, such as the tie rod in tension depicted in Fig. 9, a design factor might be defined as

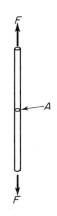

$$n = \frac{\text{ultimate load}}{\text{imposed load}} = \frac{F_u}{F} = \frac{S_u A}{F}$$

The above definition seems to imply that n is a definite number. However, the ultimate strength of the steel S_u is not a definite stress, but shows a statistical distribution as depicted in Fig. 10, as a histogram. The mean of the distribution is generally considered the ultimate stress S_u, i.e.,

$$S_u = \mu_s$$

Distributions of statistical data have various properties. One of these is the *expected value*.

FIG. 9. A simple tie rod in tension.

17

The expected value of the quantity S is defined as follows:

$$\text{Probability} \left| f(S_1) \right| f(S_2) \left| \ldots \right| f(S_k)$$
$$\text{Value of } S \left| \; S_1 \; \right| \; S_2 \; \left| \ldots \right| \; S_K$$

$$E(S) = S_1 f(S_1) + S_2 f(S_2) + \ldots + S_k f(S_k)$$

$$E(S) = \sum_{i}^{k} S_i f(S_i) = \mu_s$$

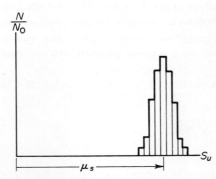

FIG. 10. A histogram of a test for the ultimate strength of steel.

It is clear that the expected value of the variable S is the population mean μ_s.

The *absolute mean deviation* of a distribution S with an expected value of μ_s is the expected value of $|S - \mu|$, i.e.,

mean absolute deviation of S

$$= E(|S - \mu|)$$

The *variance* of a distribution S is the mean squared deviation of S from its mean (second area moment about mean), i.e.,

$$\text{Var}(S) = E\left(|S - \mu|^2\right) = \sum_{i}^{k} (S_i - \mu)^2 f(S_i)$$

The *standard deviation* of a distribution S is the square root of the mean squared deviation of S from its mean (a radius of gyration from mean), i.e.,

$$\sigma_s = \sqrt{E\left(|S - \mu|^2\right)} = \sqrt{\text{Var}(S)}$$

Also

$$\sigma_s^2 = E(S^2) - \mu^2$$

The distribution of the ultimate strength of a material has attributes such as expected value, mean absolute deviation, variance, and standard deviation to describe its distribution. What value of S_u should be placed in the equation for n? An engineering sophomore will use the value of S_u found in a table of properties with a single entry and write

$$n = \frac{A S_u}{F}$$

18

What he is really writing is

$$n = \frac{AE(S_u)}{F}$$

Since the tie rod material could exhibit an ultimate strength less than μ_s, the design factor could overestimate the safety margin.

The applied force F might be a definite number (this rod is designed to carry a static load of 10,000 lbf) or it could be an indefinite number. For example, if a million tie rods were made to this design for the use intended, the *user* could apply loads other than 10,000 lbf and affect the safety margin. A general use presents the designer with a hopeless problem, so he adopts the *design load* concept. In such a case F is a definite number of his choosing, such as 10,000 lbf, and is advertised as the *design load*.

The indefiniteness of S_u is transmitted to n. The expected value of n is

$$E(n) = E\left(\frac{A}{F}S\right) = \frac{A}{F}E(S)$$

The variance of n is

$$\mathrm{Var}(n) = \mathrm{Var}\left(\frac{A}{F}S\right) = \left(\frac{A}{F}\right)^2 \mathrm{Var}(S)$$

The standard deviation of n is

$$\sigma_n^2 = \left(\frac{A}{F}\right)^2 \sigma_s^2$$

For $\mu_s = 50{,}000$ lbf/in.^{2}, $A = 1$ in.^{2}, $F = 10{,}000$ lbf, $\sigma_s = 1{,}000$ psi, the expected value of n is

$$E(n) = \frac{A}{F}E(S) = \frac{1}{10^4} \times 50{,}000 = 5$$

The standard deviation of n is

$$\sigma_n^2 = \left(\frac{A}{F}\right)^2 \sigma_s^2 = \frac{(10^3)^2}{10^8} = 0.01$$

$$\sigma_n = 0.1$$

What does this say about the variation of n? The probability of a value of n falling outside a range $\pm k\sigma$ from the mean for *any* distribution is equal to or less than $1/k^2$ (Bienayme-Chebyshev theorem). If the distribution of n has a single peak and a high-order contact with the abscissa at plus or minus infinity, then the probability of a value of n falling outside the range $\pm k\sigma$ from the mean is equal to or less than $1/2.25k^2$ (Camp-Meidell theorem). If the distribution of n satisfies the Camp-Meidell conditions, then the probability of an observation of n outside $\pm 3\sigma$ of the mean of n is equal to or less than

$$\frac{1}{2.25(3^2)} = 0.0494$$

We can say that 95 per cent of the observations of n will be in the range $4.7 < n < 5.3$. That is, the range 4.7 to 5.3 is laid down with 95 per cent certainty. When using n as a tactical figure of merit, its statistical attributes must be considered, because a comparison of means (expected values) may be misleading.

For the case of the mass-produced item (say the tie rod) that has a normal use where the imposed load has variations that can be assessed (the weight of a hand-pushed mine cart plus its heaping load of coal), then the effect of this variation on n can be assessed. Now

$$n = f(S, F)$$

$$\Delta n = \frac{\partial n}{\partial S} \Delta S + \frac{\partial n}{\partial F} \Delta F$$

If Δn represents a deviation from the mean of n, ΔS a deviation from the means of S, and ΔF a deviation from the mean of F, then for S and F independent

$$\frac{\partial n}{\partial S} = \frac{A}{F} = \frac{1}{10^4} = 10^{-4}$$

$$\frac{\partial n}{\partial F} = -\frac{AS}{F^2} = \frac{-1(50,000)}{10^8} = -5(10^{-4})$$

Now

$$\text{Var}\,(\Delta n) = \text{Var}\left(\frac{\partial n}{\partial S}\Delta S\right) + \text{Var}\left(\frac{\partial n}{\partial F}\Delta F\right)$$

$$\text{Var}\,(\Delta n) = \left(\frac{\partial n}{\partial S}\right)^2 \text{Var}\,(\Delta S) + \left(\frac{\partial n}{\partial F}\right)^2 \text{Var}\,(\Delta F)$$

$$\sigma_n^2 = (10^{-4})^2\sigma_S^2 + [5(10^{-4})]^2\sigma_F^2$$

If previous conditions apply and $\sigma_F = 10^3$, then

$$\sigma_n^2 = 10^{-8} \cdot 10^6 + 25(10^{-8})10^6 = 0.26$$

$$\sigma_n = \sqrt{0.26} = 0.51$$

If the Camp-Meidell conditions apply to the distribution of n, then 95 per

20

cent of the observations of n lie in the range $3.47 < n < 6.53$. Again, in the use of n as a tactical figure of merit, its statistical nature must be examined in order to interpret the meaning of the ordering of alternatives.

In hoisting operations using wire rope, the stresses in the rope arise from:

1. tension due to the load and load carrier;
2. tension due to the weight of rope;
3. bending about fair-leads, sheaves, or winch drum.

An "endurance limit" for wire rope running repeatedly (a million cycles) over a sheave is given by

$$F = \frac{S_u D d}{2000}$$

where

F = allowable tensile force in wire rope for a million flexures over sheave, lbf

S_u = ultimate strength of individual wires in rope, psi

D = sheave diameter, in.

d = rope diameter, in.

A design factor for quasistatic and repetitive cases can be defined as follows:

Quasistatic

$$n_s = \frac{\text{(rope ultimate strength)} - \text{(equivalent bending load)}}{\text{(rope tension)}}$$

$$n_s = \frac{F_a - F_b}{F_t}$$

Repetitive

$$n_f = \frac{\text{(rope endurance strength)} - \text{(equivalent bending load)}}{\text{(rope tension)}}$$

$$n_f = \frac{F_u - F_b}{F_t}$$

Notice that the design factors as defined above have a subtractive term present. Now

$$n_f = f(F_u, F_b, F_t)$$

$$\Delta n_f = \frac{\partial n_f}{\partial F_u} \Delta F_u + \frac{\partial n_f}{\partial F_b} \Delta F_b + \frac{\partial n_f}{\partial F_t} \Delta F_t$$

Now

21

$$\frac{\partial n_f}{\partial F_u} = \frac{1}{F_t}$$

$$\frac{\partial n_f}{\partial F_b} = -\frac{1}{F_t}$$

$$\frac{\partial n_f}{\partial F_t} = \frac{-(F_u - F_b)}{F_t^2}$$

and

$$\mathrm{Var}\,(\Delta n_f) = \frac{1}{F_t^2}\,\mathrm{Var}\,(\Delta F_u) + \frac{1}{F_t^2}\,\mathrm{Var}\,(\Delta F_b) + \frac{(F_u - F_b)^2}{F_t^4}\,\mathrm{Var}\,(\Delta F_t)$$

or

$$\sigma_n^2 = \frac{1}{F_t^2}\left[\sigma^2{}_{F_u} + \sigma^2{}_{F_b} + \frac{(F_u - F_b)^2}{F_t^2}\sigma^2{}_{F_t}\right]$$

Note that despite the *subtractive* nature of the numerator of the design factor equation, the effect of statistical variations in F_u and F_b on the standard deviation of n_f is *additive*.

2.4 COST AS A FIGURE OF MERIT

Cost is almost always an element in a merit function. It is not a simple element, due to the complex nature of economics. Money has a time value since human nature is such that most people would rather have a dollar today than the promise of a dollar at some future date. To lend money (and exchange a dollar now for more than a dollar later) is to postpone satisfactions that money can provide, and the charge for the postponement is *interest*. Interest is usually computed as a fraction of principal in a time interval, and varies with scarcity of money and the future outlook.

A corporation earning 5 per cent on its capitalization and considering a new company project must demand that the new enterprise return to the company at least 5 per cent for comparable risk, otherwise it would invest the money involved in other areas of the company where the demonstrated return is 5 per cent.

An element in cost is taxation, and the bases of taxation are many. A profit may be taxed, a throughput of a pipeline may be taxed, a ton-mile of transportation may be taxed, a payroll may be taxed. The tax situation must enter into the cost element of the merit function.

The merit of an enterprise may be viewed as the total payroll, or the total production, or the gross income, or the profit (before or after taxes) or the unit cost of production.

22

Accounting practices sometimes obscure the cost of an alternative. A man considers driving his car between city A and city B either directly or with a short detour for some purpose not connected with the trip. What is the cost of the detour? The accounting approach is to establish the cost of driving the car one mile and multiplying by the excess of miles involved in the detour. Is this the actual cost? The accounting approach indicates that at $.10 per mile for a 100-mile detour the cost is $10.00. Should not the cost be the difference in expenses between detouring and not detouring? This cost can only be obtained by doing it both ways, something we normally cannot or will not do. This cost difference is called the incremental cost and is equal to the costs of fuel and oil and any repair occasioned by the detour leg of the journey. It is probable that this cost is much less than $.10 per mile.

A classroom in a private school has 40 seats and a class of 20 is conducted in it. The course tuition is $100. What is the cost of adding another student? The accounting costs run as follows:

Instructor: $1,000
Room rental: $200
Student materials supplied by student

The $1,200 costs are prorated per student and amount to $60 per pupil. If one gets used to thinking in these terms, it is easy to say that of the additional tuition of $100, $60 is absorbed in costs and $40 goes into the cash drawer of the institution. In fact the difference in cost between having and not having the twenty-first student may be zero. The costs of registration and intramural paper work are zero if it will be done by registrar's and departmental offices that are not working to capacity. If the incremental cost of adding a student is zero, let us add more students. The problem comes when the class becomes too large to instruct, another classroom is needed, and a second instructor is required. The incremental cost associated with the student that forces sectioning of the course is very large indeed. The institution could afford to pay this student a considerable sum not to enroll! Incremental costs are more meaningful than accounting costs in considering alternatives.

Costs and probabilities often become related and are involved in decision and merit. Consider the wisdom of an inspection procedure in a situation in which the following is known: If a part is good, no incremental cost is incurred by the manufacturer; if a part is bad it is discovered at zero cost, but the cost of removing it from the assembly and replacing it with another part has been established as W dollars. Several alternatives confront the production department:

1. Continue as things have been—i.e., do nothing.
2. Install an inspection procedure which will detect $f_1(100)$ per cent of the bad parts and cost x dollars per part to place in effect.

3. Install an inspection procedure which will detect $f_2(100)$ per cent of the bad parts and cost y dollars per part to place in effect.
4. Install a perfect inspection procedure which will detect 100 per cent of the bad parts and cost z dollars per part to place in effect.

Table 2.3 exhibits the incremental costs of good and bad parts under each alternative.

TABLE 2.3

Alternative	Cost of a Good Part, dollars	Cost of a Bad Part, dollars
A (no inspection)	0	W
B (simple inspection)	x	$x + (1 - f_1)W$
C (complex inspection)	y	$y + (1 - f_2)W$
D (ultimate inspection)	z	z

The probability of picking a bad part from the assembly-line bin is p. The probability of picking a good part is $(1 - p)$. The expected incremental cost of alternative A is, per part,

$$E(A) = 0(1 - p) + Wp = Wp$$

The expected incremental cost of alternative B is, per part,

$$E(B) = x(1 - p) + [x + (1 - f_1)W]p = x + (1 - f_1)Wp$$

The expected incremental cost of alternative C is, per part,

$$E(C) = x(1 - p) + [x + (1 - f_2)W]p = x + (1 - f_2)Wp$$

The expected incremental cost of alternative D is, per part,

$$E(D) = z(1 - p) + zp = z$$

Figure 11 depicts a plot of unit incremental cost as a function of the probability of encountering a bad part p for all the alternatives. The heavier line represents segments of curves for alternatives offering least cost. Not only does the cost depend on the probability of a bad part, but the appropriate alternative is also a function of p. When the current probability is close to a shift in alternative, the future expectation of the value of the probability p must be considered in making a decision.

The term *risk* is usually used when odds are predictable. Underwriting life insurance policies involves risk, because mortality tables are available. The term *uncertainty* is usually used when the odds are not predictable. Uncertainty occurs in areas in which we have had no experience or understanding. The outcome of a war or a manned spaceflight involves uncertainty.

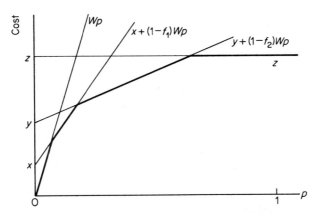

FIG. 11. The expected incremental cost of alternative inspection schemes plotted against the probability of encountering a bad part.

Where risk is involved, the expected value of a parameter can be useful, but this is not always the case. As an example let the risk be established at 0.5—i.e., the outcome, win or lose, is equally likely. Let the payoff also be known to be twice the wager upon winning and nothing upon losing. The expected value of the return is

$$E(\$) = 2x(0.5) + 0(0.5) = x$$

where x is the amount of money risked. The expected return is equal to the money committed. In an environment of alternatives yielding higher return, this investment has little merit. If the payoff is five times the investment and nothing upon losing, then the expected value of the return is

$$E(\$) = 5x(0.5) + 0(0.5) = 2.5x$$

or $2\frac{1}{2}$ times the investment. In an environment of alternatives yielding expected values of return in the neighborhood of $1.1x$, this opportunity might seem like an attractive investment. But if the amount of money risked were most or all of the resources of the investor, should the risk be assumed? A loss means bankruptcy. However favorable the return, the situation reduces itself to an all-or-nothing proposition. Thoughtful persons shy away from this investment, even with excellent odds on a favorable outcome. Can you ever risk ruin?

For small fractions of resources the expected return might qualify as a tactical merit function

$$m = E(\$) = n \, (1 + f) \, x$$

25

If one likes the idea of zero merit for a return equal to the committed capital, then the tactical merit function might be

$$m = E(\$) - (1 + f)x = (n - 1)(1 + f)\, x$$

where f is the current rate of return in the company. The merit function should also be made sensitive to the extent of resources, so that when R is risked, the merit is zero. A possible expression is

$$m = \left(1 - \frac{x}{R}\right)[E(\$) - (1 + f)x]\frac{1}{R} = (n - 1)(1 + f)\frac{x}{R}\left(1 - \frac{x}{R}\right)$$

where R is the extent of resources. Figure 12 displays this function. Note that this tactical merit function implies an optimum investment of one-half of resources, for any expected return.

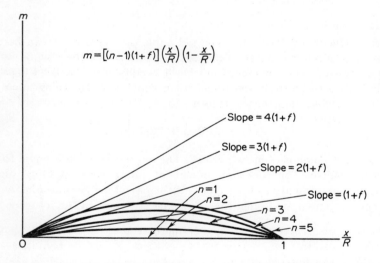

FIG. 12. A plot of a merit function sensitive to the fraction of resources x/R risked and sensitive to the available rate of return f within the company. The variable n is the number of times the usual rate of return that the expected return represents.

2.5 RELIABILITY AS A FIGURE OF MERIT

Engineers speak of the reliability of systems and the reliability of components. One definition of the reliability of a component is the probability that the component functions during the period it is summoned to perform.

26

Reliability of a component is a fraction that can be statistically determined by experiment. It is usually found to be a function of the age of the component. The reliability of a system or complex of components is often inferred from the reliability of its parts.

The probability of failure to respond to command is simply $(1 - R)$ where R is the reliability. A plot of failure rate vs. component age might look as depicted in Fig. 13. Three zones or intervals are recognized. The first is during the period of newness and is referred to as the *infant-mortality interval*. A second interval of fairly constant failure rate is observed; and since a reasonably uniform probability distribution is in evidence, the interval is referred to as the *random-failure interval*. The

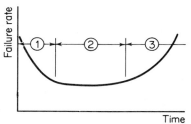

FIG. 13. The first domain is called the infant-mortality interval, the second domain is called the random-failure interval, and the third domain is called the wear-out interval.

last interval is that in which cumulative effects of wear begin to show, failure increases to intolerable levels, and the component is either repaired, rebuilt, or retired. This final interval is called the *wear-out interval*.

The reliability of a single bearing in particular circumstances might be R_1. The probability of failure is p_1 or $(1 - R_1)$, therefore

$$R_1 = (1 - p_1)$$

Similarly for the second bearing,

$$R_2 = (1 - p_2)$$

Considering the occurrence to be the functioning of the unit of two bearings, the probability of success is the product of the probabilities—i.e., the reliability of both bearings is

$$R = R_1 R_2 = (1 - p_1)(1 - p_2)$$

If the bearings are identical, the reliability can be expressed

$$R = (1 - p_1)^2$$

For the series system depicted in Fig. 14,

$$R = R_1 R_2 R_3 = (0.7)(0.8)(0.9) = 0.504$$

In general the reliability of a series system of components is

$$R = R_1 R_2 R_3 \ldots R_k$$

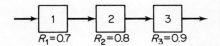

FIG. 14 A complex with components in series.

and for identical elements in series $R = R_1^k$.

If two components are provided on an either-or basis, such as boiler feedwater pumps (one active, one standby), then the situation may be depicted as shown in Fig. 15. The probability of both failing simultaneously (a simultaneous failure is necessary to a failure of a parallel complex) is the product of the failure probabilities of the individual components, i.e.,

$$p = p_1 p_2 = (1 - R_1)(1 - R_2)$$
$$(1 - R) = (1 - R_1)(1 - R_2)$$
$$R = 1 - (1 - R_1)(1 - R_2)$$

If the components are identical,

$$R = 1 - (1 - R_1)^2$$

In general, for a complex of parallel components,

$$R = 1 - (1 - R_1)(1 - R_2)\ldots(1 - R_k)$$

and for k identical components in parallel,

$$R = 1 - (1 - R_1)^k$$

For the parallel system shown in Fig. 16,

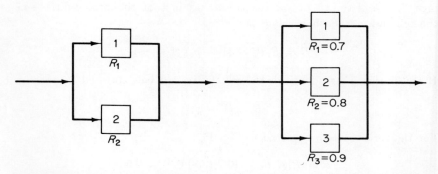

FIG. 15. A complex of two components in parallel.

FIG. 16. A complex of three components in parallel.

28

$$R = 1 - (1 - R_1)(1 - R_2)(1 - R_3)$$
$$R = 1 - (1 - 0.7)(1 - 0.8)(1 - 0.9)$$
$$R = 0.994$$

Notice that the reliability of a series complex is inferior to the individual component reliabilities, and the reliability of the parallel complex is superior to the individual component reliabilities. It is possible to build systems with overall reliability higher than that of the components by using parallel (redundant) arrangements. In high reliability complexes (such as military units or electric-power utilities), redundancy has been used for a long time. Although it is a costly procedure, it is often the only answer to a reliability problem.

Reliability may appear in a merit function as a specification—i.e., the reliability must equal or exceed R_1. In this circumstance it can be present as a Boolean factor. Reliability may itself be a tactical figure of merit, and the suitable alternatives are ordered according to reliability. As an example of the latter case, consider the problem of two elements

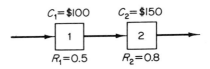

FIG. 17. A complex of two components in series.

in series as shown in Fig. 17. What redundancy pattern will produce the highest reliability if $550 is available for equipment? Component 1 is available at a cost of $100 with a reliability of 0.5, and component 2 is available at a cost of $150 with a reliability of 0.8. Figure 18 indicates the general redundancy pattern. Complex A consists of a parallel arrangement of components of type 1, and complex B consists of a parallel arrangement of components of type 2. For elements in parallel,

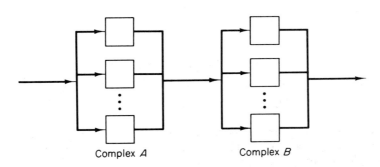

Complex A Complex B

FIG. 18. Two complexes in series whose individual components are in parallel.

29

$$R_A = 1 - (1 - R_1)^j$$
$$R_B = 1 - (1 - R_2)^k$$

where j is the number of components of type 1 in parallel and k is the number of components of type 2 in parallel. The system consists of complex A and complex B in series, and the system reliability R is given by

$$R = R_A R_B = [1 - (1 - R_1)^j][1 - (1 - R_2)^k]$$

The cost equation is expressed as

$$\$ = jC_1 + kC_2$$

where j and k are integers and $\$$ must be equal to or less than 550. The tactical figure of merit can be the system reliability R. Thus

$$m_{jk} = [1 - (1 - 0.5)^j][1 - (1 - 0.8)^k]$$
$$m_{jk} = (1 - 0.5^j)(1 - 0.2^k)$$

The exponents j and k are related through the cost equation and

$$j = \frac{550 - 150k}{100}$$

When

$$k = 1, \quad j = \frac{550 - 150(1)}{100} = \frac{400}{100} = 4$$

$$k = 2, \quad j = \frac{550 - 150(2)}{100} = \frac{250}{100} \cong 2$$

$$k = 3, \quad j = \frac{550 - 150(3)}{100} = \frac{100}{100} = 1$$

Now

$$m_{41} = (1 - 0.5^4)(1 - 0.2^1) = 0.75$$
$$m_{22} = (1 - 0.5^2)(1 - 0.2^2) = 0.72$$
$$m_{13} = (1 - 0.5^1)(1 - 0.2^3) = 0.496$$

The highest merit is exhibited by alternative $j = 4$, $k = 1$ with a cost of $\$ = jC_1 + kC_2 = 4(100) + 1(150) = 550$ dollars. The alternative of highest merit is displayed in Fig. 19.

The reliability of a component is very difficult to predict. It is usually determined by test. Reliabilities of systems can be inferred from reliabili-

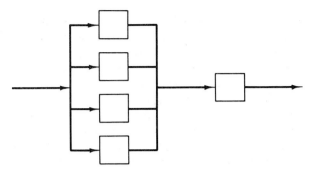

FIG. 19. The alternative with the highest reliability for a cost of $550 or less consists of the illustrated arrangement of four $R=0.5$ components in series with one $R=0.8$ component.

ties of components. Hence reliability is more often found in merit functions of systems than in merit functions of components.

2.6 TIME AS A FIGURE OF MERIT

Time can appear in a function of merit either implicitly or explicitly. Time assumes engineering importance either as absolute time (calendar time, as in a completion date) or relative time (interval time, as in a process time constant).

Absolute time is important when a market exists in the future up to a specified date. A corporation or governmental agency might accept bids, up to a specified date, to provide a system to meet definite specifications. Alternatives of superior quality will have to be discarded if the calendar time available to do the requisite engineering work is insufficient.

Relative time is important when a time interval in a system is critical. A company marketing equipment with a response time of 0.001 seconds, faced with future competition providing time constants of 0.0002 seconds, will make its merit function sensitive to response time. If there is only one way to accomplish a task for a specific application and response time is important, then a minimum of response time may be sought; and the response time, expressed negatively or reciprocally, can be the figure of merit.

Times other than cutoff dates can often be related to costs, and the time factors in a function of merit may appear as a cost. For example, if the processing time of a production element must be less than four days, a Boolean variable can assign zero merit to all alternatives exhibiting a processing time in excess of 4 days, and the cost of effecting the alternative (which involves process time) can be encoded into the merit function.

Consider the problem of specifying the gear ratio between the traction motors and the wheels of a subway or commuter train. If the system is being built with equipment having a gear ratio tailor-made for the service and the distance between stations is S, what is the optimal gear ratio to minimize time between stations, i.e., the start-to-stop time?

The d-c series traction motor has torque-speed characteristics as displayed in Fig. 20. At low speeds armature current is limited to permissible values by resistor banks and series and parallel electrical arrangements of motor wiring. During this controlled current period, the motor torque varies in a somewhat sawtoothed fashion, but its average is shown as the initial horizontal line in the diagram. The running characteristic is exhibited when full line voltage is across the traction motor.

A free body of the railway car is represented in Fig. 21. The principal forces during movement which affect train speed are the tractive efforts of the wheels and the drag forces. Presuming negligible inertia in the rotating parts (wheels, gears, and armatures), then from Newton's law,

$$F = \frac{W}{g}a$$

$$\frac{4nT}{R} - f(v) = \frac{W}{g}\frac{dv}{dt}$$

$$dt = \frac{WR\,d\omega}{g\left[4nT/R - f(v)\right]}$$

where W is the weight of the car and its passengers, a is the acceleration of the car, v is the velocity of the car, n is the stepdown gear ratio, T is the motor torque, R is the radius of the wheels, ω is the angular velocity of the wheels, and g is the gravitational constant. Figure 22 shows the train speed-time curve asymptotic to an ordinate called the *balancing speed*. This is the speed that would be obtained on level track in still air and is called the balancing speed of the equipment. There are other balancing speeds under conditions of grade, curvature, and line voltage.

The train will brake for the approaching station before attaining balancing speed. The braking in recently built equipment is initially dynamic braking, wherein the traction motors as electrical generators dissipate energy across resistor banks or deliver energy back to the third rail (overhead catenary). As the train slows, this braking effort fades and must be augmented by mechanical air brakes of conventional types. The distance from the station at which braking commences is a function of train speed, as is the duration of the braking phase. A superposition of the braking and accelerating curves is shown in Fig. 23. The area under the *v-t* curve is the distance traversed start to stop.

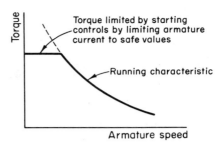

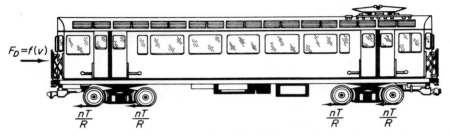

FIG. 20. Torque-speed characteristics of a typical d-c traction motor.

FIG. 21. Free-body diagram of an electrically propelled rapid transit car with four traction motors. Resistance to motion is due to bearing and rolling friction and aerodynamic drag, all of which are functions of vehicle velocity.

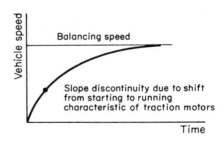

FIG. 22. On level tangent track in still air with constant line voltage, a rapid transit car will asymptotically approach a speed called the balancing speed. Several similar cars in train will exhibit a higher balancing speed than a single car.

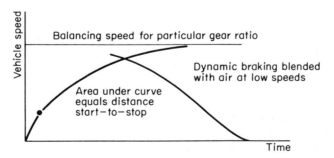

FIG. 23. The distance between stations can be shown to be the area under the speed-time curve.

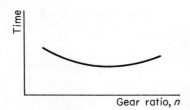

FIG. 24. The time start-to-stop will exhibit a minimum for some gear ratio n between the traction motor shaft and the axle of the car wheels.

Different gear ratios will lead to different acceleration curves on the *v-t* plot, and different train speeds will move the deceleration curve for service braking to the left or to the right, affecting the start-to-stop time. The designer charged with the preliminary design must relate start-to-stop times to the gear ratio. Clearly, a very high reduction ratio will involve a low balancing speed, and a long traveling time between stations. A very low reduction ratio will involve poor acceleration and attainment of low speeds on a short run and a long time elapsed between stations. At some intermediate gear ratio, a minimum start-to-stop time will be exhibited. Figure 24 suggests this.

This simple problem involves complicated integrations. It is admirably suited to computer solution. The possibility of simulating an entire route with variable station distances is open, and the minimum schedule time for an entire run might be the quantity sought. The effects of grade, curvature, speed limits at switches, junctions, and special track work can easily be introduced. If the equipment is to be used interchangeably in local and express (skipstop) service, then the optimum gear ratio associated with each service will be different. The use of trailers (nonpowered cars) affects the ratios also. The cost of power will differ and a compromise (trade-off) between cost of service and speed of service will have to be made.

2.7 TRADE-OFF FUNCTIONS

The engineer is constantly confronted with conflicting objectives. He tries to keep costs low, safety as well as capacity high, and meet a host of other specifications on gross size, compatibility with other equipment, etc. Clearly, safety increases cost, capacity increases cost. For a given budget, how shall he distribute safety and capacity? A marketplace appears wherein a certain amount of safety can be traded for a different amount of capacity. How will safety and capacity be measured? What is the legal tender of this marketplace? How can one establish values?

One approach is to think in terms of money. If, in a simple problem, cost is a function of design factor n and capacity C, then

$$\$ = f(n, C)$$

and

$$d\$ = \frac{\partial \$}{\partial n} dn + \frac{\partial \$}{\partial C} dC$$

The partial derivatives $\partial \$/\partial n$ and $\partial \$/\partial C$ must be examined. If it is more costly to increase the design factor when capacity is high and cost is directly proportional to design factor, then the derivative is

$$\frac{\partial \$}{\partial n} = aC$$

When the design factor is held constant and the capacity is varied, the increase in cost is proportional to the magnitude of the design factor, i.e.,

$$\frac{\partial \$}{\partial C} = bn$$

Substituting back into the differential relationship, we have

$$d\$ = aC \, dn + bn \, dC$$

Integrating the partial derivative $\partial \$/\partial n$, we obtain

$$\frac{\partial \$}{\partial n} = aC$$
$$\$ = aCn + f_1(C)$$

Integrating the partial derivative $\partial \$/\partial C$, we obtain

$$\frac{\partial \$}{\partial C} = bn$$
$$\$ = bnC + f_2(n)$$

The cost function determined either way is identical, i.e.,

$$aCn + f_1(C) \equiv bnC + f_2(n)$$

It follows from the property of an identity that $f_1(C) = 0$ and $f_2(C) = 0$ and that $a = b$. Therefore, setting $a = K$,

$$\$ = KnC$$

If the designer decides that the merit of the design is to be measured by the reciprocal of cost, then his tactical figure of merit becomes

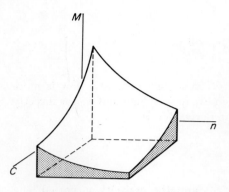

$$m = \frac{1}{\$} = \frac{1}{KnC}$$

If limitations are imposed, such as $n \geq 5$, $C \geq 5$ tons, and K is evaluated from the fact that the cost of one combination of design factor and capacity is known, say the cost of a $(n = 2.5,\ C = 4)$ crane hook is \$40, then $K = 4$ and

FIG. 25.   The merit surface M(n, C).

$$M = \frac{B_1(n)\,B_2(C)}{4nC}$$

where $B_1(n)$ and $B_2(C)$ are Boolean functions of n and C that are zero when $n < 5$ and $C < 5$. A plot of this merit surface is shown in Fig. 25.

For this example, the alternative with the highest figure of merit would be the one where $n = 5$ and $C = 5$. The extremum of the merit surface need not be a maximum or minimum in the calculus sense. A maximum or minimum found by a differentiation process is only occasionally the merit extremum sought.

The previously posed question of how much of a change in a design factor is equal in value to a change in capacity can be answered from the merit function. The change in n for a change in C at constant merit M is

$$n = \frac{B_1(n)\,B_2(C)}{4CM}$$

$$\frac{\partial n}{\partial C} = \frac{\Delta n}{\Delta C} = \frac{-B_1(n)\,B_2(C)}{4C^2 M}$$

or

$$\Delta n = \frac{-B_1(n)\,B_2(C)\Delta C}{4C^2 M} = \frac{-\$\Delta C}{4C^2}$$

For an increase in capacity C, the equivalent change in the design factor (the change of equal merit) is given above. The Boolean functions may be replaced by unity, or left in, as suits the engineer. The meaning of a zero Boolean function is that you are outside the marketplace and trades are meaningless.

The above function is called a *trade-off function* by some engineers. Since it is deducible from the merit function, in a way, the merit function itself is a trade-off function.

Cost (as a negative or reciprocal quantity) makes a natural figure of

36

merit; and the contributions of all other elements may be assessed by thinking in terms of dollars, one variable at a time. There are situations in which the principal attention is focused upon another parameter and cost is subordinate, although not completely out of the picture: it may be considered to be "hovering" in the background holding a veto power. In aircraft design, a minimum-weight wing structure for a specified aero-dynamic wing body is a desirable commodity, but not an infinite cost to discover the optimal parameters. Cost may hover in the background as a Boolean variable (cost may not exceed available resources), and the figure of merit allowed to increase until the Boolean "chop" is exercised.

Engineering costs are overhead on the production of products, and the optimal framing configuration of structural steel for a building (minimizing the weight of steel present) may be so costly that an experienced designer's judgment in getting within 15 per cent of optimal weight may be a cheaper alternative to an optimal solution and its cost.

Let us take the case of a motor-driven pump (cost $1,000) with a reliability of 0.9, which can be improved to a reliability of 0.99 by a single redundancy, and associated valves, piping, and controls, for a total of $3,000. A designer knows, in considering the development of a single motor-driven pump with a reliability of 0.99, that the market value of this pump cannot exceed $3,000. Here is a direct market reading on the dollar worth of reliability. The improvement in reliability from 0.9 to 0.99 is worth only $2,000 in the marketplace.

An approach to the creation of a figure of merit function should be clear at this point; however, the responsibility for generating a meaningful figure of merit lies with the designer, using all the inputs available to him and incorporating the line decisions of management.

2.8 QUALITATIVE PARAMETERS IN FIGURES OF MERIT

How does one construct a figure of merit for the taste of tea, for the beauty of an automobile, for the lines of a ship, for the convenience of use, for consumer eye-appeal? The answer is that we have not yet discovered how.

Suppose a qualitative factor—novelty of approach—is to be a factor in a figure of merit. One approach to the problem is to construct a figure of merit including all quantitative elements of merit, and order the solutions according to decreasing merit with the cost of each alternative tabulated alongside.

The designer must now introduce the factor of novelty of approach. Taking alternative solutions one by one, he must ask himself (or other competent persons) if the difference in novelty between the first and second alternative is worth the difference in cost. Can the product command a price differential in the marketplace to defray the increased cost of fabrication?

The answers to these questions are rooted in the cloudy area of understanding consumer tastes and in the impact of advertising in creating and extending markets. The answers will be the best judgment of those who have a history of creditable assessment of these factors.

If perfect judgment of novelty worth were available, would the final ordering be optimal? Consider a figure of merit with only two factors, X and Y. The merit surface is depicted in Fig. 26. The optimum M appears as point p in the figure. Suppose Y eludes us (we feel it qualitative) and the merit function made with X (and an uncontrolled but not random Y) traces the locus $1'2'3'$ in merit space with the maximum exhibited at b.

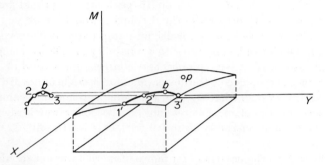

FIG. 26. A merit surface, an exploratory path upon it, and the projection of the path onto the MX plane, indicating the discrepancy between the apparent extremum at b and the true extremum at p.

The designer's merit curve is the projection of $1'2'3'$ on the XM plane, i.e., the curve 1-2-3. The curve 1-2-3 is not uniquely related to the merit surface. *To discuss the Y-merit of alternatives* 1, 2, 3 *will not help discover the extremum point p or the optimal XY combination.* Depending upon the geometry of the merit surface, the X corresponding to b may be close to optimal or a long way from it. However this is the best we can do short of shots in the dark. The quantification of parameter Y may or may not be worth a serious effort. It depends upon the problem. The pressure to quantify a qualitative factor is a wholesome one. The rewards of success in the area may be very great.

Our best understanding arises in cases where complete quantification is possible and is implemented with accuracy. Anything less is less satisfactory, but it still may be the best we know how to do.

COMPUTER REQUIREMENTS

3.1 LANGUAGE

The language employed by the computer user is referred to as a problem-oriented language. This is to say that the language and its grammar were created to fit the nature of the problems. Computational languages include MAD (*Michigan Algorithm Decoder*) and FORTRAN (FOR*mula* TRAN*slation*), which are suitable to the needs of the scientific and engineering community when dealing in algebraic and differential equations. A language called STRESS is a declarative, executive language specifically constructed for solution of problems in statically indeterminate elastic structures. A language called SNOBOL allows the manipulation and arrangement of strings of alphanumeric characters. A language called GPSS is a declarative executive language tailored to problems in queueing theory. PACER optimizes chemical process flow networks.

Because of the universality of and general acquaintanceship with the FORTRAN language, FORTRAN will be the basis for the following discussions.

3.2 FORMAT

Discussions of input-output (I/O for short) procedures on various FORTRAN language computers are available to users of particular machines through the computer manufacturer or the computational facility. These vary somewhat in small details from machine to machine. An installation using FORTRAN II might use the statement

```
    READ 10, A, B, I, J
10 FORMAT (2F10.6, 2I5)
```

or

```
    READ (1, 10) A, B, I, J
10 FORMAT (2F10.6, 2I5)
```

or

```
    READ INPUT TAPE 1, 10, A, B, I, J
10 FORMAT (2F10.6, 2I5)
```

Such details are resolved locally and the reader is presumed capable in matters of I/O on his local machine.

The format of concern here is the nature of the output display obtained from the computer as it bears on design. A man's desk in his own home is capable of being used as a written-communication center—i.e., as a place to receive the daily mail and generate responses (outgoing mail) as required. If this communication center were inundated with hundreds of letters daily, the normal procedure would become hopelessly inadequate.

Similarly a designer can keep information in mind concerning a few alternatives, but if the computer were to document a hundred alternatives, the physical keeping of input and output information together would be the only alternative to chaos. This leads to the formulation of some rules:

Rule I: An output sheet or sheets shall have as an integral part all pertinent input data, and sufficient redundancy shall be incorporated therein so that later perusal (when everything is no longer fresh in mind) can be accomplished conveniently. All sheets of a single investigation shall be identified so that should they become disassociated, they may be reassembled with confidence.

A great deal of design documentation occurs on the standard $8\frac{1}{2}$ by 11 in. sheet of paper, and it is assembled in folders of various kinds. A great inconvenience to readers and users occurs when foldout sheets are incorporated in such documents. These should be kept to a minimum. Since most of the computer output paper is larger than $8\frac{1}{2}$ by 11 in., confine the printed display to fall within a $8\frac{1}{2}$ by 11 in. area (with ample margins), so that the output paper may be either (1) trimmed to page size if the original is kept with documentation, or (2) copied and the copy kept with the documentation. Hence we cite Rule II:

Rule II: Confine output displays to $8\frac{1}{2}$ by 11 in. whenever possible.

Units are important in design work, and the units associated with output displays should be explicitly associated with the numerical quantity to which they pertain, unless there is no possibility for misinterpretation. Thus Rule III:

> *Rule III:* Indicate the physical units of numerical quantities appearing in output displays.

Conforming to these three simple rules will save the designer from considerable confusion and embarrassment in his engineering work utilizing the computer.

3.3 SELF-DOCUMENTING CARD DECKS

There is always the problem of the preservation of information relevant to the punch-card decks of computer programs in the engineering design room, even one with its own computer staff.

Programs generally travel down the following list with considerable attrition at each level:

1. Some programs solve an immediate engineering need.
2. Some programs are made useful at a later date by the originator and/or others with the same or similar problems.
3. Some programs are sufficiently useful that they are rewritten as a subroutine to be added to the new user's program decks as required.
4. Some programs are in such demand that in the interest of reducing compiling time, they are stored as library subroutines on computer tape or on disk. The formal write-up of these programs appears in the computer center subroutine manual, hopefully preserving necessary information for the potential user.

This section concerns itself with the period beginning with 1 and before reaching stage 4. This consideration involves many of the programs written in the design room, most of the loss of information, and nearly all of the attendant waste.

Computer program development is expensive in terms of the time and money that it represents. Computer use is economically justified when programming time plus computer charges represent less money for a given result than does another approach. Factors of speed and accuracy are also involved.

Even a very simple program may have hours of development time associated with it. Although the project with which it was associated has paid for it, it would be wasteful of human and fiscal resources to duplicate the same development at a later date. Also, if a project will not quite justify program development time, the future utility of a program can encourage management to underwrite part of the development cost now.

Essential to future use is preservation of information about the program that is important to the next user. This information consists of the answers to the questions, "What does the program do?" and "What has the program done to merit confidence?" To expect engineers who are in pursuit of answers ahead of deadlines to write up their programs, complete with logic flow diagrams, is asking more of people than they will give without serious compulsion. Even if a write-up is done at the time of the program development, will the program deck and the write-up be together six months later? Who has what? People take care of program decks, but write-up folders wander across decks, get stuck into files "just in case," and mostly fade into oblivion.

The key to information preservation, if this is the case, is to lump all the information into one indivisible unit, i.e., *into the program deck* itself. We are speaking here of main programs in contradistinction to subroutines, which are considered in Sec. 3.5.

What kinds of questions does the potential "borrower" of a program deck usually wish to pose?

1. What does the program do?
2. Is any well-known method or technique utilized?
3. What input is required?
4. What output is delivered?
5. Who developed the program?
6. Who knows the extent of problems that have been solved with the deck?
7. Where can the originator (or most frequent user) be reached?
8. Where can these solutions be studied?
9. What are the variables?
10. Is the computer really delivering what is asked for?

These are all reasonable requests, and a little thought will show how the answers to these questions (and similar ones unasked) can be preserved within the program deck itself.

A most valuable tool to the computer problem solver and to the borrower of solutions is the COMMENT card. A rule of thumb might be that if the number of comment cards does not exceed the number of active FORTRAN program cards, then a careful review is in order to prevent the loss of information. Sound exaggerated? Let us see.

What Does the Program Do?

Often a simple declarative sentence at the top of the deck will reveal the intent of the program and, if it cannot, an expository paragraph should follow the opening summary sentence.

EXAMPLES

```
C
C      .....  DUNKERLEY CRITICAL SPEED DETERMINATIONS  .....
C      .....  FOR MULTIDISK TURBINE SHAFT, STRAIGHT    .....
C      .....  AND UNIFORM, SOLID OR HOLLOW             .....
C


C
C      .....  ROUTINE FOR DETERMINING THE EQUATION FOR  .....
C      .....  THE MOST PROBABLE NORMAL CURVE THAT CAN   .....
C      .....  BE PASSED THROUGH GIVEN DATA              .....
C


C
C      .....  COMPUTER SYNTHESIS OF SLIDER CRANK     .....
C      .....  FUNCTION GENERATOR                     .....
C
C      .....  THIS PROGRAM KINEMATICALLY DESIGNS THE    .....
C      .....  PROPORTIONS FOR THE MOST ACCURATE SLIDER  .....
C      .....  CRANK FUNCTION GENERATOR POSSIBLE USING   .....
C      .....  THREE PRECISION POINTS, WITH LIMITS SET   .....
C      .....  BY THE DESIGNER                           .....
C
```

What Input Is Required?

List the input variables, for there may be a surprising one present (to the borrower).

EXAMPLE

```
C
C      .....  THE FOLLOWING INPUT DATA CARDS IN FORTRAN  .....
C      .....  EQUATION FORM ARE REQUIRED                 .....
C
C      .....  N = NUMBER OF TURBINE DISKS, INTEGER          .....
C      .....  SPAN = LENGTH BETWEEN BRGS, INCHES, FPN       .....
C      .....  DIN = INSIDE DIA. OF HOLLOW SHAFT, IN., FPN   .....
C      .....  DOUT = OUTSIDE DIA. OF SHAFT, INCHES FPN      .....
C      .....  E = YOUNGS MODULUS, LBF/SQIN., FPN            .....
C      .....  GAMMA = SP. WT. SHAFT MATERIAL, LBF/CUIN., FPN .....
C      .....  P(1), . . . , P(N), LOADS, LBF, L TO R, FPN    .....
C      .....  B(1), . . . , B(N), DIST, LOAD TO R BRG, IN., FPN .....
C
```

How Is Input Placed in Program?

How input is placed in the program depends on the nature of the problem. If the program was originally designed to give a solution to a single problem and only once, then input may well have been in FORTRAN declarative statements. In this case place a red card right after the listing of input variables and mode (see previous example). If the program was designed to give a solution to a number of problems, then the input data was probably read off punched cards. In this case, after reading the input variable list, the borrower checks the READ statements for variables and reads FORMAT statements for mode and location on cards.

EXAMPLE

```
C
C       .....   PLACE N, SPAN, DIN, DOUT, E,                      .....
C       .....   GAMMA, P(1),...P(N), B(1),..., B(N)               .....
Cred    .....   BEHIND THIS CARD                                  .....
Cred    .....   CABOOSE CARD FOR INPUT N,...., B(N)               .....
C
C       .....   FOLLOWING THIS CARD ARE PROGRAM STATEMENTS  .....
C       .....   1 THRU 42, STOP, END, FLAG CARDS                  .....
C
```

What Output Is Delivered?

List the output variables and units if machine output does not do this. (Who would write a program that did not label every output number with proper units?)

EXAMPLE

```
C
C       .....   OUTPUT TO THIS PROGRAM CONSISTS OF A         .....
C       .....   TABULATED HISTOGRAM REPRODUCING INPUT        .....
C       .....   DATA, THE NUMBER OF OBSERVATIONS, THE        .....
C       .....   ABSCISSA OF THE MEDIAN OF SAMPLE,            .....
C       .....   THE STANDARD DEVIATION OF THE SAMPLE,        .....
C       .....   AND THE EQUATION OF THE MOST PROBABLE        .....
C       .....   NORMAL CURVE PASSING THRU THE HISTOGRAM      .....
C
```

Who Developed the Program?

Whoever developed the program is probably the person who can best answer questions concerning the program. Indicate his name, where he can be found, and whether solutions can be seen. Put this information just under program title.

44

```
C
C      .....  COMPUTER SYNTHESIS OF SLIDER CRANK FUNCTION  .....
C      .....  GENERATOR. PROGRAM BY C. MISCHKE, IOWA         .....
C      .....  STATE UNIVERSITY, AMES, SOLUTIONS ON FILE      .....
C
```

What Is the Macrostructure of the Program?

Place COMMENT cards identifying purpose immediately before each block of the macroprogram. The macroprogram diagram should be reconstructable from inspection of the cards, and the microprogram (if this is necessary) can be constructed from the program itself (run the deck through the off-line printer). To make everything more readable, separate the program from the comments, by providing a blank COMMENT card on either side of each "in program" commentary.

EXAMPLE

```
C
C      .....  GENERAL INITIALIZATION                         .....
C
                                                             .

C
C      .....  READ INPUT DATA                                .....
C

C
C      .....  SWITCH FOR ABSOLUTE OR RELATIVE ERROR          .....
C

C
C      .....  GOLDEN SECTION SEARCH FOR LARGEST ERROR        .....
C      .....  ORDINATE  BETWEEN  PRECISION POINTS ONE        .....
C      .....  AND TWO                                        .....
C
```

What Are the Computation Variables?

The internal variables unique to the computer program and not related directly to the problem analysis (iteration indices, Boolean switches, recent path memory, future path guides, etc.) ought to be largely defined by comment cards either above the program or by inference from macroprogram COMMENT statements.

EXAMPLE

```
C
C        .....  PASS SWITCH                                          .....
C
      675 IF(J − 2) 610, 611, 612
      610 F1 = ERR
          ALPHA2 = ALEFT + 0.618*DELTA
          J = 2
          GO TO 609
      611 F2 = ERR
               .
               .
               .

C
C        .....  PRINT AND REMEMBER (L = 1, 2, 3, 4) CONFIGURATION  .....
C
```

What If I Ever Drop a Deck of Cards?

A working deck of cards should be serialized by number against the
possibility of losing their order. A small FORTRAN program can be
serialized by labeling the statement numbers sequentially throughout the
program. A long program grows by pieces and patches, and the job of
ordering statement numbers is frightening in prospect. (Consider all the
numbers buried in IF and WRITE and READ and GO TO statements.)
A better solution is to serialize the final deck, including COMMENT cards
and blanks, using columns 73 to 80. Most compilers ignore these punches
in program cards.

How Do I Know the Computer Is Converging on My Solution?

It is very helpful to provide for a *convergence monitor* when writing a
program. A convergence monitor displays those output variables which
reveal the convergence as the iterations are taking place. No engineer
will use a raw number of output, *even from his own programs*, unless he has
personal assurance that the computer is indeed doing the job. The convergence monitor answers this need for the program writer and program
user. A Boolean variable to turn the monitor on or off can be built into the
program.

The value of the monitor is great. Many programs, run successfully
many times, *sometimes have never used some branches within the program*.
This is because an eventuality could be foreseen, but the programmer does
not know any data that will activate it. A program used a hundred times
can suddenly give an erroneous result by going down an incorrect virgin
pathway within the program. The monitor is helpful in this situation.

46

What Should an Output from a Computer Solution to an Engineering Problem Look Like?

Computer solution outputs vary in appearance. Many outputs go into an $8\frac{1}{2}$ by 11 in. documentation folder, and if it is possible, accommodate to this size, for the convenience of avoiding foldouts is appreciated by readers of such documents.

If possible, the input data and the output data (particularly output summary) should be inseparable, i.e., on one and the same sheet.

The format should be neat, concise, and easy to read, and needed information should be easy to locate. An engineering report is always expository, and the computer output should be also.

3.4 SUBROUTINES

If engineering problems had to be solved and programmed from scratch on each and every occasion, the computer would find little use in the design room. The overhead of planning the computer program and debugging it would be large, and therefore in many instances the use of the computer would become economically infeasible. In this situation any notion that a complete problem, once successfully completed, would be encountered again should be dispelled. If the overhead of time and money associated with computer use is substantial, how can previously invested time and experience be salvaged so that the cost per problem becomes reasonable? The answer to this question is, surprisingly, the same whether you are talking about a human problem-solver or a machine. A human is trained to provide conditioned responses to very elementary situations. A designer functions because he can bring to bear on a problem a whole bag full of conditioned responses, arranged and ordered by intellect in such a way as to successfully solve a complicated problem. The computer can be "taught" a similar repertoire of conditioned responses which must be arranged by humans into a problem solution. Once "taught," the computer can be made to remember previous training. The computer capability corresponding to the learning of conditioned responses to elementary problems and remembering them once learned is called the *subroutine capability* of the computer.

Another closely related capability is called *function definition*. A function may generate a value which is the result of a single arithmetic statement. If this is the case, it is possible to define an arithmetic statement function (internal function) with a single declaration in the main program, such as

WIREF(D) = 42.*D*D

wherein the ultimate strength of a wire rope is given by $42d^2$, where d is the diameter in inches and WIREF is expressed in tons. The statement above is declarative and nonexecutable. It appears anywhere in the main program preceding its first computational use.

It is called implicitly by its use (appearance) in an executable arithmetic statement such as

SAFE = (WIREF(D) − TENS)/WIREF(D)

In arithmetic statement functions it is the responsibility of the main programmer to

1. define the arithmetic statement function,
2. be sure the defining declarative statement precedes its first use in an executable statement.

In so doing the programmer is cautioned on the following:

1. Place the internally defined function declaration ahead of the first executable statement in the program.
2. Dummy arguments must be individual nonsubscripted variables.
3. The function name must contain a terminal F and be at least four characters long, including the terminal F.
4. The list of arguments in the calling statement must agree in number, order, and mode with the dummy arguments in the defining declarative statement.
5. The variables in the arithmetic statement function which are not dummy arguments are considered parameters, and current values of these parameters are used.
6. The arithmetic statement function may include in its expression other functions; and if they are internally defined, their definitions must have preceding defining declarations.

The other kind of function that is useful is the externally defined function previously mentioned as the *subroutine*. An example of a subroutine might be the extraction of the square root of a quantity. This cannot be accomplished by a single arithmetic statement, and therefore a subroutine program is written for this purpose. Since the particular illustrative example chosen is often used, the computer manufacturer provides this subroutine as a program in a library of functions, and it may be summoned by the user by simply writing SQRTF(X) or SQRT(X), depending on the sort of FORTRAN used by the particular computer. Its appearance in an arithmetic expression such as

C = SQRT(A*A + B*B)

and the absolute value of $\sqrt{a^2 + b^2}$ is returned and stored in the location C. The above expression could have been written as

C = SQRT(A**2. + B**2.)

But as a practical matter the computer can multiply A times A much more quickly than it can square A by using its exponentiation technique.

Of paramount interest to the designer is the external function of *his* definition. These external functions are really separate and complete programs. Their purpose may be, on call, to compute and return a value to the main program, or to return an ordered array.

Functions which return values often have the opening declaration

FUNCTION NAME (A1, A2, ..., A6)

and are called implicitly by the use of the function NAME, in an arithmetic expression.

Subroutines which perform various roles, including the return of values to the main program, have the opening declaration

SUBROUTINE NAME (A1, A2, ..., A6)

and are called by the statement

CALL NAME (A1, A2, ..., A6)

At this point the programmer is cautioned on the following:

1. Name FUNCTION and SUBROUTINE subprograms with one to five (or six, depending on the computer) characters, the first of which must be alphabetic and the last of which *cannot* be a terminal F. The terminal F is reserved for internal functions on some computers. FUNCTION subprograms returning integer values must be given integer names.
2. Dummy arguments must be nonsubscripted variable names.
3. FUNCTION subprograms must have at least one dummy argument, but SUBROUTINE subprograms may have none or more dummy arguments.
4. The argument list must agree in number, order, and mode in the calling statement and in the definition.

A subroutine should be thoroughly checked out before use in order that confidence in it may be established. A common method of checkout is to call a subroutine with data that will exercise all its responses. For example if subroutine TRIAN (A, B, C, I) is to determine whether the line segments A, B, and C can be assembled into a triangle, sets of sides from known triangles and known nontriangles can be given the TRIAN and the responses noted.

The subroutine TRIAN accepts the three side lengths and returns an integer $I = 1$ (a triangle), $I = 2$ (limiting case, sides collinear), and $I = 3$ (no triangle). Testing this subroutine with combinations like 5, 12, 13 will give the expected reply. It is the borderline cases that test the finer logic imbedded in the routine, The combination 1.0000000, 1.0000000, 2.0000000, the combination 1.0000001, 1.0000000, 2.0000000, and the combination 0.9999999, 1.0000000, 2.0000000 are better test exercises for the subroutine TRIAN.

3.5 CATALOGING SUBROUTINES

A subroutine user, convinced of the soundness of the routine, needs to know very few things in order to use the routine with fullest effectiveness:

1. What is the number of arguments in the subroutine call?
2. What is the order of the arguments in the subroutine call?
3. What are the modes of the arguments in the subroutine call?
4. What declarative statements are required in the calling program?
5. Are any additional subroutines required?
6. What are the definitions of the arguments used?
7. What are the units of measurement of the arguments?
8. Where can I find the analysis upon which the subroutine is based, diagrams, and additional information?
9. Which arguments represent information carried into the subroutine (i.e., must be defined in calling program in advance of the call)? Which arguments represent values returned to the main program by the subroutine (and are now defined in the calling program)?
10. Who wrote the routine?

With a little organization, these questions can be answered simply and conveniently. Examples from the IOWA CADET algorithm documentation follow.

A subroutine which requires three variables as input and returns four variables can be denoted as

NAME1 (A1, A2, A3, B1, B2, B3, B4)

where the A's designate floating point quantities carried to the subroutine from the calling program and the B's represent floating point quantities returned to the calling program. A subroutine requiring one integer variable among the four sent to it and one integer variable among the three variables returned to the calling program, can be written as

NAME2 (A1, A2, I3, A4, B1, J2, B3)

where the I denotes an integer variable going to the subroutine and J represents an integer variable returned by the subroutine.

A list of the variables, their definitions, and units of physical measurement will establish the number, order, and mode of the arguments. All ten questions can be answered by the subroutine writeup format which appears below.

FOURBAR KINEMATIC CHAIN POSITION ANALYSIS
ME007 (I1, A2, A3, A4, A5, A6, B1, B2)   Mischke

This subroutine computes the abscissa angles of the coupler vector and the follower vector of a plane four-bar mechanism as depicted on page 101, Fig. 4.3, *Elements of Mechanical Analysis*, Mischke.

CALLING PROGRAM REQUIREMENTS

None

VARIABLES

I1 = 1 uncrossed configuration, integer
   = 2 crossed configuration, integer
A2 = abscissa angle of crank vector, radians
A3 = length of crank vector, length
A4 = length of coupler vector, length
A5 = length of follower vector, length
A6 = length of grounded link, length
B1 = abscissa angle of coupler vector, radians
B2 = abscissa angle of follower vector, radians

In the above program there are no requirements on the calling program. The calling program might require a DIMENSION statement. The affected variable and the magnitude of the storage allocation required would be specified. Perhaps an additional subroutine is required, defining a function that this subroutine uses and which only the programmer knows. Such a situation occurs in subroutine ME010:

RADIAL FLATFACED FOLLOWER FUNCTION GENERATOR CAM
ME010 (A1, A2, A3, B1, B2)   C. Mischke

This subroutine obtains points on the cam profile of a radial flat-

51

faced follower cam used as a function generator as depicted on page 161, Fig. 6.17, *Elements of Mechanical
Analysis*, Mischke.

CALLING PROGRAM REQUIREMENTS

Provide a subroutine FUNCT (THETA, YY, DYY)
wherein YY and DYY are functions of THETA returned
by the subroutine FUNCT upon the tendering of the angle
THETA. DYY is the first derivative of YY with respect
to THETA.

VARIABLES

A1 = value of function of THETA to be generated by the
cam follower
A2 = value of the derivative of the function of THETA to
be generated by the cam follower
A3 = the angle THETA of current cam position, radians
B1 = x coordinate of cam profile point, units of YY
B2 = y coordinate of cam profile point, units of YY

Blank sheets, such as the one on the opposite page, should be provided
for convenient recording of the vital information necessary to the next
subroutine user. This documentation is the minimum required. For users
interested in the anatomy of the subroutine, the compilation printout
can be provided on the back of this page or as the following page.

3.6 ERROR MESSAGES

Users of subroutines who are not familiar with the particular methods
used within the subroutine are likely to err at some point and provide an
argument value outside the acceptable range, or of inappropriate sign.
In order to debug a snarl in the main program, a diagnostic message from
the offending subroutine can be very helpful in finding the trouble.

Error messages resulting in printouts can be provided by the subroutine
writer. A logical error in a main program may send a negative argument
to a subroutine, and the subroutine, in attempting to take, say, a square
root, will be unable to do so, and the user's program will be aborted from
the computer; the only diagnostic message might be an error code indicating the attempt to take the square root of a negative number. If there are
a number of square roots in the main program, the user might waste a
great deal of time in hand calculation trying to prove which step provided
the error. If the subroutine were to print out *****ERROR MESSAGE
SUBROUTINE ME006 ARGUMENT A3 NEGATIVE***** and stop

_____
(Title)

_____   _____
(Call)   (Programmer)

SUMMARY & REFERENCE

CALLING PROGRAM REQUIREMENTS

VARIABLES

the program, then the user will seek to unearth the reason for the existence of the identified negative variable instead of one of his uses of SQRT.

A series of IF statements at the beginning of a subroutine can test for the prohibited values of variables and refer to WRITE statements citing the appropriate error. The computer may be stopped with a STOP (or CALL EXIT) statement by allowing the offending calculation to abort the program or, as in MAD, to use a return variable—a statement label in the main program that brings the computer to a halt in a manner of the programmer's choosing. An error variable can be used in a subroutine's call to return error specie to the calling program, so again the program may be halted in a manner of the programmer's choosing.

The most common error committed by someone using a subroutine he has not written is that of sending a numerical value of inappropriate magnitude to the subroutine. The user will appreciate knowing which subroutine is involved, which argument in the call list is the offending one, and specifically what was the numerical value which triggered the trouble. Many times the error is one of logic in the designer's own executive or MERIT program, and a succinct error message will quickly identify the trouble. Sample error messages are:

*****ERROR MESSAGE SUBROUTINE GOLD1*****
   A2, 0.9246071E 00, IS NOT SMALLER THAN A3, 0.6643291E 00

*****ERROR MESSAGE SUBROUTINE GRID4*****
   A3(5) = 0.42926780E 00 GREATER THAN A4(5) = 0.33333333E 00

*****ERROR MESSAGE SUBROUTINE ROOT1*****
   VALUE OF A4, 0.2164921E 01, IS NOT WITHIN RANGE 0 to 1

*****ERROR MESSAGE SUBROUTINE ME0034*****
   VALUE OF I1, 5, LIES OUTSIDE ALLOWABLE RANGE 1 THRU 4

THE SEARCH FOR EXTREMES

4.1 ECONOMY IN EFFORT

Presuming one can successfully obtain a meaningful merit function, the problem of discovering the configuration corresponding to the largest figure of merit becomes central. In simple cases the general geometry of the merit surface might be visualized from inspection of the merit function and the general location of the extremes ascertained. It is in this domain that search is initiated and directions of progress are apparent. In most problems, however, the "shape" of the merit surface is not known because there are so many independent variables that geometrically oriented thinking simply is not tractable. The simple reason is human lack of experience with, say, ten-dimensional geometry and the properties of hypersurface. Where, then, does one look?

One is reminded of the tipsy tippler looking for his housekey on the sidewalk under the corner street lamp who replied to inquiry as follows:

Passerby: What are you doing?
Searcher: Looking for my housekey.
Passerby: Do you have any idea where you lost it?
Searcher: Yes, somewhere up the block.
Passerby: Why aren't you looking for it up there?
Searcher: Because the light's better here.

Since the searcher did not know exactly where he had dropped the key, he assigned a small, but finite, probability of finding it near the street light. He considered the probability of finding the key up the dark block was zero. Exploitation of what knowledge of probabilities we have is not always a sure road to successful search, but it may be all we have. We do our best and take our lickings.

The object of our searches will be an extremum, in particular the largest ordinate of the formal figure of merit function or the tactical figure of merit function. An a priori knowledge of the ordinates is presumed to be zero, but a knowledge of the domain within which suitable alternatives are to be found is presumed complete, for the moment. For the purpose of drawing a distinction, consider the problem of discovering, in one-dimensional search, the interval in which the extreme of a unimodal function lies—i.e., of narrowing down the interval in which the extremum lies from the initial domain to some fraction of the initial domain. At the start of the search we can say the extremum lies within the search interval. At the end of the search we still do not know the exact location of the extreme ordinate, but the tolerance on our specification of where it is has been reduced to acceptable limits.

A unimodal function has a single peak in a given interval, and each successive ordinate is progressively larger than the last until the peak is reached; then each successive ordinate is progressively less than the last. Nonunimodal functions can be divided into a number of contiguous unimodal regimes. Examples of unimodal functions appear in Fig. 27. We are given

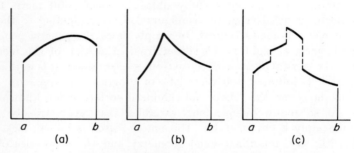

FIG. 27. Examples of unimodal functions.

the unimodality of the function y of independent variable x. In narrowing the interval in which the extremum may be found with certainty from the original range $a \leq x \leq b$ to something less, a problem arises concerning the expenditure of function evaluations. Suppose four function evaluations may be expended. Should we expend them simultaneously or one at a time?

The simultaneous approach is something of a shotgun approach, and a four-ordinate simultaneous function evaluation might appear as indicated in Fig. 28. In Fig. 28(a) the extremum lies in the interval $x_3 \leq x \leq b$, and in Fig. 28(b) in the range $x_2 \leq x \leq x_4$. In the absence of knowledge of the relationship between x and y, four ordinates would be placed, equally spaced, in the interval; and the domain of the extremum is narrowed to 0.4 of the interval (a, b).

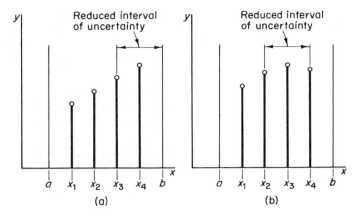

FIG. 28. Simultaneous evaluation of the function in four locations and the reduction in the interval of uncertainty that results.

If we expend our ordinate evaluations, first as a pair to determine the trend of the function, then singly in the reduced certain domain of the extremum, we would have with the first step knowledge that the extremum is certainly in the interval $x_1 \leq x \leq b$ as indicated in Fig. 29. By now placing an ordinate between x_1 and x_2, we obtain the situation depicted in Fig. 30, and have a new reduced interval of $x_3 \leq x \leq b$. The placing of our last ordinate evaluation between x_2 and b yields the still further reduced interval $x_3 \leq x \leq x_4$, as shown in Fig. 31. If we placed initial ordinates at the third points of the original interval and successive ordinates bisecting previous spacings, then the final region of uncertainty is one-third of the interval (a, b).

The second method employed exploited the results of prior trials, and ordinate evaluations were expended where they contributed the most-needed

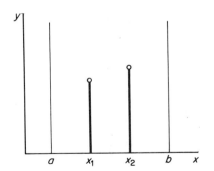

FIG. 29. A pair of simultaneous function evaluations in the interval (a, b)

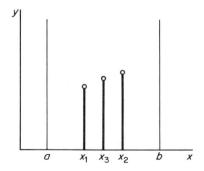

FIG. 30. An additional ordinate x_3 has been placed between x_1 and x_2.

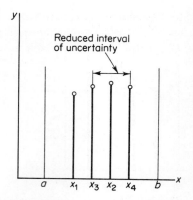

FIG. 31. An additional ordinate x_4 has been placed between x_2 and b.

Reduced interval of uncertainty

information. The first method is called a *simultaneous search plan*, and the latter is called a *sequential search plan*. The second approach is preferable as it expends fewer functional evaluations in reducing the interval of certainty to a specified level. The former plan is used where there is no time available to obtain partial results and to act on that information for future evaluations. Since the number of function evaluations is an index to effort expended in narrowing the region of uncertainty, economy of search effort and expeditious search techniques go hand in hand.

If the computer is to execute the search and it can calculate quickly, why worry over some extra function evaluations? If one evaluation of a function takes sizable computer time, then whether there are 10^2 or 10^6 function evaluations necessary *is* significant.

4.2 EXHAUSTIVE SEARCH

Consider a unimodal function y in the interval $a \leq x \leq b$ to be evaluated at n evenly spaced abscissas—as shown in Fig. 32—in a simultaneous

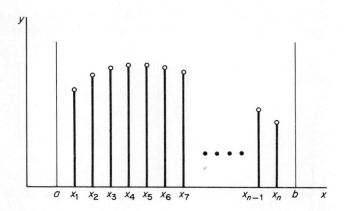

FIG. 32. Simultaneous evaluation of n ordinates in the interval (a, b), forming the pattern of ordinates for an exhaustive search in the interval (a, b).

search. The abscissa spacing is $1/(n + 1)$ of the interval (a, b) and the interval of uncertainty has been reduced to two spaces. The fractional reduction of the original interval of uncertainty is $2/(n + 1)$. Table 4.1, which indicates search effort, appears below.

Clearly

$$f = \frac{2}{(n + 1)}$$

and

$$n = \left\{ \frac{(2 - f)}{f} \right\}$$

where the nearest integer greater than $(2 - f)/f$ is enclosed in braces. For $f = 0.01$

$$n = \left\{ \frac{(2 - 0.01)}{0.01} \right\} = 199$$

As a practical matter in programming such a search routine, it can be desirable to evaluate the function at each end of the interval also. Although this is not helpful in reducing the interval of uncertainty, it is useful when points for plotting purposes are sought and the use of an exhaustive search routine to spray an interval full of equally spaced ordinates is convenient.

TABLE 4.1

Number of Function Evaluations, n	Fractional Reduction of Interval of Uncertainty, f
1	1
2	2/3
3	1/2
4	2/5
.	.
.	.
.	.
199	1/100
.	.
.	.
.	.
n	$2/(n + 1)$

4.3 INTERVAL-HALVING

In the previous section we discovered that, in a simultaneous search for a fractional reduction in the interval of uncertainty $f = 0.1$, 19 functional evaluations would be required; that for $f = 0.01$, 199 evaluations would be involved; and that for $f = 0.001$, 1,999 evaluations would be necessary. In view of the rapidly increasing cost of reducing the interval of uncertainty, it might be advantageous to nest the search by spending 19 function evaluations to reduce the interval to 0.1, then spend 19 more in the *reduced* interval to contract the interval of uncertainty to 0.01, and finally spend 19 more in the twice-reduced interval. The resultant expenditure in functional evaluations is $19 + 19 + 19 = 57$ to accomplish in a combined sequential and simultaneous strategy that which requires 1,999 evaluations in a simultaneous approach. The gain in economical expenditure of function evaluations is impressive. The choice of f for each simultaneous subsearch was arbitrary. What is the best choice of f for the subsearch?

We had

19 evaluations reducing original interval to 0.1
19 evaluations reducing original interval to $(0.1)^2$
19 evaluations reducing original interval to $(0.1)^3$

and in general we would have

n evaluations reducing the original interval to $2/(n + 1)$
n evaluations reducing the original interval to $[2/(n + 1)]^2$
.
.
.
n evaluations reducing the original interval to $[2/(n + 1)]^m$

The total expenditure of function evaluations is $N = mn$, and the final reduction in the interval of uncertainty is designated F. Thus

$$F = \left(\frac{2}{n + 1}\right)^m$$

and since $m = N/n$

$$F = \left(\frac{2}{n + 1}\right)^{N/n}$$

Solution of the above equation for N yields

$$N = \frac{n \ln (1/F)}{\ln [(n + 1)/2]}$$

A minimum of N for a specified F is associated with a definite n. Inasmuch as n is limited to integer values and differentiation of the equation for N with respect to n leads to a transcendental equation, the smallest value of N will be found by simple substitution.

$$N|_{n=1} = \infty$$

$$N|_{n=2} = \frac{2}{\ln 3/2} \ln (1/F) = 4.93 \ln (1/F)$$

$$N|_{n=3} = \frac{3}{\ln 4/2} \ln (1/F) = 4.32 \ln (1/F)$$

$$N|_{n=4} = \frac{4}{\ln 5/2} \ln (1/F) = 4.37 \ln (1/F)$$

Higher values of n result in continuously increasing values of N. The strategy associated with the least N is the one involving the placing of $n = 3$ ordinates within the search interval. The optimal choice of f for the fractional reduction sought during each subsearch is $f = 2/(n + 1) = \frac{1}{2}$. This optimal blending of sequential and simultaneous approaches is called *interval-halving*.

Consider a unimodal function y in the interval $a \leq x \leq b$ which will be evaluated with three equally spaced ordinates in the intervals depicted in Fig. 33. In any of the eventualities depicted in Fig. 33, the interval of uncertainty has been reduced to half of the original interval. This allows

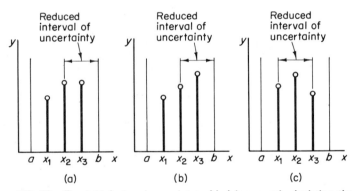

FIG. 33. The initial step in an interval-halving search depicting the eventualities (a) two ordinates equal; (b) all ordinates unequal; $x_1 < x_2 < x_3$; and (c) all ordinates unequal, $x_3 < x_1 < x_2$, for a unimodal function. The reduced interval of uncertainty is indicated for each eventuality.

half of the interval to be discarded and attention turned to the remaining interval of uncertainty. Notice that in each of the situations of Fig. 33 the central ordinate has already been evaluated. Now two more ordinates are evaluated at the $\frac{1}{4}$ and $\frac{3}{4}$ points of the shortened interval of uncertainty, as shown in Fig. 34. We observe from examination of Fig. 34 that the new region of uncertainty can be again halved, and that the extremum now lies within a range of $\frac{1}{4}$ of the original interval. Only five functional evaluations have been expended up to this time. Table 4.2 indicates the search effort expended. Clearly

$$f = \frac{1}{2^{(n-1)/2}}$$

and

$$n = \left\{1 + \frac{2 \ln 1/f}{\ln 2}\right\}$$

For $f = 0.01$

$$n = \left\{1 + \frac{2 \ln 1/0.01}{\ln 2}\right\} = \{14.4\} = 15$$

TABLE 4.2

Number of Function Evaluations, n	Fractional Reduction of Interval of Uncertainty, f
3	1/2
5	1/4
7	1/8
9	1/16
.	.
.	.
.	.
n	$1/2^{(n-1)/2}$

TABLE 4.3

Number of Function Evaluations, n	Fractional Reduction of Interval of Uncertainty, f
2	$(1 + \delta)/2$
4	$(1 + 3\delta)/4$
6	$(1 + 7\delta)/8$
8	$(1 + 15\delta)/16$
.	.
.	.
.	.
n	$[1 + (2^{n/2} - 1)\delta]/2^{n/2}$

The interval-halving technique has reduced the function evaluations for an interval of uncertainty of $\frac{1}{100}$ of the original interval from 199 to 15, a remarkable reduction.

A little thought shows that the central ordinate evaluation in the original evaluation is unnecessary. In addition, the other two original function evaluations could be very close to the central ordinate and still indicate the half-interval to be retained (see Fig. 35). The limit of how close these evaluations may approach the central ordinate is that spacing which still allows one to determine which ordinate is larger *with certainty*. If the spacing between the ordinate pairs is δ, then Table 4.3 indicates the search effort expended.

The magnitude of the quantity δ is imposed by the ability

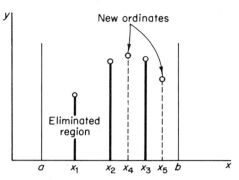

FIG. 34. The second step in an interval-halving search of a unimodal function indicating the two new ordinates and the eliminated region.

to recognize a difference between ordinates erected a distance δ apart, with a certainty that the difference is real and discernible, and that the ordering that results is flawless. In experimental work the order of magnitude of δ may be in the neighborhood of a fraction of a per cent of the interval. In com-

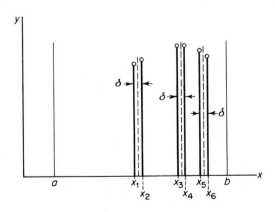

FIG. 35. Successive placement of ordinate pairs in a dichotomous search.

puter work it may be smaller, but not necessarily as small as 0.00000001. If a function of merit contains a parameter such as the size of a bolt, a small

63

change in abscissa may not change the bolt size, and both of the adjacent ordinates might have the same magnitude. Since

$$f = \frac{1 + (2^{n/2} - 1)\delta}{2^{n/2}}$$

it follows that

$$n = \left\{ \frac{2 \ln \left(\dfrac{1 - \delta}{f - \delta} \right)}{\ln 2} \right\}$$

It is seen that n approaches infinity as δ approaches f. (You cannot find the largest bearing ball of a group whose mean diameter is $\frac{1}{2}$ in. and standard deviation 0.001 in. with a 1-ft rule.) As δ approaches zero, the expression for n becomes

$$n = \left\{ \frac{2 \ln 1/f}{\ln 2} \right\}$$

which is one less function evaluation than the previous equivalent expression for the case of interval-halving. The saved ordinate is the original central ordinate, which is no longer required.

For $f = 0.01$

$$n = \left\{ \frac{2 \ln 1/0.01}{\ln 2} \right\} = \{13.4\} = 14$$

"Interval-halving" by using closely spaced pairs of function evaluations is called *dichotomous search*.

4.4 GOLDEN SECTION SEARCH

As impressive as was the effort reduction in function evaluation introduced by the first version of the interval-halving technique, there lingers an intuitive feeling that further improvement is possible. In the interval-halving technique, following the initial triple function evaluation, function evaluations were expended two by two. One of these two is the largest and tells us that the maximum is "within its half of the current search interval." The other tells us less. It says "it is *not* here." If we could put in the new ordinate and obtain the largest ordinate so far, there would be no need to "use up" the second. We have no guarantee that the first evaluation will or will not be the smaller, so we have to use both evaluations. Perhaps the way to avoid this situation is to devise a way of using one ordinate at a time.

Consider the unimodal function y in the interval $a \leq x \leq b$ evaluated at two intermediate ordinates as shown in Fig. 36. In the case depicted by Fig. 36(a), the extremum lies in the interval $x_1 \leq x \leq b$. In the case depicted by Fig. 36(b), the extremum lies in the interval $a \leq x \leq x_2$. We shall take the first case and continue (see Fig. 37). We wish now to continue the search, expending a single function evaluation for each interval of uncertainty reduction. We wish to define ξ and η such that, if region $a \leq x \leq x_1$ is eliminated, the ordinate x_2 is in the proper location—that it is the *first* ordinate of the new interval, $\overline{\Delta x} = (b - x_1)$—i.e., located at $\xi \overline{\Delta x}$ from x_1, the new left end of the interval of uncertainty (see Fig. 38). Similarly, if the region $x_2 \leq x \leq b$ was eliminated by x_1 being greater than

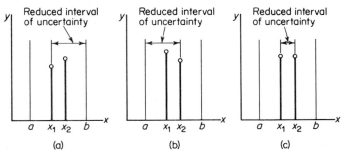

(a)   (b)   (c)

FIG. 36. The initial step of placing unequally spaced ordinate pairs in an interval (a, b) of a unimodal function depicting the eventualities (a) ordinates unequal, $x_1 < x_2$; (b) ordinates unequal, $x_1 > x_2$; and (c) ordinates equal, $x_1 = x_2$ and the corresponding reduction in the interval of uncertainty.

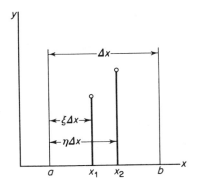

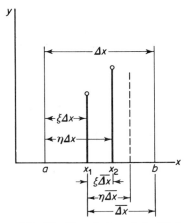

FIG. 37. The definitions of ξ and η for golden section search.

FIG. 38. The placing of the third ordinate for case (a) of Fig. 36.

65

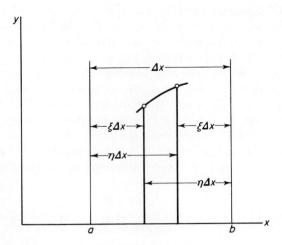

FIG. 39. The geometry and symmetry of the placement of ordinates in the golden section search of a unimodal function.

x_2, then x_1 would be in the proper location to be the *second* ordinate in the new interval $\overline{\Delta x}' = (x_2 - a)$—i.e., located at $\eta \overline{\Delta x}'$ from a. This readiness for either alternative demands a symmetry in the location of x_1 and x_2. The geomerty of Fig. 39 indicates this symmetry. In Fig. 39, we sum the distances which add to Δx and obtain

$$\xi \Delta x + (\eta \Delta x - \xi \Delta x) + \xi \Delta x = \Delta x$$

or

$$\xi + \eta = 1$$

From the relationship between Δx and $\overline{\Delta x}$ we obtain another requirement from Fig. 38

$$\Delta x = \xi \Delta x + \overline{\Delta x} \qquad (4.1)$$

$$\xi \Delta x + \xi \overline{\Delta x} = \eta \Delta x \qquad (4.2)$$

From equations (4.1) and (4.2) we obtain

$$(1 - \xi) = \frac{\overline{\Delta x}}{\Delta x} = \frac{\eta - \xi}{\xi}$$

The outer equality yields

$$\xi(1 - \xi) = \eta - \xi = (1 - \xi) - \xi$$

66

The resulting quadratic in ξ is

$$\xi^2 - 3\xi + 1 = 0$$

from which

$$\xi = \frac{3}{2} \pm \frac{1}{2}\sqrt{5}$$

Since $\xi < 1$, the negative sign prevails, and

$$\xi = \frac{3 - \sqrt{5}}{2} = 0.381966011$$

and it follows that

$$\eta = 0.618033989$$

and

$$\frac{\overline{\Delta x}}{\Delta x} = (1 - \xi) = 0.618033989$$

Table 4.4 indicates the search effort expended.

TABLE 4.4

Number of Function Evaluations, n	Fractional Reduction of Interval of Uncertainty, f
2	0.618033989
3	$(0.618033989)^2$
4	$(0.618033989)^3$
.	.
.	.
.	.
n	$(0.618033989)^{n-1}$

Clearly,

$$f = (0.618033989)^{n-1}$$

and

$$n = \left\{ 1 + \frac{\ln f}{\ln (0.618033989)} \right\}$$

When $f = 0.01$

$$n = \left\{ 1 + \frac{\ln (0.01)}{\ln (0.618033989)} \right\} = \{1 + 9.58\} = \{10.58\} = 11$$

Figure 40 indicates graphically the relative efforts necessary to carry out a one-dimensional search using the methods mentioned so far in this chapter.

4.5 MULTIDIMENSIONAL SEARCHES

When a function of one independent variable is explored for an extremum, a convenient geometric model is a functional locus in a plane with the

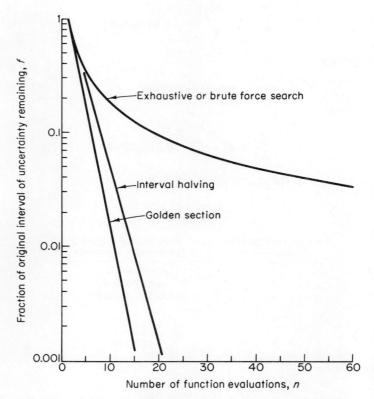

FIG. 40. A graph indicating the relative effectiveness of exhaustive, interval-halving and golden section search strategies.

search interval as a line segment, as indicated by Fig. 41. When a function of two independent variables is explored, the concept of a surface above a plane is a useful geometric interpretation, as indicated in Fig. 42. A function of three independent variables can be given a geometric interpretation by using three space variables and thinking of a function whose value is dependent upon the point's location in space, as in Fig. 43.

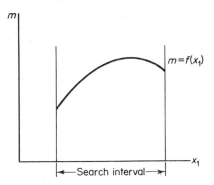

FIG. 41. A merit function of a single independent design variable.

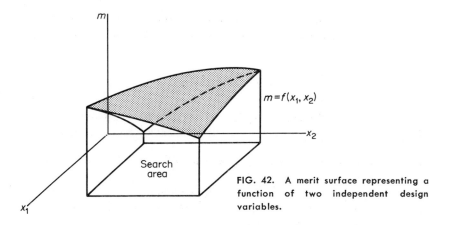

FIG. 42. A merit surface representing a function of two independent design variables.

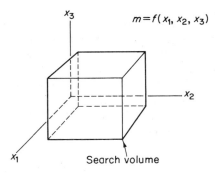

FIG. 43. A merit hypersurface exists defined by three independent design variables. Visualization is possible by imagining that at every location defined as a point x_1, x_2, x_3 there is, a number whose magnitude is the ordinate to the merit hypersurface.

69

When a function of more than three independent variables arises, geometric visualization becomes impossible. We have the convenience of geometric thinking in simple problems; in more complicated problems algebraic methods must be used, despite the lack of geometric insight. An intuitive approach to multidimensional problems is to use algebraic methods (as we must)—develop, prove, and gain experience with them in problems with two independent variables—and then extend the method into n-dimensional space.

A function of n variables

$$y = f(x_1, x_2, \ldots, x_n)$$

can be represented in a hyperspace of $(n + 1)$ orthogonal axes, or an $(n + 1)$ space. The function y is said to define a hypersurface. Thus the merit function

$$m = f(x_1, x_2, x_3)$$

is represented in a 4 space hyperspace, and m defines a hypersurface.

The difficulties encountered in multidimensional searches include:

1. multidimensionality overpowers the effective search techniques available in a 1 space;
2. the very enormity of n space is overwhelming;
3. a lack of objective comparisons of searching techniques prevents construction of optimal search plans.

Suppose a search region has c cells and that we wish to evaluate the merit function in the b best cells. The probability of choosing *at random* a cell that is in the best group (b in number) is b/c. The probability of missing a cell of the best group in a single try is $(1 - b/c)$. The selection of two cells at random involves a $(1 - b/c)^2$ probability of a double miss. The probability of finding one or more (at least one) cells in n tries is $[1 - (1 - b/c)^n]$. If the fraction b/c is denoted as f, then $p(f)$, the probability of finding at least one cell of the best group ($b = cf$), is

$$p(f) = 1 - (1 - f)^n$$

or

$$n = \left\{ \frac{\ln (1 - p(f))}{\ln (1 - f)} \right\}$$

70

If $f = 0.01$, $p(f) = 0.99$, then

$$n = \left\{ \frac{\ln (1 - 0.99)}{\ln (1 - 0.01)} \right\} = 460$$

In other words it would take 460 tries to have a 0.99 certainty of selecting, at random, one or more best cells (of a group $fc = 0.01c$).

Multivariable searches are not unlike a strange form of mountain climbing (to use a three-dimensional example), wherein the climbing director is at a radio but out of sight of the mountain, and has a robot mountain climber who can report local elevations above sea level and move from place to place on command. The climb director has no picture of the mountain, would like a picture of the mountain, but cannot afford the necessary survey. He settles for less. He is always torn between two alternatives:

1. Should he explore in a locality so as to gain a clear picture of the local lay of the land and so gain the most elevation in the next climbing move? or
2. Should he move again in a previously elevation-gaining direction settling for more but smaller gains per function evaluation?

In the beginning the climbing director must explore a randomly chosen region because nothing is known. Then, having some feel for the local topography, he orders moves in the most promising direction. If elevation is gained more moves in the same direction are ordered, then a little local exploration is in order to improve the direction of movement. Local exploration is ordered any time a move does not result in a gain in elevation. As the summit is approached, more exploration is required to find the very top in case of nearly flat-domed mountains.

4.6 SEQUENTIAL LINEAR SEARCH

Suppose the extremum of the merit surface of Fig. 44 is required within the region $0 \leq x_1 \leq a$, $0 \leq x_2 \leq b$. One opening move could be to select a line such as $x_1 = c$ and conduct a linear search along it using dichotomous or golden section search plans. Such a linear search would terminate in an extreme at $x_2 = d$. A search along line $x_2 = d$ will terminate in an extreme at $x_1 = e$. A search along $x_1 = e$ will terminate at a point near the summit.

While this linear exploration approach seems effective, it can lead to a trap. Consider the merit surface depicted in Fig. 45. A linear search begun at $x_1 = a$ will terminate at $x_2 = b$, an extreme. A search along $x_2 = b$ will terminate in the same extreme,—i.e., at (a, b). This extreme is a *false*

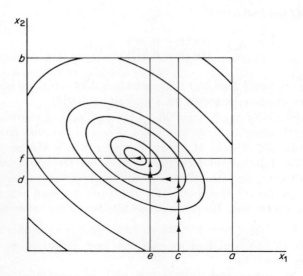

FIG. 44. Contour map of a merit surface indicating paths of sequential linear searches.

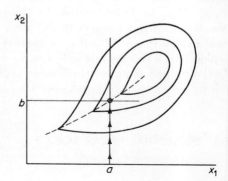

FIG. 45. Contour map of a merit surface containing a ridge and indicating the false extremum at the termination of a sequential linear search.

extremum brought about by the existence of a ridge in the merit surface. In Fig. 46 the merit surface exhibits a rising ridge. A linear search along the base line of plane R will detect the merit trace $\overline{apb}$ and report p as the extremum. A shift in direction along the base line of plane S will detect the merit trace $\overline{cpd}$ and report p as the extremum. The search plan would terminate at p although there are higher points in the merit surface.

Because entrapment at a false extremum is possible when ridges exist in merit surfaces (or hyperridges in hypersurfaces), this search plan is not recommended unless the topography of the merit surface is well known.

72

Another piece of information that can be deduced from knowledge of the tangent plane is the generation of the strike of the tangent plane—i.e., a line in the plane on one side of which are found increases in the merit function and on the other side of which are found decreases in merit function. The direction of this line is necessarily perpendicular to the direction of steepest ascent. Since

$$\Delta p = \frac{\partial p}{\partial x_1}\Delta x_1 + \frac{\partial p}{\partial x_2}\Delta x_2 = p_1\Delta x_1 + p_2\Delta x_2 \geq 0$$

then it follows that the extremum is to be found when combinations of Δx_1 and Δx_2 result in

$$p_1\Delta x_1 + p_2\Delta x_2 \geq 0$$

or

$$p_1(x_1 - a) + p_2(x_2 - b) \geq 0$$
$$p_1 x_1 + p_2 x_2 - (p_1 a + p_2 b) \geq 0$$

The equality is the equation of the line of constant merit in the tangent plane. This line divides the search area into regions: one a region of higher

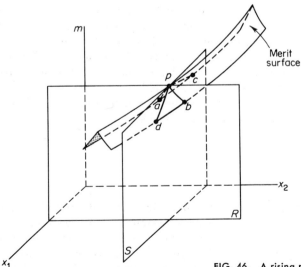

FIG. 46.   A rising ridge in a merit surface.

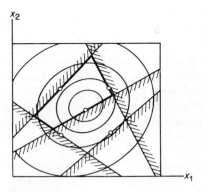

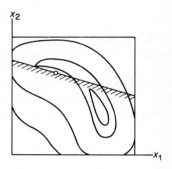

FIG. 47. The area elimination technique is applied by determining the
contour tangents through five points
and then eliminating low ground. The
darkly outlined area contains the
summit.

FIG. 48. If a contour line is concave, the possibility of eliminating
higher ground is present in the
method of area elimination.

merit (reduced area of certainty) and the other a region of lower merit (an eliminated region).

Regional or area elimination might be used as suggested by Fig. 47. A number of arbitrarily spaced points are evaluated for tangent plane location and the elimination lines drawn to define a reduced area of certainty. The search domain is reduced by five exploration points (fifteen function evaluations). There is a hidden danger in this method because of the possibility of eliminating the region containing the extremum. This can happen when a contour line is concave in some location. Figure 48 indicates the elimination of the extremum due to the location of a survey point on the concave portion of the contour line. Another drawback of this method is that the elimination is on a Boolean basis, and "high ground" just a little lower than the survey point is eliminated just as surely as if it had been low ground. Thus alternatives of low merit and alternatives of not quite so high merit are eliminated in the same stroke.

4.8 GRADIENT SEARCH

To avoid the trap of the false extremum it is desirable to take another approach to the problem of locating the extremum of the merit surface or hypersurface. The plan could be to pick a point at random, determine which way is the steepest upgrade from that point, and move in that direction. If the search area is the rectangle of the $x_1 x_2$ plane of Fig. 49, then an arbitrary ordinate to the merit surface is evaluated at (a, b). This ordinate is indicated on the figure. Shifting now to Fig. 50, we evaluate m_1 at position $(a + \Delta x_1, b)$ and m_2 at position $(a, b + \Delta x_2)$ and have three ordinate evaluations in the locality of m_0. These three ordinates are m_0, m_1, m_2. A plane passing through these three points in the merit surface is approximately tangent to the merit surface, because in the limit as $\Delta x_1 \rightarrow 0$ and $\Delta x_2 \rightarrow 0$, the plane so defined becomes coincident with the tangent plane to the merit surface at (a, b). Since we cannot let Δx_1 and Δx_2 approach zero too closely, we must settle for a good approximation. This *approximation to the tangent plane* (hereafter called the tangent plane) is denoted functionally as $p(x_1, x_2)$ and has the equation

$$p(x_1, x_2) = p_0 + p_1 x_1 + p_2 x_2$$

The constants p_0, p_1, and p_2 may be calculated from the simultaneous solution of the above equation at the three known ordinates m_0, m_1, and m_2.

$$m_0 = p_0 + p_1 a + p_2 b$$
$$m_1 = p_0 + p_1 (a + \Delta x_1) + p_2 b$$
$$m_2 = p_0 + p_1 a + p_2 (b + \Delta x_2)$$

Subtracting the second equation from the first yields

$$m_0 - m_1 = -p_1 \Delta x_1$$

or

$$p_1 = \frac{m_1 - m_0}{\Delta x_1}$$

Subtracting the third equation from the first yields

$$m_0 - m_2 = -p_2 \Delta x_2$$

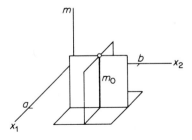

FIG. 49. An ordinate to a merit surface erected at the point (a, b).

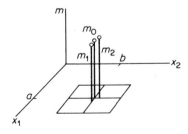

FIG. 50. Two additional ordinates to the merit surface have been erected at $a + \Delta x_1$ and $b + \Delta x_2$.

75

or

$$p_2 = \frac{m_2 - m_0}{\Delta x_2}$$

and it follows that

$$p_0 = m_0 - p_1 a - p_2 b = m_0 - \frac{(m_1 - m_0)a}{\Delta x_1} - \frac{(m_2 - m_0)b}{\Delta x_2}$$

The slope of the tangent plane in the x_1 direction is

$$\frac{\partial p}{\partial x_1} = p_1 = \frac{(m_1 - m_0)}{\Delta x_1}$$

and the slope in the x_2 direction is

$$\frac{\partial p}{\partial x_2} = p_2 = \frac{(m_2 - m_0)}{\Delta x_2}$$

If p_1 and p_2 are positive, then the plane is uphill in both the x_1 direction and the x_2 direction. If the climbing director wishes to proceed in the direction of greatest rate of ascent, then this direction is determinable from the tangent plane (examine Fig. 51). The change Δp, due to a movement Δx_1 in the x_1 direction and Δx_2 in the x_2 direction, is given by

$$\Delta p = \frac{\partial p}{\partial x_1}\Delta x_1 + \frac{\partial p}{\partial x_2}\Delta x_2 = p_1 \Delta x_1 + p_2 \Delta x_2$$

The slope of the diagonal line from point (a, b) to $(a + \Delta x_1, b + \Delta x_2)$ is

$$S = \frac{\Delta p}{\sqrt{\Delta x_1^2 + \Delta x_2^2}} = \frac{p_1 \Delta x_1 + p_2 \Delta x_2}{\sqrt{\Delta x_1^2 + \Delta x_2^2}}$$

The slope S is greatest —i.e., maximum—for a judiciously selected advance

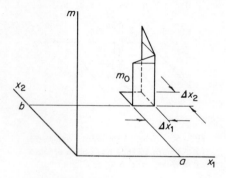

FIG. 51. The geometry of the gain in elevation for a move Δx_1 in the x_1 direction and Δx_2 in the x_2 direction from point (a, b)

whose components are $\overline{\Delta x_1}$ and $\overline{\Delta x_2}$. Satisfying the conditions

$$\frac{\partial S}{\partial \Delta x_1} = 0$$

$$\frac{\partial S}{\partial \Delta x_2} = 0$$

leads to the step $\overline{\Delta x_2}$ in the x_2 direction being given by

$$\overline{\Delta x_2} = \frac{p_2}{p_1}\overline{\Delta x_1}$$

If the searcher decides upon an advance of $\overline{\Delta x_1}$ in the x_1 direction in the case of a plane with no tilt in the x_2 direction, then $p_2 = 0$ and the appropriate x_2 coordinate of the advance is

$$\overline{\Delta x_2} = \frac{(0)}{p_1}\overline{\Delta x_1} = 0$$

and the steepest ascent is in the x_1 direction.

The previous arguments may be extended to a hyperspace of n abscissas as follows: The hyperplane $p(x_1, x_2, \ldots, x_n)$ which is tangent to the hypersurface (the tangent hyperplane) is denoted functionally as

$$p(x_1, x_2, \ldots, x_n) = p_0 + p_1 x_1 + p_2 x_2 + \cdots + p_n x_n$$

The ordinates at the survey points are

$$m_0 = p_0 + p_1 a + p_2 b + \qquad \cdots + p_n z$$
$$m_1 = p_0 + p_1(a + \Delta x_1) + p_2 b + \cdots + p_n z$$
$$m_2 = p_0 + p_1 a + p_2(b + \Delta x_2) + \cdots + p_n z$$
$$\vdots \qquad \vdots$$
$$m_n = p_0 + p_1 a + p_2 b + \qquad \cdots + p_n(z + \Delta x_n)$$

Subtracting each equation in turn from the first equation above yields

$$m_0 - m_1 = -p_1 \Delta x_1$$
$$m_0 - m_2 = -p_2 \Delta x_2$$
$$\vdots$$
$$m_0 - m_n = -p_n \Delta x_n$$

It follows that the slopes of the tangent plane in the ordinal directions are

$$p_1 = \frac{m_1 - m_0}{\Delta x_1}$$

$$p_2 = \frac{m_2 - m_0}{\Delta x_2}$$

$$\cdot \qquad \cdot$$
$$\cdot \qquad \cdot$$
$$\cdot \qquad \cdot$$

$$p_n = \frac{m_n - m_0}{\Delta x_n}$$

The change in the ordinate to the plane p due to small movement from the survey position is given by

$$\Delta p = \frac{\partial p}{\partial x_1}\Delta x_1 + \frac{\partial p}{\partial x_2}\Delta x_2 + \cdots + \frac{\partial p}{\partial x_n}\Delta x_n$$

In terms of the slopes of the tangent plane in ordinal directions this equation is written as

$$\Delta p = p_1\Delta x_1 + p_2\Delta x_2 + \cdots + p_n\Delta x_n$$

The slope of the hyperline drawn from point $(a, b, \ldots, z)$ to the point $(a + \Delta x_1, b + \Delta x_2, \ldots, z + \Delta x_n)$ is

$$S = \frac{\Delta p}{(\Delta x_1^2 + \Delta x_2^2 + \cdots + \Delta x_n^2)^{1/2}} = \frac{p_1\Delta x_1 + p_2\Delta x_2 + \cdots + p_n\Delta x_n}{(\Delta x_1^2 + \Delta x_2^2 + \cdots + \Delta x_n^2)^{1/2}}$$

In order for the slope to be a maximum the conditions

$$\frac{\partial S}{\partial \Delta x_1} = 0, \frac{\partial S}{\partial \Delta x_2} = 0, \ldots, \frac{\partial S}{\partial \Delta x_n} = 0$$

must be met. These lead to the relations

$$(\Delta x_1^2 + \Delta x_2^2 + \cdots + \Delta x_n^2)p_1 - (p_1\Delta x_1 + p_2\Delta x_2 + \cdots + p_n\Delta x_n)\Delta x_1 = 0$$
$$(\Delta x_1^2 + \Delta x_2^2 + \cdots + \Delta x_n^2)p_2 - (p_1\Delta x_1 + p_2\Delta x_2 + \cdots + p_n\Delta x_n)\Delta x_2 = 0$$

$$\cdot \qquad\qquad\qquad\qquad\qquad\qquad\qquad\qquad\qquad\qquad\qquad \cdot$$
$$\cdot \qquad\qquad\qquad\qquad\qquad\qquad\qquad\qquad\qquad\qquad\qquad \cdot$$
$$\cdot \qquad\qquad\qquad\qquad\qquad\qquad\qquad\qquad\qquad\qquad\qquad \cdot$$

$$(\Delta x_1^2 + \Delta x_2^2 + \cdots + \Delta x_n^2)p_n - (p_1\Delta x_1 + p_2\Delta x_2 + \cdots + p_n\Delta x_n)\Delta x_n = 0$$

Dividing each equation successively into the first yields

78

$$\overline{\Delta x_2} = \frac{p_2}{p_1}\overline{\Delta x_1}$$

$$\overline{\Delta x_3} = \frac{p_3}{p_1}\overline{\Delta x_1}$$

.   .

.   .

.   .

$$\overline{\Delta x_n} = \frac{p_n}{p_1}\overline{\Delta x_1}$$

The above increments correspond to the steepest ascent.

If the step size in a two-dimensional search (projected in the $x_1 x_2$ plane) is denoted Δ, then

$$\Delta = (\overline{\Delta x_1^2} + \overline{\Delta x_2^2})^{1/2}$$

If the search is n-dimensional, then the step size Δ is given by

$$\Delta = (\overline{\Delta x_1^2} + \overline{\Delta x_2^2} + \cdots + \overline{\Delta x_n^2})^{1/2}$$

or

$$\Delta = \left[\overline{\Delta x_1^2} + \left(\frac{p_2}{p_1}\right)^2\overline{\Delta x_1^2} + \left(\frac{p_3}{p_1}\right)^2\overline{\Delta x_1^2} + \cdots + \left(\frac{p_n}{p_1}\right)^2\overline{\Delta x_1}^2 \right]^{1/2}$$

or

$$\overline{\Delta x_1} = \frac{p_1\Delta}{(p_1^2 + p_2^2 + p_3^2 + \cdots + p_n^2)^{1/2}}$$

This is the correct increment $\overline{\Delta x_1}$ with which to effect the step size Δ proceeding along the steepest ascent.

4.9   IMPLEMENTING GRADIENT SEARCH IN N-SPACE

There were two useful elements deducible from the tangent plane: the domain of superior merit (area elimination) and the direction of steepest ascent. The drawback of area elimination method is the possibility that the extremum will be eliminated when concave contour lines are present. We therefore should not use area elimination. We now further investigate the method of ascent made possible by local knowledge of the gradient.

Such methods are called *gradient search plans*. The stratagem might be to follow the direction of the steepest ascent. It can be successful when

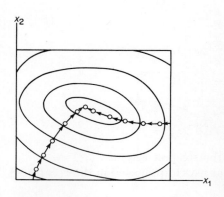

FIG. 52. Two summit-attaining gradient search paths shown on a contour map of a merit surface.

pursuit of local gradient leads inevitably to the summit. This is most likely to be true when the summit is a domelike extreme. The case of concave contour lines would not thwart the gradient search. A two-dimensional illustration in Fig. 52 shows the search path following the local gradient and attaining the summit. Notice that the lines of maximum gradient are approximately perpendicular to the contour lines. In the limit, as step size approaches zero, the search path is perpendicular to contour lines. Figure 53 shows a number of gradient lines. A gradient search started from any of the stations 1, 2, 3, ..., 13 would approximately follow the gradient lines if the step size is not too large. Concave contour lines will not confuse the method.

Consider the bimodal merit surface depicted in Fig. 54. Contour lines and gradient search paths have been drawn. Notice that the ascents begun at stations 1, 2, 3, 4, 13, 14, and 15 climb to one extremum, and ascents begun at stations 6, 7, 8, 9, and 10 climb to the other extremum. The ascents begun at stations 5 and 11 climb to the saddle point. Fortunately

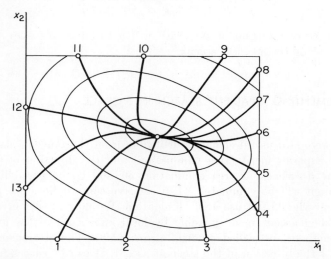

FIG. 53. Thirteen gradient lines on a contour map of a merit surface representing summit-attaining gradient search paths.

80

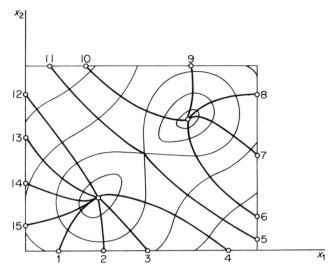

FIG. 54. Gradient lines on a bimodal surface.

only a very particular gradient line includes the saddle point on it. To a gradient search plan a saddle is not a serious obstacle. To guard against termination of search at a saddle, the terminal point can be tested for its identity, extremum, or saddle.

Next consider the unimodal merit surface depicted in Fig. 55, in which a portion of the surface is plane. A search begun at station 1 will progress until it encounters a ridge line (a locus of the discontinuity in the slope of the contour lines). What happens when a gradient search plan encounters a ridge? Figure 56 indicates, by open circles, ridge points in the plane; the arrows attached indicate the direction of steepest ascent as seen in the plane. The solid dots are points in the curved merit surface and on the ridge; the arrows attached indicate the direction of steepest ascent as seen in the curved merit surface in the neighborhood of the ridge. At the ridge there are two gradients. The gradients are such that if a search "stepped" alternately in the curved surface and in the plane surface, the search path would follow the ridge at some loss in the rate of ascent (much as a man follows a ditch approximately by stepping somewhat laterally in the sides). When the slope of the ridge line is slight, the gradient search becomes very slow. Notice that in the representation of a ridge the contour lines break and seem to "point" downhill. For a valley the contour cusps point uphill.

The gradient search on a two-dimensional surface evaluates the merit function three times to survey the neighborhood in order to find the local direction of steepest ascent. A pattern of several climbing steps is portrayed

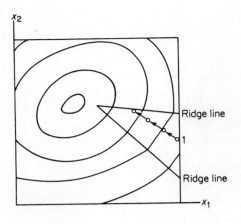

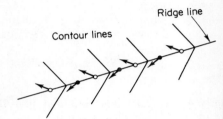

FIG. 55. A partially plane merit surface showing a gradient search path about to interact with the ridge.

FIG. 56. Gradient directions in the neighborhood of a ridge.

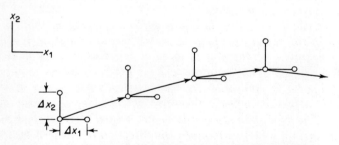

FIG. 57. Subsequent climbing steps made by a gradient search plan.

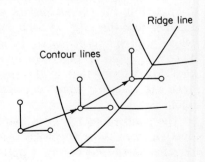

FIG. 58. A gradient search survey pattern has straddled a ridge line.

82

in Fig. 57. When the climbing steps between survey points are so coarse compared with the dimensions Δx_1 and Δx_2 that the ridge line does not cross the footprint of a survey pattern, then the proper local gradient is measured, its direction assessed, and the appropriate direction of next climbing step thereby determined. When a ridge line intersects a survey pattern (survey footprint steps on the ridge line), a situation such as that depicted in Fig. 58 occurs. The gradient measured by the survey is not correct for either side of the ridge, If the "north" survey point shows a rise to the north and the "east" survey point shows a rise to the east, then the gradient deduced will indicate steepest ascent in the northeast quadrant. Figure 59 shows the various interpretations at step 3 in Fig. 58: the ascending direction for the next step might be reported in any direction in the first or second quadrant. Step 4, acting on the false gradient measured by step 3, will have an uphill component, but it may be very small. Stepping on a ridge slows the climb. The gradient method follows ridges uphill, and so crosses over many times. Unless the survey pattern is very small compared with the step size, it is likely that the ridge will be stepped on and that slowing, both from the ridge straddling and the ridge being stepped on, will be present.

Figure 60 (a) shows a three-point survey which has stepped on a ridge line. The abscissa angle of the contour line through the survey point is β. The abscissa angle of the same contour line on the other side of the ridge line is γ. The abscissa angle of the ridge is δ. The triangle $\overline{abc}$ has an east-west side of length Δx_1. The two adjacent angles are $(\pi - \beta)$ and α. The length of side s is given by the law of sines as

$$\frac{\Delta x_1}{\sin\left[\pi - (\pi - \beta) - \alpha\right]}$$

$$= \frac{s}{\sin (\pi - \beta)}$$

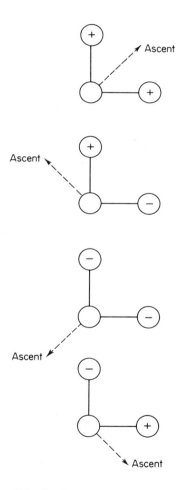

FIG. 59. Interpretations of the direction of steepest ascent that can be made from exploratory pattern.

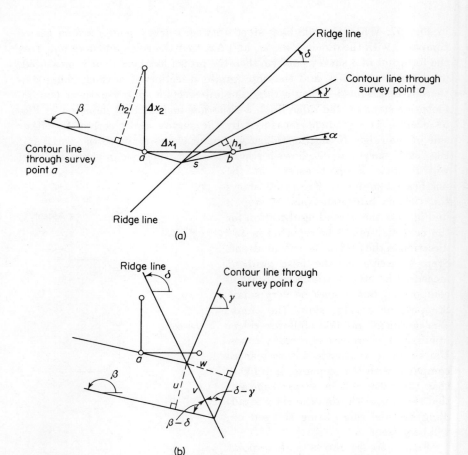

FIG. 60 Geometry of a three-point survey pattern that has stepped on a ridge line, (a) strike northeast and (b) strike northwest.

or

$$s = \frac{\Delta x_1 \sin \beta}{\sin (\beta - \alpha)}$$

The increase in the merit function above the survey point will be, at the east point,

$$\Delta m_1 = -h_1 G_1 = G_1 s \sin (\alpha - \gamma) = \frac{G_1 \Delta x_1 \sin \beta \sin (\alpha - \gamma)}{\sin (\beta - \alpha)}$$

where G_1 is the gradient in locale of the east point. The increase in the merit function at the north survey point, above the value at the survey point will be

84

$$\Delta m_2 = G_2 h_2 = G_2 \Delta x_2 \cos(\pi - \beta) = -G_2 \Delta x_2 \cos \beta$$

The implied gradient in the easterly direction is

$$p_1 = \frac{G_1 \sin \beta \sin (\alpha - \gamma)}{\sin (\beta - \alpha)}$$

and the implied (correct) gradient in the northerly direction is

$$p_2 = -G_2 \cos \beta$$

The gradient in the easterly direction in the absence of the ridge is $p_1' = G_2 \sin \beta$. The gradient direction in the neighborhood of the survey point is denoted ξ' and

$$\tan \xi' = \frac{p_2}{p_1'} = \frac{-G_2 \cos \beta}{G_2 \sin \beta} = -\frac{1}{\tan \beta}$$

The direction of steepest ascent implied by the survey is

$$\tan \xi = \frac{p_2}{p_1} = \frac{-G_2 \cos \beta \sin (\beta - \alpha)}{G_1 \sin \beta \sin (\alpha - \gamma)} = \tan \xi' \left[\frac{G_2 \sin (\beta - \alpha)}{G_1 \sin (\alpha - \gamma)} \right]$$

In moving from contour to contour to the left of the ridge, the direction of steepest ascent is shown to be along u of Fig.61, and

$$G_2 = \frac{\Delta m}{u}$$

In moving from contour to contour to the right of the ridge line, the largest gradient is along w of Fig. 61, and

$$G_1 = \frac{\Delta m}{w}$$

and

$$\frac{G_2}{G_1} = \frac{w}{u}$$

Now

$$u = v \cos \left(\beta - \frac{\pi}{2} - \delta \right) = v \sin (\beta - \delta)$$

$$w = v \sin (\delta - \gamma)$$

therefore

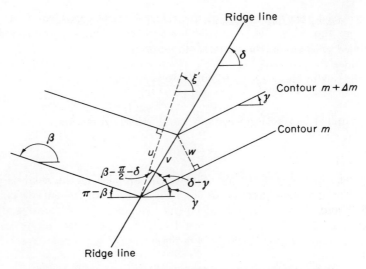

FIG. 61. Contour geometry in neighborhood of northeast ridge.

$$\frac{G_2}{G_1} = \frac{\sin (\delta - \gamma)}{\sin (\beta - \delta)}$$

It follows that

$$\tan \xi = \tan \xi' \left[\frac{\sin (\delta - \gamma) \sin (\beta - \alpha)}{\sin (\beta - \gamma) \sin (\alpha - \gamma)} \right]$$

The worst condition occurs when the ridge is the edge of a cliff and $\gamma = \delta$ then

$$\tan \xi = \tan \xi'(0)$$

and

$$\xi = 0 \text{ or } \pi$$

since $\sin (\delta - \delta)$ is zero and $\gamma > \alpha$. This indicates that the surveyed direction of steepest ascent is in the x_1 direction. As this condition is approached $\tan \xi$ becomes negative, since $(\alpha - \gamma)$ is a negative angle. The appropriate angle is $\xi = \pi$, and the surveyed direction of steepest ascent is in the $-x_1$ direction.

A gradient search stepping on a cliff edge would recoil from the edge with a step in the $-x_1$ direction. The recoil step would permit another local survey away from the cliff edge and pursuit of the local gradient. A gradient search ought not to have encountered this ridge of Figs. 60(a) and 61 while

86

moving in the area to the left of the ridge, since the gradient is directed away from the ridge line. A gradient search could have encountered this ridge line while moving to the east of the ridge.

Consider the ridge of Fig. 60(b), which could be encountered in searching to the left of the ridge line. It still follows that

$$\tan \xi = \frac{p_2}{p_1} = \tan \xi' \frac{G_2 \sin (\beta - \alpha)}{G_1 \sin (\alpha - \gamma)}$$

and

$$\tan \xi = \tan \xi' \frac{\sin (\delta - \gamma) \sin (\beta - \alpha)}{\sin (\beta - \gamma) \sin (\alpha - \gamma)}$$

and everything is as before. A precipitous slope to the right of the ridge line, say a vertical cliff, leads to a recoil in the $-x_1$ direction as before, and continuation of the search up the left slope toward a possible re-encounter with the ridge later on.

The gradient search method follows a ridge in the following ways:

1. When the search steps over the ridge, the path of search is directed back toward the ridge, resulting in a zigzag following of the ridge upgrade. Gaining altitude in this fashion can be a painfully slow process.
2. When the survey pattern steps on the ridge, the search path recoils from the ridge and continues from the recoil step.
3. When the search survey pattern steps on a cliff edge, the recoil is in the negative abscissa direction.

4.10 PATTERN SEARCH IN N-SPACE

Gradient searching schemes work well in n-dimensional space when there are no ridges and the summit is domelike. It is true that mild ridges increase the time to attain the summit, but the strong ridges likely to be encountered in computer-aided design can cause the designer problems when he does not know they are there and he relies on a gradient search method. A surface as simple as that depicted in Fig. 25 (p. 36) has four sharp ridges, introduced into the problem by the regional constraints. A gradient search in this circumstance can have real problems if such a ridge is encountered. The direction to the extreme is "along the ridge," yet the gradient direction points toward an infeasible area on the basis plane. The problem is now stategic, since "up" is no longer indicated by the gradient. A gradient search method can be evolved which will "mix" its strategy when it encounters an irresolvable ridge, abandon the gradient, and turn to "follow" the ridge.

A search technique somewhat akin to gradient searching but capable of steering along a rising ridge is called pattern search. Briefly it operates as follows:

1. A base point is established in feasible space.
2. From the base point an exploratory survey is made by systematically incrementing the abscissas of the space. Rather than determine the direction of steepest ascent, the method settles for an improvement. The coordinates of the perturbed base point are used to specify a second point. If the merit ordinate is superior to the base point, the new point becomes a second (and superior) base point.
3. A line connecting the two base points, projected from the first toward the second and extrapolated beyond, indicates the direction of "rising ground."
4. A step equal to the distance between base points is taken, and at this new location an exploratory search is carried out and the best perturbations of coordinates used. This has the effect of reaching out along the line of base points and then "steering" a little laterally according to the local topography.
5. If the up direction is substantially that of the base line extension, the third position—now a third base point—is further from the second base than the second is from the first.
6. Continued successes result in bolder and bolder extrapolation steps. This continues until the extrapolation step oversteps a ridge and no merit ordinate is superior to that at the last base point. At this point the size of the local exploration is reduced, the last successful base point taken as the first, and a new pattern developed.
7. Search is terminated when the reduction in exploration size has been reduced below a predetermined level.

Figure 62 shows a pattern search that encounters a regional constraint,

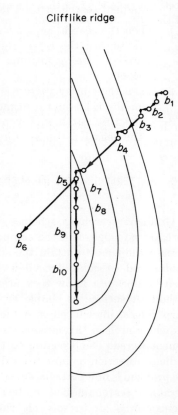

FIG. 62. Pattern search technique.

here a cliff on the merit surface. Base point $\mathbf{b}_1$ is established within the feasible area of the basis plane, the $x_1 x_2$ plane. An exploration is carried out in the neighborhood of $\mathbf{b}_1$ by adding a small amount δ to the x_1 coordinate of $\mathbf{b}_1$. The merit is inferior to that at $\mathbf{b}_1$, so exploration in the $-x_1$ direction is undertaken. This does result in an increase in merit, so the x_1 increment, $-\delta$, is noted. Similarly the x_2 increment is discovered to be $-\delta$. Perturbing $\mathbf{b}_1$ with these values established location $\mathbf{b}_2$, which is found to have superior merit to $\mathbf{b}_1$. The location $\mathbf{b}_2$ is designated a second base point.

An extrapolation from $\mathbf{b}_1$ through $\mathbf{b}_2$ is carried out, a small exploration carried out, and, when point $\mathbf{b}_3$ is discovered to be superior in merit to point $\mathbf{b}_2$, $\mathbf{b}_3$ is designated the third base point. Notice that the distance from $\mathbf{b}_1$ to $\mathbf{b}_2$ is half the distance from $\mathbf{b}_2$ to $\mathbf{b}_3$.

Similar explorations and extrapolations bring us to $\mathbf{b}_5$. An attempt to establish $\mathbf{b}_6$ meets with failure, so $\mathbf{b}_6$ is the same as $\mathbf{b}_5$. A new pattern is begun treating $\mathbf{b}_6$ as the initial base, reducing step size δ to, say, half its previous size, and $\mathbf{b}_7$ is established. The pattern is moving in the $-x_2$ direction due to the fact that the exploratory step in the $-x_1$ direction stepped "off the cliff." The pattern of extrapolation and exploration is again defeated after establishment of base $\mathbf{b}_{10}$. Again the step size is reduced and base point $\mathbf{b}_{10}$ is established as $\mathbf{b}_{11}$, an initial base point. Repeated attempts fail, and when the step size is reduced to a predetermined magnitude, the search terminates with last base point reported as the extreme.

In order to avoid deciding what the step size in each abscissa direction should be, it is prudent to normalize the coordinates and conduct the search on a basis plane of unit area (or in other problems, on a basis space of unit size). This is simply accomplished by equating the normalized abscissa x_{im} as follows:

$$x_{im} = \frac{x_i - x_{iL}}{x_{iR} - x_{iL}}$$

where

x_{im} = normalized abscissa in the i direction
x_i = abscissa in the i direction
x_{iL} = smallest value of abscissa x_i encountered
x_{iR} = largest value of abscissa x_i encountered

4.11 GRID SEARCH IN N-SPACE

Search methods that appear to move an "exploratory bug" in the merit surface and are sensitive to gradient (or nearly so) have a small exploratory pattern. Due to the smallness of this pattern the method can be confused on encounter with an irresolvable ridge, such as a "cliff." Visualize a hemi-sphere cut by a plane perpendicular to the base and intersecting the sphere along a small circle. Let us consider the smaller fragment of the hemisphere as the merit surface. If a gradient-sensitive search climbs the surface, it will, in general, encounter the cliff edge at an altitude inferior to the extreme altitude of the merit surface. Unless means are included in the search strategy for sensing the strike of the cliff and the direction of improving altitude, the search will be defeated. This is the fate of gradient-sensitive search schemes when used alone, simply because once the cliff is encountered the "up direction" is no longer in agreement with the direction of the gradient.

Exploratory lattices begun at this juncture can result in some improvement in altitude, but they are drawn closer and closer to the cliff edge and can be likewise defeated because of the smallness of their pattern size. No indication is available of how much enlargement in pattern size is necessary or desirable to produce success.

The "cliff-type" ridges encountered in design problems are often irresolvable by pattern size reduction. The "cliff" orientations (usually due to functional constraints and penalty ordinates) are askew to the coordinate system. This condition invites the traps of false optimum inherent in sequential linear searches, since kindred techniques are usually incorporated in the exploratory features of gradient-sensitive searches.

In such circumstances it is desirable that pattern size not be small upon initial encounter with a cliff-type ridge. In order to satisfy this requirement, a grid-type search can be used. Thinking in terms of a three-dimensional problem (two design variables) will help visualize the nature of the grid-type search. The region of uncertainty is mapped into and onto a unit area (volume or hypervolume as appropriate) so that the interval of uncertainty at the initiation of the search is bounded by abscissas 0 and 1 on all design variables. On this unit square (cube or hypercube) is drawn a grid of orthogonal lines intersecting at their third-points. The merit ordinate is evaluated at these nodes as well as at the center of the pattern, which initially includes the entire region of uncertainty. This involves $2m + 1$ function evaluations, where m is the number of design variables. Note is made of the location of the largest of these ordinates. This position becomes the center of a reduced grid having a size that is a fraction of the original grid size. If a reduction of side length r of $\frac{2}{3}$ is selected, the new nodes are at new (not previously evaluated) positions. This is done purposely in order to maintain an influx of new information concerning the merit surface. The information is useful in correcting poor moves that result from the coarseness of the grid, and the consequently sketchy information upon which decision must be made.

The search continues, following the most promising ordinate uncovered from each grid, and the grid contracts in size until a previously established grid size is attained. If no false moves are made, the search is capable of pursuing an extreme to any location in the domain of uncertainty. Due to the coarseness of the grid some poor moves are bound to occur. Therefore, although r cannot be less than $\frac{2}{3}$, it is desirable that it be somewhat greater, though less than, 1. Table 4.5 indicates the cost of the search in function evaluations for a given fractional reduction in the domain of uncertainty as measured along an abscissa.

TABLE 4.5

Number of Function Evaluations, n	Fractional Reduction in Domain of Uncertainty Measured along an Abscissa, f
$2^m + 1$	r
$2(2^m) + 1$	r^2
$3(2^m) + 1$	r^3
.	.
.	.
.	.
$b(2^m) + 1$	r^b

It is clear that the linear fractional reduction in the interval of uncertainty is

$$f = r^b$$

Since

$$n = b(2^m) + 1$$

it follows that

$$f = r^{(n-1)/2^m}$$

from which the number n of functional evaluations required is

$$n = \left\{1 + \frac{2^m \ln f}{\ln r}\right\}$$

For $f = 0.01$, $r = \frac{2}{3}$, and $m = 1$

$$n = \left\{1 + \frac{2^1 \ln 0.01}{\ln (2/3)}\right\} = \{23.7\} = 24$$

For $f = 0.01$, $r = \frac{2}{3}$, and $m = 2$

$$n = \left\{1 + \frac{2^2 \ln 0.01}{\ln (2/3)}\right\} = \{46.4\} = 47$$

When $f = 0.01$, $r = \frac{2}{3}$, and $m = 4$

$$n = \left\{ 1 + \frac{2^4 \ln 0.01}{\ln (2/3)} \right\} = \{182.1\} = 183$$

Notice that the increase in function evaluations is approximately exponential with dimensionality—i.e., approximately exponential with the number of design variables. As $r \to 1$ the number of function evaluations increases without bound.

The cam problem discussed in Sec. 5.4 and the curved beam problem illustrated in Sec. 5.7 will employ a grid-type searching scheme because of the "cliffs" introduced by the functional constraints in the problems.

No single searching scheme has universal applicability for the simple reason that the geometric complexities of n space can be formidable, and, depending upon the character of the problem at hand, particular approaches exhibit differing effectiveness. Matching a searching scheme to a problem is still a skill evolved from experience. The reader is referred to the extensive literature of optimization, some of which is cited in Appendix 4. Considerably more study than the very brief introduction of this chapter is essential for those who intend to pursue the more complex problems of engineering design.

The grid-type search documented in Appendix 2 has a feature in addition to those indicated in the preceding discussion. In order to increase the flow of information of the ordinates to the merit surface in the exploration locale, the exploratory pattern alternates between that of a "square" about the mid-ordinate and that of a "star" similar to that employed in gradient search. This alternation of search pattern has the effect of allowing movement of the search in eight possible directions (four opportunities after each search pattern). In this way some cliffs can be followed for a distance toward rising ground. Additional improvements can be made to increase the cliff-following ability of the grid-type search. Their programming tends to become machine-specific and they are not treated here.

For the alternating star-square exploratory pattern it is left to the reader to demonstrate that the number of functional evaluations is

$$n = \left\{ 1 + (2^{m-1} + m) \frac{\ln f}{\ln r} \right\}$$

which is more economical of function evaluations than the square pattern when the number of independent design variables is three or greater.

PROBLEMS AS THEY
CONFRONT THE ENGINEER

5.1 IOWA CADET: AN ALGORITHM FOR COMPUTER-AIDED DESIGN

The advent of computer hardware allowing the substitution of a time-sharing mode of operation for a batch system of program processing so dramatically reduces turnaround time in the debugging process that engineering designers can conveniently use the computer and obtain usable answers very rapidly. The extent to which engineering designers will avail themselves of this tool will be great if convenient alogrithms of use are available.

An algorithm which permits expeditious use of a computer facility as well as the fruits of previous labor is the previously mentioned IOWA CADET. The software elements are a battery of search programs, a library of useful engineering-analysis routines, and the convenient documentation of these programs.

In the beginning just a few search programs will suffice, the most important being the multidimensional searching program that will crawl over a merit hypersurface and discover the location of the largest ordinate to the degree of accuracy specified by the designer. Gradient, pattern, and grid-searching technique are useful. Such subprograms are documented in Appendix 2.

The multidimensional search programs can be used for one-dimensional searches; however, there exist much more effective one-dimensional search techniques. The golden section search technique is very efficient, and such a subprogram is documented in Appendix 2.

The design library consists of analysis routines which the designer finds useful in his day-to-day work. These subroutines are simply automated conditional responses to familiar situations. The battery of subroutines useful in a design room for agricultural implements differs markedly from that useful in a structural design office. Since useful routines vary greatly from job situation to job situation, it is false hope to become complacent and await the availability of proprietary routines (developed by computing machinery companies) that will solve your particular engineering design problems. Only broad, general-interest routines can find a market. Only the designer knows what is important to *him* in his work. Only the designer can envision the library that will be of value to him. *If it is to exist, only he can develop it or supervise its creation.*

Given the existence of search programs and a design library, how can they be utilized?

1. The designer writes an EXECUTIVE PROGRAM to read in all necessary information and to document the problem and its output information. This EXECUTIVE PROGRAM calls the SEARCH subroutine.
2. The SEARCH subroutine is a library program that will crawl over a multidimensional hypersurface and discover the location and magnitude of the largest ordinate to the hypersurface. The SEARCH program does this by calling the subprogram MERIT in such a way as to find the largest ordinate of merit.
3. The designer writes the MERIT subroutine which generates alternative solutions to his problem, tests them against the constraints of the problem, and, if they are satisfactory, calculates their merit according to the rules laid down by the designer. In generating alternatives and calculating the solution figure of merit, the MERIT subroutine calls design library subroutines.

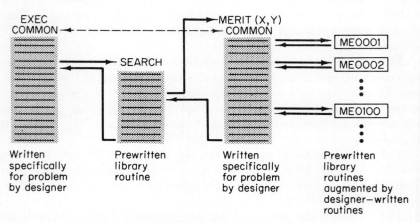

FIG. 63. IOWA CADET* algorithm for simple synthesis.

Computer Augmented Design Engineering Technique.

4. The DESIGN subroutines are really analysis subprograms that
have been written, checked out, found useful, and documented in
a convenient manner in order to facilitate ease of use. As problems
require new subroutines, these are written by the designer, used,
and then documented and deposited in the library for subsequent
utilization. Thus a nucleus design library grows in useful directions
and as time elapses, grows in value inasmuch as it is custom-built
to serve the needs of a particular designer of a specific design office.

In the beginning of an operation, such as in an engineering school
seeking to provide a computer-aided design experience for its students,
the initial design library will be of modest scope and prewritten by the
design faculty. As larger problems are solved and new routines added to
the library, an impressive capability can be amassed for student and faculty
use. Figure 63 illustrates in its simplest form the algorithm just described.

5.2 PROPER PROPORTIONS FOR A CAN

As our first example of the use of the IOWA CADET algorithm for the
computer-aided solution of an engineering problem, let us consider
the task of determining the proportions of the right circular cylindrical
container fabricated of sheet metal that will
have the least mass for a specified interior
volume. For a given gauge of sheet metal this
is equivalent to seeking a minimum of sheet
metal area. This problem is posed simply in
order to exemplify the use of the algorithm.

In order to obtain an order-of-magnitude
solution, let us initially ignore the excess of
metal that must be provided in order to
dish the ends for strength and crimp the
ends to the cylindrical sleeve. We shall also
ignore the overlap necessary for the soldered
seam, the thickness of the metal itself, and
the edge allowances for crimping. Figure 64
indicates the essential geometry of the can. The volume is given by

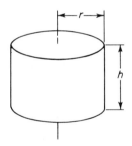

FIG. 64. The essential geometry
of a right circular cylinder.

$$V = r^2 h$$

and for a specified volume V the altitude h is determined from

$$h = \frac{V}{\pi r^2}$$

95

The lateral area of the can is composed of the sleeve area plus the area of the two circular ends. This lateral area A is given by

$$A = 2\pi r^2 + 2\pi rh$$

The area may be expressed as a function of the single independent variable r by substituting for h in the previous equation

$$A = 2\pi r^2 + \frac{2V}{r}$$

In order to minimize the area with respect to the independent variable r, we differentiate the expression for A with respect to r and equate to zero. Thus

$$\frac{dA}{dr} = 4\pi r - \frac{2V}{r^2} = 0$$

from which

$$r^3 = \frac{V}{2\pi}$$

and the optimal radius is given by

$$r = \left(\frac{V}{2\pi}\right)^{1/3}$$

The associated height is

$$h = \frac{V}{\pi r^2} = \frac{V(2\pi)^{2/3}}{\pi V^{2/3}} = 2r \tag{5.1}$$

The optimal proportions provided by this simple mathematical model, which ignores fabrication allowances, indicate that an equality exists between the altitude h and the diameter d. We shall now improve the modeling of the physical situation by introducing the following additional parameters:

r_1 = dishing allowance on the container ends, in.
r_2 = crimping allowance on the container ends, in.
r_3 = seam allowance for forming the cylindrical sleeve, in.
h_1 = crimping allowance for attaching an end, in.

Figure 65 indicates the essential geometry of this more realistic model. Ignoring the corner chamfers on the sleeve blank and the thickness of the sheet metal itself, we find that for our revised model the interior volume is given by

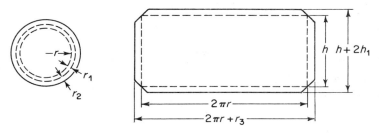

FIG. 65. The geometry of parts of a right circular cylindrical sheet-metal can.

$$V = \pi r^2 h$$

and the area of sheet metal provided to fabricate a can is predicted by

$$A = 2\pi(r + r_1 + r_2)^2 + (2\pi r + r_3)(h + 2h_1)$$

Let us now suppose that the numerical work associated with the problem is sufficiently complex to require computer assistance. We identify the tactical figure of merit function as the volume-to-area ratio V/A,

$$\frac{V}{A} = \frac{\pi r^2 h}{2\pi(r + r_1 + r_2)^2 + (2\pi r + r_3)(h + 2h_1)} \qquad \text{(merit function)}$$

which we will seek to maximize. For a given volume of container there is a functional constraint which does not allow the altitude of the can to be independent of the radius. Thus the equation

$$h = \frac{V}{\pi r^2} \qquad \text{(functional constraint)}$$

constitutes the functional constraint for this problem.

The search for the optimal V/A ratio is carried out over a one-dimensional domain wherein the radius r is the independent variable. There may or may not be regional constraints. We shall reject solutions with a negative radius and declare

$$0 \le r \le 10 \qquad \text{(regional constraint)}$$

as the regional constraint.

Inasmuch as we are faced with a one-dimensional search problem, we shall choose the efficient golden section search method and utilize the IOWA CADET library subroutine GOLD1. The documentation of GOLD1 in Appendix 2 indicates that the subroutine calls another subroutine MERIT1 (X, Y) in carrying out the process of reducing the interval of uncertainty

97

from a span of 10 in., $0 \le r \le 10$, to a specified fraction of this initial interval.

We are ready to compose the subroutine MERIT1(R, Y)

```
      SUBROUTINE MERIT1(R, Y)
      COMMON VOL, R1, R2, R3, H1, H, AREA
      PI = 3.14159
      H = VOL/(PI*R*R)
      AREA = 2.*PI*(R + R1 + R2)*(R + R1 + R2)
1           + (2.*PI*R + R3)*(H + 2.*H1)
      Y = VOL/AREA
      RETURN
      END
```

The subroutine simply calculates the figure of merit Y, and in order to do so requires knowledge of the radius R (which comes from the search routine GOLD1 through the call list) and the voulme VOL. The fabrication allowances R1, R2, R3, and H1 are supplied to MERIT1 from the executive program via the COMMON statement. Since for documentation reasons we desire knowledge of the altitude H and the surface area AREA in the executive program, the values of H and AREA are passed back to the executive program, via the COMMON statement. Hence the declarative statement

COMMON VOL, R1, R2, R3, H1, H, AREA

in the subroutine MERIT1.

We have remaining the task of composing the executive program for this problem. It should perform the following functions:

1. State the problem.
2. Define the variables.
3. Read in necessary information.
4. Pass information to MERIT1.
5. Call subroutine GOLD1, which searches the domain of the figure of merit, reducing the interval of uncertainty to desirable size and reporting results of the search.
6. Document input information.
7. Document output information.
8. The executive program should be written in such a way so that it can be used to solve many problems involving variation of the parameters, hence all parametric information should be read from cards.

An examination of the executive program which follows shows that these requirements have been met.

98

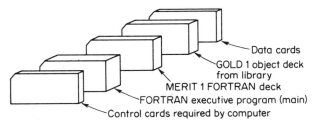

FIG. 66. Assembly of punch card decks to solve can problem.

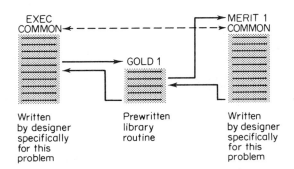

FIG. 67. IOWA CADET program structure for can problem.

The program deck is assembled as shown in Fig. 66, which represents in card form the program structure depicted in Fig. 67. The problem is now run on the computer.

```
C       OPTIMAL PROPORTIONS FOR A RIGHT CYLINDRICAL CONTAINER
C
C       NOMENCLATURE
C
C       VOL=VOLUME OF CONTAINER, IN3
C       H=HEIGHT OF CONTAINER, IN
C       R=RADIUS OF CONTAINER, IN
C       D=DIAMETER OF CONTAINER, IN
C       R1=DISHING ALLOWANCE ON CONTAINER ENDS, IN
C
C       R2=CRIMPING ALLOWANCE ON CONTAINER ENDS, IN
C       R3=SEAM ALLOWANCE FOR FORMING CYLINDRICAL SHELL, IN
C       H1=CRIMPING ALLOWANCE FOR ATTACHING END, IN
C       AREA=AREA OF SHEET METAL USED IN FABRICATION, IN2
C
        COMMON VOL,R1,R2,R3,H1,H,AREA
C
C       ..... READ INPUT DATA .....
C
      5 READ(1,2)VOL,R1,R2,R3,H1,RHIGH,RLOW,F
      2 FORMAT(8F10.5)
        I=1
C
C       ..... INITIATE GOLDEN SECTION SEARCH FOR MAXIMUM VOLUME TO    .....
C       ..... AREA RATIO WHICH IS THE FIGURE OF MERIT.  A MAXIMUM      .....
C       ..... VOLUME   TO AREA RATIO IMPLIES A MINIMUM SHEET METAL     .....
```

```
C       ..... AREA FOR A GIVEN CONTAINER VOLUME                      .....
C
        CALL GOLD1(I,RLOW,RHIGH,F,Y,X,XLOW,XHIGH,J5)
C
C       ..... DOCUMENT SEARCH RESULTS .....
C
        D=2.*X
        WRITE(3,1)VOL,R1,R2,R3,H1
    1 FORMAT('1OPTIMAL PROPORTIONS FOR RIGHT CIRCULAR CYLINDRICAL CAN',/
     1,' BASED ON MINIMUM WEIGHT',//,
     2' INPUT DATA',//,
     3' VOLUME OF CONTAINER, IN3, ...............................',F10.5,/,
     4' DISHING ALLOWANCE ON CONTAINER ENDS, IN, ..............',F10.8,/,
     5' CRIMPING ALLOWANCE ON CONTAINER ENDS, IN, ............',F10.8,/,
     6' SEAM ALLOWANCE FOR FORMING CYLINDRICAL SHELL, IN, ....',F10.8,/,
     7' CRIMPING ALLOWANCE FOR ATTACHING END, IN, .............',F10.8)
        WRITE(3,3)H,D,AREA
    3 FORMAT(/,' OUTPUT DATA',//,
     1' HEIGHT OF CAN, IN, .....................................',F10.5,/,
     2' DIAMETER OF CAN, IN, ...................................',F10.5,/,
     3' AREA OF SHEET METAL USED, IN2,.........................',F10.5)
C
C       ..... FOR COMPARISON INDICATE OPTIMAL PROPORTIONS USING THE   .....
C       ..... SIMPLIFIED THEORY AND DETERMINE THE SHEET METAL AREA    .....
C       ..... NEEDED TO FABRICATE A REAL CAN USING THESE PROPORTIONS  .....
C
        RAD=(VOL/(2.*3.14159))**0.333333
        HI=VOL/(3.14159*RAD*RAD)
        H=HI
        DIA=2.*RAD
C
C       ..... CALL MERIT1 TO COMPUTE SHEET METAL AREA, VALUE OF       .....
C       ..... WHICH IS RETURNED VIA COMMON.                          .....
C
        CALL MERIT1(RAD,YY)
        WRITE(3,4)HI,DIA,AREA
    4 FORMAT(/,' OPTIMAL PROPORTIONS IGNORING SEAMS, TABS AND DISHING',/
     1/,
     2' HEIGHT OF CAN,IN, .....................................',F10.5,/,
     3' DIAMETER OF CAN, IN, ..................................',F10.5,/,
     4' AREA OF SHEET METAL USED, IN2, ........................',F10.5)
        GO TO 5
        END


        SUBROUTINE MERIT1(R,Y)
        COMMON VOL,R1,R2,R3,H1,H,AREA
        PI=3.14159
        H=VOL/(PI*R*R)
        AREA=    2.*PI*(R+R1+R2)*(R+R1+R2)+(2.*PI*R+R3)*(H+2.*H1)
        Y=VOL/AREA
        RETURN
        END



        CONVERGENCE MONITOR SUBROUTINE GOLD1
```

N	Y1	Y2	X1	X2
2	0.6069737E 00	0.3283069E 00	0.3825839E 01	0.6184157E 01
3	0.7467008E 00	0.6069737E 00	0.2368318E 01	0.3825839E 01
4	0.6163253E 00	0.7467008E 00	0.1467520E 01	0.2368318E 01
5	0.7467008E 00	0.7216181E 00	0.2368318E 01	0.2925039E 01
6	0.7263275E 00	0.7467008E 00	0.2024242E 01	0.2368318E 01
7	0.7467008E 00	0.7441732E 00	0.2368318E 01	0.2580965E 01
8	0.7427955E 00	0.7467008E 00	0.2236891E 01	0.2368318E 01
9	0.7467008E 00	0.7469471E 00	0.2368318E 01	0.2449539E 01
10	0.7469471E 00	0.7463315E 00	0.2449539E 01	0.2499742E 01
11	0.7470390E 00	0.7469471E 00	0.2418517E 01	0.2449539E 01

12	0.7469819E 00	0.7470390E 00	0.2399343E 01	0.2418517E 01
13	0.7470390E 00	0.7470303E 00	0.2418517E 01	0.2430367E 01
14	0.7470275E 00	0.7470390E 00	0.2411193E 01	0.2418517E 01
15	0.7470390E 00	0.7470397E 00	0.2418517E 01	0.2423043E 01
16	0.7470397E 00	0.7470377E 00	0.2423043E 01	0.2425840E 01
17	0.7470397E 00	0.7470397E 00	0.2421314E 01	0.2423043E 01

```
LEFTHAND ABSCISSA OF INTERVAL OF UNCERTAINTY .........   0.9999998E-02
RIGHTHAND ABSCISSA OF INTERVAL OF UNCERTAINTY ........   0.1000000E 02
FRACTIONAL REDUCTION OF INTERVAL OF UNCERTAINTY ......   0.9999999E-03
EXTREME ORDINATE DISCOVERED DURING SEARCH ............   0.7470397E 00
ABSCISSA OF EXTREME ORDINATE .........................   0.2421314E 01
NEW LEFTHAND ABSCISSA OF INTERVAL OF UNCERTAINTY .....   0.2418517E 01
NEW RIGHTHAND ABSCISSA OF INTERVAL OF UNCERTAINTY ....   0.2425840E 01
NUMBER OF FUNCTION EVALUATIONS EXPENDED IN SEARCH ....          17
OPTIMAL PROPORTIONS FOR RIGHT CIRCULAR CYLINDRICAL CAN
BASED ON MINIMUM WEIGHT

INPUT DATA

VOLUME OF CONTAINER, IN3, ............................. 100.00000
DISHING ALLOWANCE ON CONTAINER ENDS, IN, .............0.09999996
CRIMPING ALLOWANCE ON CONTAINER ENDS, IN, ............0.19999999
SEAM ALLOWANCE FOR FORMING CYLINDRICAL SHELL, IN, ....0.29999995
CRIMPING ALLOWANCE FOR ATTACHING END, IN, ............0.09999996

OUTPUT DATA

HEIGHT OF CAN, IN, ...................................   5.42936
DIAMETER OF CAN, IN, .................................   4.84263
AREA OF SHEET METAL USED, IN2,....................... 133.86168

OPTIMAL PROPORTIONS IGNORING SEAMS, TABS AND DISHING

HEIGHT OF CAN,IN, ...................................   5.03081
DIAMETER OF CAN, IN, ................................   5.03079
AREA OF SHEET METAL USED, IN2, ...................... 134.04379
```

The convergence monitor for subroutine GOLD1 has been actuated by the call (I = 1). Figure 68 indicates the figure of merit curve for the particular case where

$V = 100$ cu in.

$R1 = 0.1$ in.

$R2 = 0.2$ in.

$R3 = 0.3$ in.

$H1 = 0.1$ in.

The height of the can is 5.429 in. and the diameter is 4.842 in. The area of sheet metal used is 133.86 sq in.

Note that the executive program also figured the optimal proportions for the container ignoring fabrication allowances. Observe also that the simplified model of Eq. (5.1) gives equal height and diameter. The rather mild discrepancy between the two models (the optimal value of diameter) is due to the peaking of the two merit functions near the same abscissa. The corresponding ordinates, however, differ to a greater degree. In study-

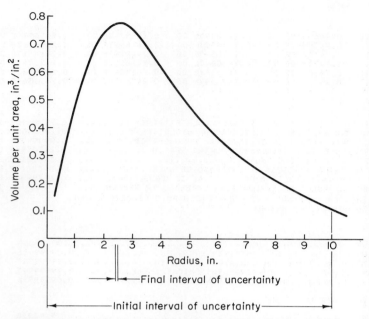

FIG. 68. The figure of merit for the can problem indicating the initial and final interval of uncertainty.

ing Fig. 69 notice that the displacement of the practical optimum from the simple optimum is consistently toward the smaller radius, giving the practical optimal configuration a slightly larger height. The good agreement between the optimal radius in the two models should not mislead one into expecting the necessary area to produce a can of a specified volume with similar accuracy, A study of Fig. 69 will reveal why.

An inspection of the documentation of the computer program reveals that numbers such as R1, R2, R3, and H1 are not expressed precisely. This occurs because the IBM 360 computer is a hexidecimal machine operating with base 16 arithmetic. There is no concise representation for a number like 0.1 and the machine carries it as 0.09999996. By controlling format differently we can cause roundup to occur and read the printout as 0.100. A nonengineering reader might be puzzled if confronted with the number 0.09999996 after reading 0.1.

5.3 THE PROPER GEAR RATIO FOR A RAPID TRANSIT CAR

Consider the following situation: A city contemplating the opening of a rapid transit line has engaged a consulting engineering firm to recommend equipment for the contemplated new line. The project engineer is con-

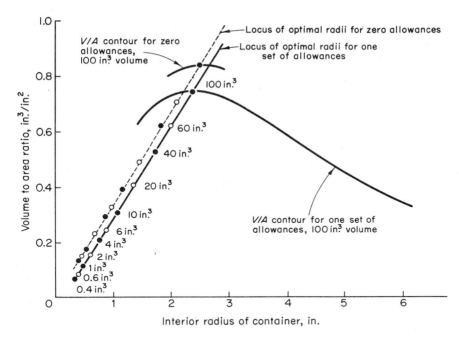

FIG. 69. Comparison of solutions obtained from simple mathematical model and the revised model incorporating fabrication allowances.

sidering the performance that can be obtained with rapid transit equipment recently built for another city. His thought is that costs will be considerably less if the supplier builds equipment using the principal jigs and plans already in existence. A simple variable with which to modify performance and not incur great increases in price is the gear ratio between the traction motors and the axles of the powered wheels. Failing to obtain a satisfactory resolution of problems in this manner, the project engineer has other alternatives, such as changing both the gear ratio and the traction motors.

The project engineer assigns you the problem of determining the optimal gear ratio for a rapid transit car which results in a minimum of elapsed time between the start of motion at one station and the cessation of motion at the next station. Phase 1 of the problem is to determine this ratio for a single-car train running on level tangent track with equally spaced station stops. The solution to phase 1 will be considered here.

Resistance to motion of a railway car occurs because of rail-wheel rolling friction, axle journal-bearing friction, curve resistance, grade resistance, and air resistance. For our problem resistance due to grade and curvature of track is zero. Resistance in pounds per ton of car weight is given by the Davis formula modified for the fact that this car is not following others, but is the first car of a one-car train:

$$r = 1.3 + \frac{29}{w} + 0.03v + 0.0024\frac{AV^2}{wn} \tag{5.2}$$

where

r = resistance, lbf/ton of car
w = average weight carried per axle, tons
V = train speed, miles per hour
n = number of axles
A = cross-sectional area, square feet

In Sec. 2.6 a preliminary analysis of the dynamics of this problem was made. The plan of attack begins with the recognition that several subroutines will be needed to conveniently write the merit function. Such subroutines would ordinarily be in the design library of a railway equipment manufacturer, but we shall compose simplified versions for the purpose of broadening our understanding.

The subroutine DRAG will be needed to determine the retarding force on the car corresponding to the present velocity of the vehicle. The call will be DRAG (V, A1, W1, RETARD), where the arguments in call list represent

V = vehicle speed, miles per hour
A1 = cross-sectional area, square feet
W1 = vehicle weight, tons
RETARD is the drag force in pounds.

A COMMON statement will be required, but its contents are presently unknown. We can expect the cross-sectional area A and the vehicle weight W to be in the common declaration, and to prevent the compiler from rejecting the program because the same quantity appears both in the subroutine call and in the COMMON statement, the dummy variables A1 and W1 are placed in the call list. Thus we write

```
SUBROUTINE DRAG (V, A1, W1, RETARD)
COMMON (to be completed at end of programming)
A = A1
W = W1
WT = W/4.
S = 1.3 + 29./WT + 0.03*V + 0.0024 *A*V*V/(4.*WT)
RETARD = S*W
RETURN
END
```

We note that we need not have any variables in COMMON which are used in the subroutine DRAG, inasmuch as all necessary values are entered via the call list.

104

The next subroutine of use would be one which, if given the speed of the vehicle, would return the distance necessary to stop the car and the elapsed time in braking the car to a halt. This subroutine will be given the name BRAKE, and the call will be BRAKE (V, BDIST, BTIME) where

V = vehicle speed in miles per hour
BDIST = distance necessary to stop the vehicle in feet
BTIME = time duration of braking in seconds

The service braking pressure will be insufficient to cause a wheel skid. The coefficient of adhesion utilized during service braking will be designated COEFF2. In this simplified example the braking will be presumed to be a constant deceleration event and the programming proceeds as follows:

```
SUBROUTINE BRAKE (V, BDIST, BTIME)
COMMON (to be completed at the end of programming)
VEL = V*88./60.
BDIST = VEL*VEL/(2.*COEFF2*32.174)
BTIME = SQRT(2.*BDIST/(COEFF2*32.174))
RETURN
END
```

We note that it is necessary to have the parameter COEFF2 in the common statement since it does not appear in the call list.

The next useful subroutine will be named TMOTOR, and its purpose is to return the magnitude of the traction motor torque corresponding to any vehicle speed. The motors utilized will be the approximate equivalent of General Electric 1240, which in their running characteristic exhibit the following relationship between motor torque (in inch-pounds) and the angular velocity (in radians per second) of the armature shaft:

$$T = \frac{29.9(10)^9}{\omega^{3.13}}$$

Below an angular velocity of 106 radians per second, current limiting devices will maintain the torque at a level of 12150 inch-pounds. The programming proceeds as follows:

```
SUBROUTINE TMOTOR (V, R1, RATIO1, TM)
COMMON (to be completed at the end of programming)
R = R1
RATIO = RATIO1
VEL = V*88./60.
OMEGA = 12.*VEL*RATIO/R
IF(OMEGA — 106.)2, 1, 1
1 TM = 29.9E09/(OMEGA**3.13)
```

```
    RETURN
2 TM = 12150.
    RETURN
    END
```

We can expect the gear ratio RATIO and the wheel radius R to appear in the COMMON declaration, hence the dummy variables RATIO1 and R1 are employed in the call list to prevent the compiler from rejecting the program (for containing the same variable in the subroutine call list and the COMMON declaration list). We note that the COMMON declaration need not have been present in this subprogram.

The next useful subprogram will be named EFFORT and will be called by EFFORT (RATIO1, TM, R1, TE). The tractive effort can be expressed in terms of the motor torque and the gear ratio and wheel radius as

$$TE = 4.*RATIO*TM/R$$

and we program as follows:

```
    SUBROUTINE EFFORT (RATIO1, TM, R1, TE)
    COMMON (to be completed at the end of programming)
    RATIO = RATIO1
    R = R1
    TE = 4.*RATIO*TM/R
    IF(TE — W*2000.*COEFF1)1, 2, 2
2 TE = W*2000.*COEFF1
    L = 1
1 RETURN
    END
```

It is necessary to note that when the tractive effort exceeds the adhesive force available at the rail (about 20 per cent of car weight), the wheels will slip, unless anti-wheelslip devices are brought into play to limit the motor torque. The setting of integer L to unity alerts the engineer to the fact that anti-wheelslip devices are required by a particular gear ratio. The COMMON declaration must return L to the executive program, and will also contain RATIO and R.

Now that these incidental subroutines are written, we can plan the general arrangement of the programming elements to solve the problem. Fundamentally we expect the plot of the reciprocal of the elapsed time between the stations (start to stop) and the gear ratio to exhibit a maximum such as depicted by Fig. 70. When the gear ratio is very large, very low average and balancing speeds result, and the elapsed time is consequently

106

very large. When the gear ratio is small, the acceleration is very small and again the elapsed time is very large. Somewhere within the domain of positive gear ratios there is one that corresponds to minimum elapsed time (and hence maximum ordinate in Fig. 70). A golden section search will be effective in this one-dimensional situation. We select library routine GOLD2

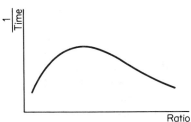

FIG. 70. The general trend of the merit function for the rapid transit car problem.

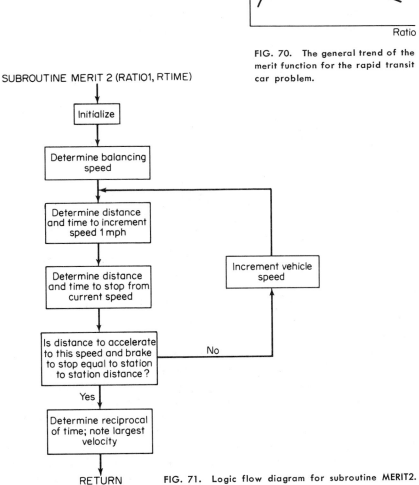

FIG. 71. Logic flow diagram for subroutine MERIT2.

which calls subroutine MERIT2. For every tendered value of the gear ratio, MERIT2 must return an ordinate RTIME, which is the reciprocal of the elapsed time between stations. The purpose of MERIT2 is therefore clear, and we structure it as indicated in Fig. 71.

The balancing speed corresponding to a given gear ratio must be determined. At this speed the tractive effort TE is equal to the drag force RETARD. If the accelerating force FACC = TE − RETARD, then clearly when FACC is zero, the associated velocity is the balancing speed. Treating FACC as a function of vehicle speed V, we utilize another library subroutine ROOT1 which will locate zero places in a function within a specified interval of uncertainty. In order to effectively search for the zero place, the subroutine ROOT1 calls another subroutine EQUAT1 which must return to ROOT1 the ordinate FACC corresponding to a tendered value of V. Such a subroutine could be structured as follows:

```
SUBROUTINE EQUAT1 (V, FACC)
COMMON (to be completed at the end of programming)
CALL DRAG (V, A, W, RETARD)
CALL TMOTOR (V, R, RATIO, TM)
CALL EFFORT (RATIO, TM, R, TE)
FACC = TE − RETARD
RETURN
END
```

For this subroutine values must be supplied to it through the COMMON declaration. These include A, W, R, RATIO.

The structure of the subroutine MERIT2 is displayed as written below. The programs are arranged as indicated in Fig. 72. The COMMON declaration is composed of the common needs of all these subroutines and the executive program.

```
COMMON COEFF1, COEFF2, R, W, A, RATIO, L, VBIG,
1 BSPEED, VLOW, VHIGH, F, MPRINT, DIST
```

A complete program follows, with convergence monitor printout. The single-car train weighs 29 tons, has a frontal area of 80 ft^2, and uses 32-in.-diameter wheels. It is running on level tangent track with limiting rail-wheel adhesion of 0.20 and braking adjusted to demand 0.15 adhesion during service stops. There are 4 d-c traction motors similar to GE 1240. The distance between stations is 4,000 ft.

The optimal gear ratio is 2.61. The average speed between stations is 44.2 mph and involves an elapsed time of 61.8 seconds. The maximum speed obtained between stations is 65.0 mph. The balancing speed at this ratio is 70.7 mph.

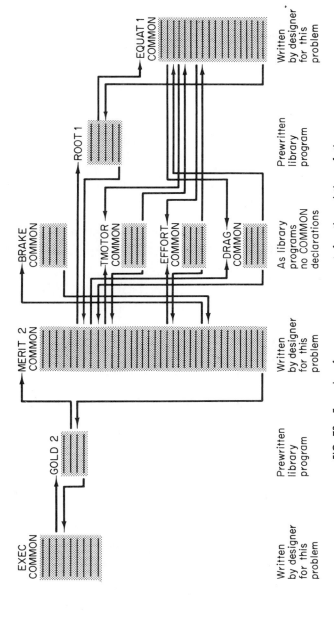

FIG. 72. Example of program arrangement for the solution of the rapid transit car gear-ratio problem using the IOWA CADET algorithm.

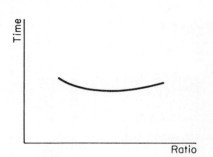

FIG. 73.   Variation of start-to-stop time with gear ratio.

The opportunity is present to introduce multicar trains and curvature, grade, and speed restrictions, as well as variable interstation distances. In short it becomes possible to model the line and study performances. We are close to a simulation, a valuable contribution which the computer makes quite easily. Figure 73 can be constructed to determine how sensitive performance is to gear value.

This problem shows a one-dimensional optimization problem in which the computer is helpful to the engineer.

```
C     EXECUTIVE PROGRAM FOR DETERMINING THE OPTIMAL GEAR RATIO BETWEEN
C     THE TRACTION MOTOR AND THE WHEELS ON A ELECTRICALLY PROPELLED RAPID
C     TRANSIT CAR IN ORDER TO MINIMIZE START-TO-STOP TIME BETWEEN EQUALLY
C     SPACED STATIONS ON LEVEL TANGENT TRACK.                 MISCHKE
C
C     VARIABLES
C
C     V=VELOCITY OF VEHICLE, MILES/HR
C     W=WEIGHT OF VEHICLE: TONS
C     A=CROSS SECTIONAL AREA OF CAR, SQ FT
C     RATIO=GEAR RATIO BETWEEN TRACTION MOTOR AND WHEELS
C     R=RADIUS OF WHEELS
C
C     L=0  NO WHEEL SLIP DURING ACCELERATION
C       =1   WHEEL SLIP DURING ACCELERATION
C     VLOW=LOWER EXTENT OF V-DOMAIN
C     VHIGH=HIGHER EXTENT OF V-DOMAIN
C     F=FRACTIONAL REDUCTION IN INTERVAL OF UNCERTAINTY DESIRED
C
C     TM=TRACTION MOTOR TORQUE, IN-LBF
C     TE=TRACTIVE EFFORT OF VEHICLE, LBF
C     OMEGA=ANGULAR SPEED OF MOTOR, RAD/SEC
C     WT=VEHICLE WEIGHT, TONS/AXLE
C     RETARD=DRAG FORCE ON VEHICLE, LBF
C
C     COEFF1=ADHESION LIMIT BETWEEN RAILS AND WHEELS
C     COEFF2=WORKING ADHESION DURING SERVICE BRAKE APPLICATION
C     RLOW=LOWER EXTENT OF RATIO-DOMAIN
C     RHIGH=HIGHER EXTENT OF RATIO DOMAIN
C     RTIME=RECIPROCAL OF ELAPSED TIME STATION TO STATION,  1./SEC
C     DIST=DISTANCE BETWEEN STATIONS, FEET
C
      COMMON COEFF1,COEFF2,R,W,A,RATIO,L,VBIG,BSPEED,VLOW,VHIGH,F,
     1 MPRINT,DIST
      DIMENSION IABC(20)
C
C     ..... READ INPUT DATA .....
C
    1 READ(1,2)W,A,R,COEFF1,COEFF2,DIST
    2 FORMAT(5F10.5,F10.0)
```

110

```
      3 READ(1,4)VLOW,VHIGH,RLOW,RHIGH,F,MPRINT
      4 FORMAT(5F10.5,I5)
      5 READ(1,6)(IABC(I),I=1,20)
      6 FORMAT(20A4)
        L=0
C
C     ..... INITIATE GOLDEN SECTION SEARCH TO FIND THE GEAR RATIO  .....
C     ..... AT WHICH THE RECIPROCAL OF ELAPSED TIME BETWEEN STATIONS ...
C     ..... HAS AN EXTREME VALUE                              .....
C
        CALL GOLD2(MPRINT,RLOW,RHIGH,F,RTIME,RATIO,RLO,RHI,J5)
C
C     ..... PREPARE OUTPUT AND PRINT DOCUMENTATION .....
C
        TIME=1./RTIME
        SSPEED=(DIST/5280.)/(TIME/3600.)
        WRITE(3,7)W,A,R,COEFF1,COEFF2,DIST
      7 FORMAT('1RAPID TRANSIT CAR OPTIMIZATION PROGRAM'//' INPUT DATA'//,
       1' WEIGHT OF CAR, TONS ...............................',F15.2,/,
       2' FRONTAL AREA OF CAR, SQ FT ........................',F15.2,/,
       3' RADIUS OF CAR WHEELS, INCHES ......................',F15.2,/,
       4' ADHESION LIMIT BETWEEN WHEEL AND RAIL .............',F15.2,/,
       5' WORKING ADHESION VALUE DURING SERVICE BRAKING .....',F15.2,/,
       6' DISTANCE BETWEEN STATIONS, FEET   .................',F15.3)
        WRITE(3,18)(IABC(I),I=1,20)
     18 FORMAT(/,20A4)
        IF(L)1,8,10
      8 WRITE(3,9)
      9 FORMAT(//,' NO WHEELSLIP DURING ACCELERATION'//)
        GO TO 12
     10 WRITE(3,11)
     11 FORMAT(//,' WHEELSLIP DURING ACCELERATION'//)
     12 WRITE(3,13)RATIO,TIME,SSPEED,VBIG,BSPEED
     13 FORMAT(
       1' OPTIMAL GEAR RATIO ................................',F15.5,/,
       2' ELAPSED TIME BETWEEN STATIONS, SECONDS ............',F15.2,/,
       3' AVERAGE SPEED BETWEEN STATIONS, MILES/HR ..........',F15.2,/,
       4' MAXIMUM SPEED ATTAINED BETWEEN STATIONS, MILES/HR ....',F15.2,/,
       5' BALANCING SPEED AT THIS RATIO, MILES/HR ...........',F15.2)
        GO TO 1
        END


        SUBROUTINE MERIT2(RATIO1,RTIME)
        COMMON COEFF1,COEFF2,R,W,A,RATIO,L,VBIG,BSPEED,VLOW,VHIGH,F,
       1 MPRINT,DIST
C
C     ..... INITIALIZE .....
C
        RATIO=RATIO1
        L=0
        ATIME=0.
        ADIST=0.
        VOLD=0.
        DELTA=1.
        VBIG=0.
        V=1.
C
C     ..... DETERMINE BALANCING SPEED FOR THIS RATIO USING ROOT1   .....
C
        MPRINT=0
        CALL ROOT1(MPRINT,VLOW,VHIGH,F,BSPEED,B2,B3,B4,J8,J9)
        MPRINT=1
C
C     ..... DETERMINE ACCELERATING FORCE, AND BY AN APPROXIMATE   .....
C     ..... INTEGRATION TECHNIQUE, ESTABLISH MERIT ORDINATE       .....
C
      6 IF(V-BSPEED)10,11,11
     11 DT=2.
        GO TO 12
     10 CALL DRAG(V,A,W,RETARD)
        CALL TMOTOR(V,R,RATIO,TM)
        CALL EFFORT(RATIO,TM,R,TE)
        CALL BRAKE(V,BDIST,BTIME)
```

111

```
            FACC=TE-RETARD
            DT=2000.*W/(32.174*FACC)
        12  AT=ATIME+DT
            AD=ADIST+(V+VOLD)*0.5*DT*5280./3600.
            DSTOS=AD+BDIST
            TSTOS=AT+BTIME
            IF(DIST-DSTOS)5,4,4
         5  IF(DELTA-0.01)9,7,7
         7  DELTA=DELTA/10.
            V=VOLD+DELTA
            GO TO 6
      C
      C
      C     ..... ACCUMULATE ACCELERATION TIME AND ACCELERATION DISTANCE .....
      C     ..... NOTE VOLD, THEN INCREMENT V                             .....
      C
         4  ATIME=AT
            ADIST=AD
            VOLD=V
            V=V+DELTA
            GO TO 6
      C
      C
      C     ..... CALCULATE MERIT ORDINATE AND NOTE LARGEST ATTAINED V   .....
      C     ..... AT THIS RATIO.                                         .....
      C
         9  RTIME=1./TSTOS
            VBIG=V
            RETURN
            END


            SUBROUTINE TMOTOR(V,R1,RATIO1,TM)
            COMMON COEFF1,COEFF2,R,W,A,RATIO,L,VBIG,BSPEED,VLOW,VHIGH,F,
           1 MPRINT,DIST
            R=R1
            RATIO=RATIO1
            VEL=V*88./60.
            OMEGA=12.*VEL*RATIO/R
            IF(OMEGA-106.)2,1,1
      C
      C
      C     ..... MOTOR ON RUNNING CHARACTERISTIC .....
      C
         1  TM=29.9E09/(OMEGA**3.13)
            RETURN
      C
      C
      C     ..... MOTOR ON STARTING CHARACTERISTIC .....
      C
         2  TM=12150.
            RETURN
            END


            SUBROUTINE EFFORT(RATIO1,TM,R1,TE)
            COMMON COEFF1,COEFF2,R,W,A,RATIO,L,VBIG,BSPEED,VLOW,VHIGH,F,
           1 MPRINT,DIST
            RATIO=RATIO1
            R=R1
      C
      C
      C     ..... DETERMINE TRACTIVE EFFORT .....
      C
            TE=4.*RATIO*TM/R
      C
      C
      C     ..... DETERMINE IF WHEELS SLIP .....
      C
            IF(TE-W*2000.*COEFF1)1,2,2
      C
      C
      C     ..... WHEELSLIP EQUIPMENT OPERATIVE .....
      C
         2  TE=W*2000.*COEFF1
            L=1
      C
      C
      C     ..... WHEELS DO NOT SLIP .....
      C
         1  RETURN
            END
```

112

```
      SUBROUTINE DRAG(V,A1,W1,RETARD)
      COMMON COEFF1,COEFF2,R,W,A,RATIO,L,VBIG,BSPEED,VLOW,VHIGH,F,
     1 MPRINT,DIST
      A=A1
      W=W1
      WT=W/4.
      S=1.3+29./WT+0.03*V+0.0024*A*V*V/(4.*WT)
      RETARD=S*W
      RETURN
      END


      SUBROUTINE EQUAT1(V,FACC)
      COMMON COEFF1,COEFF2,R,W,A,RATIO,L,VBIG,BSPEED,VLOW,VHIGH,F,
     1 MPRINT,DIST
C
C     ..... THIS SUBROUTINE DETERMINES THE ACCELERATING FORCE    .....
C     ..... FOR THE SUBROUTINE ROOT1.                            .....
C
      CALL DRAG(V,A,W,RETARD)
      CALL TMOTOR(V,R,RATIO,TM)
      CALL EFFORT(RATIO,TM,R,TE)
      FACC=TE-RETARD
      RETURN
      END


      SUBROUTINE BRAKE(V,BDIST,BTIME)
      COMMON COEFF1,COEFF2,R,W,A,RATIO,L,VBIG,BSPEED,VLOW,VHIGH,F,
     1 MPRINT,DIST
C
C     ..... THIS BRAKING SUBROUTINE BASED UPON A CONSTANT        .....
C     ..... DECELERATION APPROXIMATION.                          .....
C
      VEL=V*88./60.
      BDIST=VEL*VEL/(2.*COEFF2*32.174)
      BTIME=SQRT(2.*BDIST/(COEFF2*32.174))
      RETURN
      END
```

CONVERGENCE MONITOR SUBROUTINE GOLD2

N	Y1	Y2	X1	X2
2	0.1325857E-01	0.1205516E-01	0.4437694E 01	0.6562305E 01
3	0.1481423E-01	0.1325857E-01	0.3124611E 01	0.4437694E 01
4	0.1565030E-01	0.1481423E-01	0.2313081E 01	0.3124611E 01
5	0.1564945E-01	0.1565030E-01	0.1811528E 01	0.2313081E 01
6	0.1565030E-01	0.1598705E-01	0.2313081E 01	0.2623056E 01
7	0.1598705E-01	0.1510083E-01	0.2623056E 01	0.2814632E 01
8	0.1541933E-01	0.1598705E-01	0.2504656E 01	0.2623056E 01
9	0.1598705E-01	0.1536908E-01	0.2623056E 01	0.2696231E 01
10	0.1528829E-01	0.1598705E-01	0.2577831E 01	0.2623056E 01
11	0.1598705E-01	0.1559307E-01	0.2623056E 01	0.2651006E 01
12	0.1533265E-01	0.1598705E-01	0.2605782E 01	0.2623056E 01
13	0.1598705E-01	0.1583791E-01	0.2623056E 01	0.2633732E 01
14	0.1607842E-01	0.1598705E-01	0.2616457E 01	0.2623056E 01
15	0.1613457E-01	0.1607842E-01	0.2612379E 01	0.2616457E 01
16	0.1616909E-01	0.1613457E-01	0.2609859E 01	0.2612379E 01
17	0.1619043E-01	0.1616909E-01	0.2608301E 01	0.2609859E 01

```
LEFTHAND ABSCISSA OF INTERVAL OF UNCERTAINTY .........  0.1000000E 01
RIGHTHAND ABSCISSA OF INTERVAL OF UNCERTAINTY ........  0.1000000E 02
FRACTIONAL REDUCTION OF INTERVAL OF UNCERTAINTY ......  0.9999999E-03
EXTREME ORDINATE DISCOVERED DURING SEARCH ............  0.1619043E-01
ABSCISSA OF EXTREME ORDINATE .........................  0.2608301E 01
NEW LEFTHAND ABSCISSA OF INTERVAL OF UNCERTAINTY .....  0.2605782E 01
NEW RIGHTHAND ABSCISSA OF INTERVAL OF UNCERTAINTY ....  0.2612379E 01
NUMBER OF FUNCTION EVALUATIONS EXPENDED IN SEARCH ....           17
```

INPUT DATA

```
WEIGHT OF CAR, TONS .....................................        29.00
FRONTAL AREA OF CAR, SQ FT ..............................        80.00
RADIUS OF CAR WHEELS, INCHES ............................        16.00
ADHESION LIMIT BETWEEN WHEEL AND RAIL ...................         0.20
WORKING ADHESION VALUE DURING SERVICE BRAKING ..........          0.15
DISTANCE BETWEEN STATIONS, FEET  .......................       4000.000
```

TRACTION MOTORS ARE SIMILAR TO GE 1240 WITH FIELD SHUNT ONE

NO WHEELSLIP DURING ACCELERATION

```
OPTIMAL GEAR RATIO ............,........................,        2.60830
ELAPSED TIME BETWEEN STATIONS, SECONDS .................        61.76
AVERAGE SPEED BETWEEN STATIONS, MILES/HR ...............        44.16
MAXIMUM SPEED ATTAINED BETWEEN STATIONS, MILES/HR ....         65.01
BALANCING SPEED AT THIS RATIO, MILES/HR ...............         70.66
```

5.4 A COMPUTATIONAL CAM OF MINIMAL MASS

Computational schemes can utilize analog mechanical devices in order to perform computational operations within a device called a *control* or *analog computer*. In an analog device a quantity such as shaft rotational displacement is used to represent the change in a variable, and the angular position of the shaft itself can be compared to the magnitude of the variable. Under these circumstances it is easy to appreciate how a spur-gear pair connecting parallel shafts can perform multiplication by a fixed number.

There are circumstances in the course of computational evolutions that require an analog rotation to be converted to an equivalent analog translation, A device capable of performing this conversion is the pinion and rack. Another device is the radial follower cam. The second device has the advantage of not only changing the mode of representation from rotational to translational but incorporating a functional transformation in the process. Control of the functional transformation is accomplished by specifying a particular contour for the cam.

Figure 74 shows a knife-edge offset radial follower cam, which is a suitable type where the load driven by the cam is small. The XY coordinate system is fixed in the earth (or in the guides of the follower) with the origin coincident with the point of contact between the cam and follower when the shaft is in the position associated with zero of the rotational variable. The xy coordinate system is fixed in the cam with the origin at the center of cam rotation in XY. At the zero position of the rotational variable, the corresponding axes of the two coordinate systems are parallel. The abscissa angle between the x axis and the X axis is designated θ. The location of the origin of the XY frame in the xy frame is specified by (a, b).

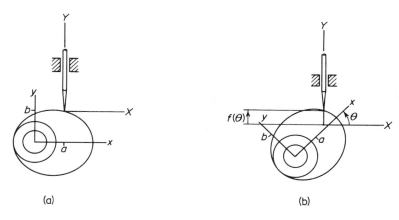

FIG. 74. A cam with an offset knife-edge follower used as a function generator in (a) its initial position and (b) in a subsequent position defined by angle θ.

We may think of a as representing the offset of the follower path from the center of the cam bearing. We may interpret b as the elevation of the initial point of contact above the x axis. Figure 74(b) indicates the geometry associated with a rotational displacement θ of the cam. The point of contact between the cam and follower moves up the Y axis and the distance is a function of theta $f(\theta)$ determined by the cam contour. The location of the point of contact in the XY frame determines values of $f(\theta)$ and the location of the point of contact in the xy frame locates points on the cam contour. The transformation equation can be shown to be

$$x = (Y + b) \sin \theta + (X + a) \cos \theta \qquad (5.3)$$

$$y = (Y + b) \cos \theta - (X + a) \sin \theta \qquad (5.4)$$

We note that the point of contact is constrained to lie on the Y axis, and therefore $X = 0$. The Y coordinate can be interpreted as a desired function of θ, and Eqs. (5.3) and (5.4) can be written as

$$x = (f(\theta) + b) \sin \theta + a \cos \theta \qquad (5.5)$$

$$y = (f(\theta) + b) \cos \theta - a \sin \theta \qquad (5.6)$$

A problem encountered with this type of cam is one of the cocking and binding of the follower in the follower guides when the knifeedge contact is too far from normal with the cam contour. Such deviation from normality is measured by an angle called the *pressure angle*, which is denoted by the symbol α in Fig. 75. From the geometry of the figure it is easy to determine that

115

$$\alpha = \theta + \arctan \frac{dy}{dx}$$

The value of dy/dx can be found by determining $dy/d\theta$ and $dx/d\theta$ in Eqs. (5.5) and (5.6)

$$\frac{dy}{d\theta} = -\,[f(\theta) + b]\sin\theta + f'(\theta)\cos\theta - a\cos\theta \qquad (5.7)$$

$$\frac{dx}{d\theta} = [f(\theta) + b]\cos\theta + f'(\theta)\sin\theta - a\sin\theta \qquad (5.8)$$

and it follows from Eqs. (5.7) and (5.8) that

$$\frac{dy}{dx} = \frac{dy/d\theta}{dx/d\theta} = \tan(\psi - \theta)$$

where

$$\psi = \arctan\frac{f'(\theta) - a}{f(\theta) + b}$$

The pressure angle may be expressed as

$$\alpha = \theta + \arctan[\tan(\psi - \theta)] = \theta + \psi - \theta = \psi$$

or

$$\alpha = \arctan\frac{f'(\theta) - a}{f(\theta) + b} \qquad (5.9)$$

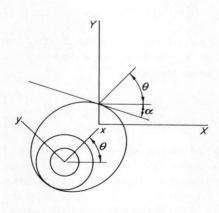

It is clear that points on the contour of the cam are determined by knowledge of the function $f(\theta)$ and of the parameters a and b using Eqs. (5.5) and (5.6). It is also clear that the local value of the pressure angle α is determined by $f(\theta)$, $f'(\theta)$, a, and b using Eq. (5.9). In an approximate way, the magnitude of the parameter b controls the physical size of the cam, and from Eq. (5.9) it is seen that a large value of b depresses the magnitude of the pressure angle α.

FIG. 75. The pressure angle α of the cam at position θ.

Let us consider the problem of providing the specifications for a computational cam that will generate the function $\ln \theta$ with the input variable θ varying between 60° and 160°. We shall add to the problem the limitation that the pressure angle α may not exceed 30° and the requirement that of all possible cams that could meet these specifications, the one selected shall involve a minimum plate area. This is somewhat akin to minimum weight specification. See Fig. 76.

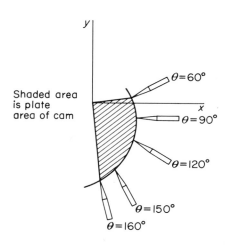

Shaded area is plate area of cam

FIG. 76.   The plate area of the cam.

In planning a machine computation program it is necessary to choose a figure of merit. The figure of merit selected to solve this problem is the reciprocal of the plate area of the cam. The functional constraint is the fact that the pressure angle may not exceed 30°. The regional constraints are the ranges of values permitted the parameters a and b. Given the function to be generated, it is clear that the independent variables at the designer's disposal are the parameters a and b. The search problem becomes two-dimensional, and for such a search we shall select library function GRID4, which is capable of carrying out grid-type searches in as many as eight design variables. The documentation of GRID4 indicates that this subroutine calls a subroutine MERIT4, which generates the ordinate to the merit surface for tendered values of the independent variables. This routine, MERIT4, we must write.

In writing the MERIT4 subroutine we shall face the problem of incorporating the functional constraint of the limit on the size of the pressure angle. We cannot simply identify the values of a and b which locate points in the feasible plane area to be excluded from consideration by virtue of excessive pressure angle. One approach to resolving this problem is to calculate the merit ordinate without regard to the violation of the pressure angle constraint, and then if the constraint is violated, *penalize* the merit ordinate in such a way as to make that point have a very poor merit—say, zero or less. Another way this can be done is to arrange it so that the slope above the infeasible area directs the search back to the feasible domain. Without prior knowledge of the configuration of the merit surface this may seem like a formidable task, but there are some things that we can do.

If we know the coordinates of one point in feasible space, a simple stratagem is available to us. The merit ordinate in feasible space is designed to be always positive, and it is calculated in accordance with the appropriate

117

merit subroutine. When the merit ordinate of a point in infeasible space is required, the merit calculation is pursued to the point wherein the violation of a functional constraint is ascertained. A negative merit ordinate is then returned. In order to ensure that the slope of the negative merit surface will direct a gradient-sensitive search back into feasible space, a smooth unimodal second hypersurface is placed under the merit hypersur-

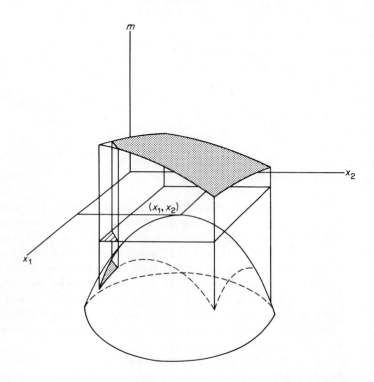

FIG. 77. The shaded surface is the merit surface with and without penalty. The location (x_1, x_2) is a known point in feasible space. The cross-hatched domain within regional constraints is that domain in violation of the functional constraints.

face. This second surface is called the *penalty* surface. The apex of the penalty surface is placed at the known point in feasible space, and the ordinate of the apex is zero. Thus the penalty surface has no extremes in infeasible space and a gradient-sensitive search straying into infeasible space is guided unerringly back toward feasible space. Figure 77 suggests the geometry involved.

A subroutine generating the penalty surface is part of the IOWA CADET design library, and its listing is as follows:

118

```
      SUBROUTINE PENAL (N, GOOD, X, Y)
      DIMENSION GOOD(9), X(9)
      Y = 0.
      DO 100 I = 1, N
      Y = Y + (GOOD(I) − X(I))*(GOOD(I) − X(I))
  100 CONTINUE
      Y = −Y
      RETURN
      END
```

The MERIT function for this problem will be one constructed to respond
to interrogations of GRID4 multidimensional search routine. It must accept
a tendered value of offsets a and b, determine the plate area of the cam
and determine whether the functional constraint of the limiting value of
the pressure angle is violated. If this proves to be the case, subroutine
PENAL is called to supply a penalty negative ordinate for return to GRID4.

A subroutine FUNCT is provided to supply an ordinate and first derivative of the function to be generated by the cam when a value of rotational
angle θ is supplied.

A complete listing of the program which implements the plan depicted
in Fig. 78 follows.

```
C      EXECUTIVE PROGRAM TO DETERMINE THE CONTOUR AND OFFSET OF A
C      KNIFE-EDGED RADIAL FOLLOWER CAM OF MINIMUM SIZE TO GENERATE
C      A SPECIFIED FUNCTION.                              MISCHKE
C
C      THETA1=INITIAL ANGULAR POSITION OF CAM SHAFT, DEG.
C      THETA2=FINAL ANGULAR POSITION OF CAM SHAFT, DEG.
C      PLIMIT=HIGHEST PERMISSIBLE PRESSURE ANGLE, DEG.
C      ALOW=LOWER LIMIT OF FOLLOWER PATH OFFSET, IN.
C      AHIGH=UPPERLIMIT OF FOLLOWER PATH OFFSET, IN.
C
C      BLOW=LOWER LIMIT OF INITIAL FOLLOWER POSITION, IN.
C      BHIGH=UPPER LIMIT OF INITIAL FOLLOWER POSITION, IN.
C      AREA=AREA OF CAM PLATE, SQ.IN.
C      RAREA=RECIPROCAL OF AREA (FIGURE OF MERIT)
C
C      A=FOLLOWER PATH OFFSET, IN.
C      B=INITIAL FOLLOWER POSITION,IN.
C      XX=X-COORDINATE OF POINT ON CAM CONTOUR, IN.
C      YY=Y-COORDINATE OF POINT ON CAM CONTOUR, IN.
C      THETA=ABSCISSA ANGLE TO POINT (XX,YY), DEG.
C
       COMMON THETA1,THETA2,PLIMIT,GOOD(9),I1
       DIMENSION IABC(20),X(9),XR(9),XL(9),XLOW(9),XHIGH(9)
C
C      ..... READ IN DATA .....
C
     1 READ(1,2)THETA1,THETA2,PLIMIT,ALOW,AHIGH,BLOW,BHIGH
     2 FORMAT(7F10.5)
       READ(1,3)I1,I2,F,AA,BB,R
     3 FORMAT(2I2,4F10.5)
       READ(1,4)(IABC(I),I=1,20)
     4 FORMAT(20A4)
C
C      ..... INITIATE A GRID SEARCH FOR LARGEST FIGURE OF MERIT    .....
C      ..... WHICH IS THE RECIPROCAL OF THE PLATE AREA OF THE CAM. .....
C
```

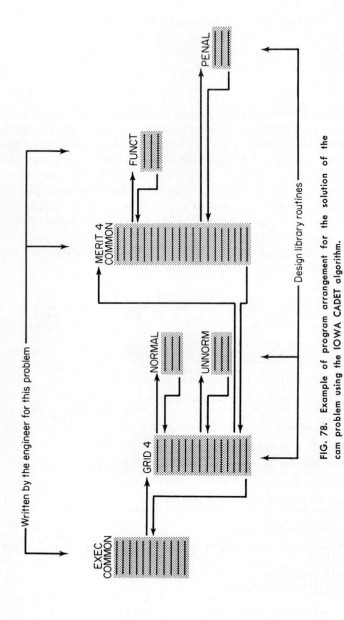

FIG. 78. Example of program arrangement for the solution of the cam problem using the IOWA CADET algorithm.

```fortran
      GOOD(1)=AA
      GOOD(2)=BB
      XL(1)=ALOW
      XL(2)=BLOW
      XR(1)=AHIGH
      XR(2)=BHIGH
      CALL GRID4(I1,I2,XL,XR,F,R,RAREA,X,XLOW,XHIGH,NN)
C
C     ..... PREPARE OUTPUT .....
C
      AREA=1./RAREA
      A=X(1)
      B=X(2)
C
C     ..... DOCUMENT SEARCH .....
C
      WRITE(3,5)THETA1,THETA2,PLIMIT
    5 FORMAT('1EXECUTIVE PROGRAM PRINT OUT FOR MINIMUM AREA PLATE CAM'//
     1' INPUT DATA'//
     2' INITIAL ANGULAR POSITION OF CAM SHAFT, DEG ............',F15.0,/,
     3' FINAL ANGULAR POSITION OF CAM SHAFT, DEG...............',F15.0,/,
     4' UPPER LIMIT ON PRESSURE ANGLE, DEG....................',F15.0//)
      WRITE(3,6)(IABC(I),I=1,20)
    6 FORMAT(20A4,//,' OUTPUT DATA',//)
      WRITE(3,7)A,B,AREA
    7 FORMAT(
     1' OFFSET OF PATH OF RADIAL FOLLOWER, IN .................',F15.5,/,
     2' INITIAL FOLLOWER RADIAL DISPLACEMENT, IN ..............',F15.5,/,
     3' PLATE AREA OF MINIMAL AREA CAM, SQ IN .................',F15.5//,
     4' CAM CONTOUR FOLLOWS',//,
     5' X-COORDINATE    Y-COORDINATE    SHAFT ANGLE    PRESSURE ANGLE',/,
     6'   INCHES          INCHES          DEGREES          DEGREES   ',//)
C
C     ..... DETERMINE AND DOCUMENT CAM CONTOUR.....
C
      C=180./3.14159
      DEL=(THETA2-THETA1)/10.
      THETA=THETA1-10.
      DO 100 I=1,12
      CALL FUNCT(THETA,G,DY)
      XX=(G+B)*SIN(THETA/C)+A*COS(THETA/C)
      YY=(G+B)*COS(THETA/C)-A*SIN(THETA/C)
      PANGLE=C*ATAN(ABS((DY-A)/(G+B)))
      WRITE(3,9)XX,YY,THETA,PANGLE
    9 FORMAT(4F15.5)
      THETA=THETA+DEL
  100 CONTINUE
      WRITE(3,101)R,NN
  101 FORMAT(/,' GRID SEARCH DATA',//,
     1' FRACTIONAL GRID REDUCTION UTILIZED ...................',F15.8,/,
     2' NUMBER OF MERIT FUNCTION EVALUATIONS EXPENDED ........',I15)
      GO TO 1
      END


      SUBROUTINE MERIT4(X,Y)
      COMMON THETA1,THETA2,PLIMIT,GOOD(9),I1
      DIMENSION X(9)
C
C     ..... INITIALIZE .....
C
      A=X(1)
      B=X(2)
      PBIG=-360.
      DELTA=(THETA2-THETA1)/10.
      THETA=THETA1
      AREA=0.
      C=180./3.14159
C
C     ..... DETERMINE CAM PLATE AREA FOR THIS VALUE OF A & B.      .....
C
      DO 100 I=1,10
      CALL FUNCT(THETA,G,DY)
      XX=(G+B)*SIN(THETA/C)+A*COS(THETA/C)
```

121

```
      YY=(G+B)*COS(THETA/C)-A*SIN(THETA/C)
      RR=XX*XX+YY*YY
      AREA=AREA+0.5*RR*DELTA/C
      PANGLE=C*ATAN(ABS((DY-A)/(G+B)))
      IF(PANGLE-PBIG)2,2,1
    1 PBIG=PANGLE
    2 THETA=THETA+DELTA
  100 CONTINUE
C
C     ..... IF FUNCTIONAL CONSTRAINT OF LIMITING VALUE OF THE    .....
C     ..... PRESSURE ANGLE IS VIOLATED, PENALIZE THE MERIT ORDINATE.....
C
      IF(PBIG-PLIMIT)5,6,6
    5 Y=1./AREA
      RETURN
    6 CALL PENAL(I1,GOOD,X,Y)
      RETURN
      END


      SUBROUTINE FUNCT(THETA,Y,DY)
      C=180./3.14159
      Y=ALOG(THETA/C)
      DY=C/THETA
      RETURN
      END


      SUBROUTINE PENAL(N,GOOD,X,Y)
C
C     PENALTY ORDINATE SUBROUTINE
C     PENAL(I1,A2,A3,B1)                                    MISCHKE
C
C     THIS SUBROUTINE SUBSTITUTES A MERIT SURFACE OF NEGATIVE
C     ORDINATE AND HAVING SLOPES APPROPRIATE TO LEAD A GRADIENT SEARCH
C     BACK INTO FEASIBLE SPACE WITH UP TO NINE INDEPENDENT VARIABLES.
C
C     CALLING PROGRAM REQUIREMENTS
C
C     PROVIDE A DECLARATION STATEMENT AS FOLLOWS:
C
C           DIMENSION A2(100),A3(100)
C
C     NOMENCLATURE
C
C     I1=NUMBER OF INDEPENDENT COORDINATES IN MERIT HYPERSPACE
C     A2=COORDINATES OF A POINT IN FEASIBLE SPACE, COLUMN VECTOR
C     A3=TENDERED COORDINATES, COLUMN VECTOR
C     B1=PENALTY ORDINATE CORRESPONDING TO TENDERED COORDINATES, A3
C
      DIMENSION GOOD(9),X(9)
      Y=0.
      DO 100 I=1,N
      Y=Y+(GOOD(I)-X(I))*(GOOD(I)-X(I))
  100 CONTINUE
      Y=-Y
      RETURN
      END
```

The following are outputs from the preceding program utilizing the following basic data:

$\theta_1 = $ THETA1 $= 60.$ deg
$\theta_2 = $ THETA2 $= 160.$ deg
$\alpha = $ PLIMIT $= 30.$ deg
　　　　ALOW $= 0.$ in.
　　　　AHIGH $= 1.5$ in.
　　　　BLOW $= 0.$ in.

122

BHIGH = 1.5 in.
I1 = 2 independent variables
I2 = 1 convergence monitor print
F = 0.01
AA = 1.
BB = 1.

CONVERGENCE MONITOR SUBROUTINE GRID4

NN	SIDE	Y	X(1)	X(2)
5	0.100E 01	0.516E 00	0.1COE 01	0.500E 00
9	0.700E 00	0.698E 00	0.650E 00	0.500E CO
13	0.490E 00	0.730E 00	0.772E 00	0.377E 00
17	0.343E 00	0.730E 00	0.772E 00	0.377E 00
21	0.240E 00	0.736E 00	0.833E 00	0.317E 00
25	0.168E 00	0.810E 00	0.833E 00	0.233E 00
29	0.118E 00	0.810E 00	0.803E 00	0.263E 00
33	0.824E-01	0.850E 00	0.803E 00	0.222E 00
37	0.576E-01	0.850E 00	0.803E 00	0.222E 00
41	0.404E-01	0.850E 00	0.803E 00	0.222E 00
45	0.282E-01	C.850E 00	0.803E 00	0.222E 00
49	0.198E-01	0.850E 00	0.803E 00	0.222E 00
53	0.138E-01	0.850E 00	0.800E 00	0.225E 00

LARGEST MERIT ORDINATE FOUND DURING SEARCH 0.84989303E 00
NUMBER OF FUNCTION EVALUATIONS USED DURING SEARCH 58
FRACTIONAL REDUCTION IN INTERVAL OF UNCERTAINTY EXTANT 0.96888803E-02

XLOW(1)= 0.79238486E 00 X(1)= 0.79965162E 00 XHIGH(1)= 0.80691826E 00
XLOW(2)= 0.21786785E 00 X(2)= 0.22513461E 00 XHIGH(2)= 0.23240125E 00

EXECUTIVE PROGRAM PRINT OUT FOR MINIMUM AREA PLATE CAM

INPUT DATA

INITIAL ANGULAR POSITION OF CAM SHAFT, DEG .... 60.
FINAL ANGULAR POSITION OF CAM SHAFT, DEG.............. 160.
UPPER LIMIT ON PRESSURE ANGLE, DEG.................... 30.

FUNCTION GENERATED IS Y=ALOG(THETA) FROM 60. TO 160. DEGREES

OUTPUT DATA

OFFSET OF PATH OF RADIAL FOLLOWER, IN 0.79965
INITIAL FOLLOWER RADIAL DISPLACEMENT, IN 0.22513
PLATE AREA OF MINIMAL AREA CAM, SQ IN 1.17662

CAM CONTOUR FOLLOWS

X-COORDINATE INCHES	Y-COORDINATE INCHES	SHAFT ANGLE DEGREES	PRESSURE ANGLE DEGREES
0.58213	-0.55541	50.00000	75.59627
0.63474	-0.55689	60.00000	29.78920
0.67324	-0.60593	70.00000	2.53857
0.68930	-0.69044	80.00000	8.49204
0.67672	-0.79965	90.00000	13.54532
0.63134	-0.92331	100.00000	16.16481
0.55098	-1.05151	110.00000	17.62712
0.43537	-1.17472	120.00000	18.47346
0.28609	-1.28392	130.00000	18.96492
0.10642	-1.37086	140.00000	19.24001
-0.09874	-1.42827	150.00000	19.37770
-0.32319	-1.45007	160.00000	19.42549

FRACTIONAL GRID REDUCTION UTILIZED 0.69999999
NUMBER OF MERIT FUNCTION EVALUATIONS EXPENDED 58

In the first case the fractional grid reduction utilized was $R = 0.7$. This is just a little higher than its minimum allowable value. Some attributes of the grid-type search can be seen from the inspection of the output of this program.

When $R = \frac{2}{3}$ the grid search abandons some of the feasible basis area irrevocably when it centers on a new ordinate. Thus if unsearched ground is abandoned on the basis of scanty information in the five (in this particular case) function evaluations, then the search is forever barred from regaining the ground even while in hot pursuit of growing ordinates.

The first output used 58 function evaluations to establish approximately that $a = 0.79965$, $b = 0.22513$, and that the plate area of the cam was 1.17662 sq in.

CONVERGENCE MONITOR SUBROUTINE GRID4

NN	SIDE	Y	X(1)	X(2)
5	0.100E 01	0.516E 00	0.100E 01	0.500E 00
9	0.750E 00	0.516E 00	0.100E 01	0.500E 00
13	0.563E 00	0.683E 00	0.859E 00	0.359E 00
17	0.422E 00	0.860E 00	0.859E 00	0.148E 00
21	0.316E 00	0.860E 00	0.859E 00	0.148E 00
25	0.237E 00	0.860E 00	0.859E 00	0.148E 00
29	0.178E 00	0.860E 00	0.859E 00	0.148E 00
33	0.133E 00	0.860E 00	0.859E 00	0.148E 00
37	0.100E 00	0.864E 00	0.834E 00	0.173E 00
41	0.751E-01	0.864E 00	0.834E 00	0.173E 00
45	0.563E-01	0.866E 00	0.820E 00	0.188E 00
49	0.422E-01	0.866E 00	0.820E 00	0.188E 00
53	0.317E-01	0.866E 00	0.820E 00	0.188E 00
57	0.238E-01	0.866E 00	0.820E 00	0.188E 00
61	0.178E-01	0.866E 00	0.820E 00	0.188E 00
65	0.134E-01	0.866E 00	0.820E 00	0.188E 00
69	0.100E-01	0.866E 00	0.820E 00	0.188E 00

LARGEST MERIT ORDINATE FOUND DURING SEARCH 0.86570883E 00
NUMBER OF FUNCTION EVALUATIONS USED DURING SEARCH 74
FRACTIONAL REDUCTION IN INTERVAL OF UNCERTAINTY EXTANT 0.75169429E-02

XLOW(1)= 0.81463039E 00   X(1)= 0.82026815E 00   XHIGH(1)= 0.82590580E 00
XLOW(2)= 0.18190622E 00   X(2)= 0.18754399E 00   XHIGH(2)= 0.19318163E 00

EXECUTIVE PROGRAM PRINT OUT FOR MINIMUM AREA PLATE CAM

INPUT DATA

INITIAL ANGULAR POSITION OF CAM SHAFT, DEG .... 60.
FINAL ANGULAR POSITION OF CAM SHAFT, DEG.............. 160.
UPPER LIMIT ON PRESSURE ANGLE, DEG.................... 30.

FUNCTION GENERATED IS Y=ALOG(THETA) FROM 60. TO 160. DEGREES

OUTPUT DATA

```
OFFSET OF PATH OF RADIAL FOLLOWER, IN ..................    0.82027
INITIAL FOLLOWER RADIAL DISPLACEMENT, IN ..............     0.18754
PLATE AREA OF MINIMAL AREA CAM, SQ IN ..................    1.15512

CAM CONTOUR FOLLOWS
```

X-COORDINATE INCHES	Y-COORDINATE INCHES	SHAFT ANGLE DEGREES	PRESSURE ANGLE DEGREES
0.56659	-0.59536	50.00000	81.04099
0.61249	-0.59354	60.00000	29.95560
0.64497	-0.63816	70.00000	0.25946
0.65586	-0.71727	80.00000	11.28900
0.63913	-0.82027	90.00000	16.03162
0.59074	-0.93708	100.00000	18.37592
0.50860	-1.05803	110.00000	19.62175
0.39251	-1.17378	120.00000	20.29817
0.24404	-1.27555	130.00000	20.65388
0.06647	-1.35532	140.00000	20.81830
-0.13539	-1.40602	150.00000	20.86401
-0.35542	-1.42179	160.00000	20.83415

```
GRID SEARCH DATA

FRACTIONAL GRID REDUCTION UTILIZED ....................    0.75000000
NUMBER OF MERIT FUNCTION EVALUATIONS EXPENDED ........            74
```

The second output is based on $R = 0.75$, and 74 function evaluations established $a = 0.82027$ in., $b = 0.18754$ in., and the plate area of the cam as 1.15512 sq in. The number of function evaluations increased, as we might have expected, but the plate area is not much smaller. This is an attribute of multidimensional searches such as GRID4. The abandonment of portions of the basis area is not done with certainty that the extreme is outside the abandoned region. Secondly, the search pattern is sparse and an element of luck is involved in locating the constrained extremum along a slowly rising cliff, such as is involved here.

```
CONVERGENCE MONITOR SUBROUTINE GRID4
```

NN	SIDE	Y	X(1)	X(2)
5	0.100E 01	0.516E 00	0.100E 01	0.500E 00
9	0.800E 00	0.516E 00	0.100E 01	0.500E 00
13	0.640E 00	0.712E 00	0.840E 00	0.340E 00
17	0.512E 00	0.712E 00	0.840E 00	0.340E 00
21	0.410E 00	0.712E 00	0.840E 00	0.340E 00
25	0.328E 00	0.856E 00	0.840E 00	0.176E 00
29	0.262E 00	0.856E 00	0.840E 00	0.176E 00
33	0.210E 00	0.856E 00	0.840E 00	0.176E 00
37	0.168E 00	0.856E 00	0.840E 00	0.176E 00
41	0.134E 00	0.856E 00	0.840E 00	0.176E 00
45	0.107E 00	0.858E 00	0.813E 00	0.203E 00
49	0.859E-01	0.858E 00	0.813E 00	0.203E 00
53	0.687E-01	0.858E 00	0.813E 00	0.203E 00
57	0.550E-01	0.858E 00	0.813E 00	0.203E 00
61	0.440E-01	0.858E 00	0.813E 00	0.203E 00
65	0.352E-01	0.858E 00	0.813E 00	0.203E 00
69	0.281E-01	0.858E 00	0.813E 00	0.203E 00
73	0.225E-01	0.858E 00	0.813E 00	0.203E 00
77	0.180E-01	0.858E 00	0.809E 00	0.208E 00
81	0.144E-01	0.858E 00	0.809E 00	0.208E 00
85	0.115E-01	0.858E 00	0.809E 00	0.208E 00

```
LARGEST MERIT ORDINATE FOUND DURING SEARCH ........... 0.85822439E 00
NUMBER OF FUNCTION EVALUATIONS USED DURING SEARCH ....          90
FRACTIONAL REDUCTION IN INTERVAL OF UNCERTAINTY EXTANT 0.92233382E-02


XLOW(1)= 0.80173469E 00   X(1)= 0.80865222E 00   XHIGH(1)= 0.81556964E 00
XLOW(2)= 0.20058888E 00   X(2)= 0.20750642E 00   XHIGH(2)= 0.21442384E 00
```

EXECUTIVE PROGRAM PRINT OUT FOR MINIMUM AREA PLATE CAM

INPUT DATA

```
INITIAL ANGULAR POSITION OF CAM SHAFT, DEG ............         60.
FINAL ANGULAR POSITION OF CAM SHAFT, DEG...............        160.
UPPER LIMIT ON PRESSURE ANGLE, DEG.....................         30.
```

FUNCTION GENERATED IS Y=ALOG(THETA) FROM 60. TO 160. DEGREES

OUTPUT DATA

```
OFFSET OF PATH OF RADIAL FOLLOWER, IN .................     0.80865
INITIAL FOLLOWER RADIAL DISPLACEMENT, IN ..............     0.20751
PLATE AREA OF MINIMAL AREA CAM, SQ IN .................     1.16520
```

CAM CONTOUR FOLLOWS

X-COORDINATE INCHES	Y-COORDINATE INCHES	SHAFT ANGLE DEGREES	PRESSURE ANGLE DEGREES
0.57441	-0.57363	50.00000	78.06279
0.62397	-0.57350	60.00000	29.97446
0.65976	-0.62042	70.00000	1.38511
0.67350	-0.70237	80.00000	9.69254
0.65909	-0.80865	90.00000	14.62869
0.61242	-0.92911	100.00000	17.13553
0.53134	-1.05394	110.00000	18.50659
0.41560	-1.17370	120.00000	19.28021
0.26680	-1.27948	130.00000	19.71301
0.08820	-1.36314	140.00000	19.93997
-0.11535	-1.41750	150.00000	20.03748
-0.33767	-1.43658	160.00000	20.05121

GRID SEARCH DATA

```
FRACTIONAL GRID REDUCTION UTILIZED ....................    0.79999995
NUMBER OF MERIT FUNCTION EVALUATIONS EXPENDED .........          90
```

The third output is based upon $R = 0.8$ and used 90 function evaluations to establish $a = 0.80865$ in., $b = 0.20751$ in., and the plate area of the cam as 1.16520 sq in. Figure 79 indicates the path of progress of the grid center during one of these searches. The plate areas obtained are within approximately 5 per cent of one another. A mixture of strategies is useful in gaining the little remaining altitude of the merit surface, if desired.

5.5 A GEAR TRAIN OF MINIMAL INERTIA

There are applications in servomechanisms and control devices wherein an angular displacement is transmitted through a gear reduction to another

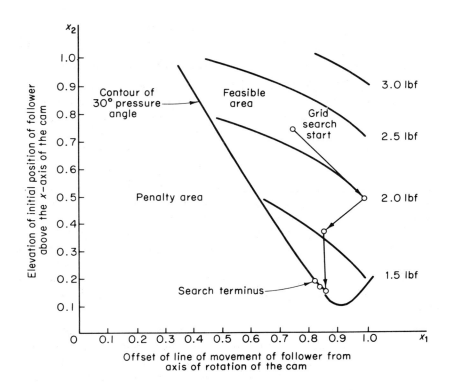

shaft. In the interest of accomplishing the angular displacement as quickly as possible, minimization of the inertia of the intervening gear train is attempted when the load inertia is small enough that the gear-train inertia represents the principal resistance to acceleration. When the overall gear ratio is specified by other considerations, should the reduction be accomplished as a single reduction, a double reduction, a triple reduction, or more?

While pursuit of the answers to these questions is interesting, we will confine out attention to the problem of determining, for a triple reduction, the appropriate distribution of the individual steps so as to minimize the gear-train inertia. Figure 80 depicts the spur gear train in which the gears and pinions are disklike. The native inertias (polar moments of inertia about principal axis of revolution) are represented by

I_M = armature inertia
I_P = pinion inertia
I_{G1} = gear 1 inertia
I_{G2} = gear 2 inertia

127

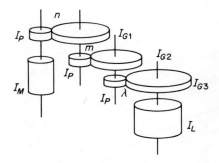

I_{G3} = gear 3 inertia
I_L = inertia of the driven load

and the other parameters are

n = first step-down ratio
m = second step-down ratio
λ = third step-down ratio
R = overall gear reduction, which equals $nm\lambda$

FIG. 80. A triple reduction spur-gear train with an overall step-down ratio $R = nm\lambda$. I_M and I_L refer to the motor armature and load rotary inertias respectively.

We shall approach this problem from a traditional analytical viewpoint in order to see diminishing returns as the problem complexity grows, then turn to a computer solution as an example of a search carried out over two independent variables.

In Fig. 81, all the inertias have been reflected to the motor shaft and the magnitude of these equivalent inertias are specified by the following rules:*

Rule I: Inertia on a second shaft is reflected onto the motor shaft as the native inertia divided by the step-down ratio squared.

Rule II: The inertia of a disk gear on a second shaft in mesh with a disk pinion on the the motor shaft is reflected to the pinion shaft as the *pinion* inertia multiplied by the step-down ratio squared.

Applying these rules to the shish kebob equivalent of Fig. 81, we obtain

$$I_e = I_M + I_P - n^2 I_p + \frac{I_P}{n^2} + \frac{m^2 I_P}{n^2} + \frac{I_P}{n^2 m^2} + \frac{\lambda^2 I_P}{n^2 m^2} + \frac{I_L}{n^2 m^2 \lambda^2}$$

Introduction of the overall ratio $R = nm\lambda$ and substitution for λ results in

$$I_e = I_M + (1 + n^2)I_P + \left(\frac{1}{n^2} + \frac{m^2}{n^2}\right)I_P + \left(\frac{1}{n^2 m^2} + \frac{R^2}{n^4 m^4}\right)I_P + \frac{I_L}{R^2} \quad (5.10)$$

In order to minimize the equivalent inertia in a formal fashion it is necessary to differentiate Eq. (5.10) with respect to n and m and equate the derivatives to zero.

---

*For development, see Charles R. Mischke, *Elements of Mechanical Analysis* (Reading, Mass.: Addison-Wesley Publishing Company, Inc., 1963), pp. 59 ff.

$$\frac{\partial I_e}{\partial n} = \left(2n - \frac{2}{n^3} - \frac{2m^2}{n^3} - \frac{2}{n^3 m^2} - \frac{4R^2}{n^5 m^4}\right)I_P = 0$$

$$\frac{\partial I_e}{\partial m} = \left(\frac{2m}{n^2} - \frac{2}{n^2 m^3} - \frac{4R^2}{n^4 m^5}\right)I_P = 0$$

In order to determine n and m, it is necessary to solve simultaneously the equations

$$n^6 m^4 - n^2 m^4 - n^2 m^6 - n^2 m^2 - 2R^2 = 0 \qquad (5.11)$$

and

$$n^2 m^6 - n^2 m^2 - 2R^2 = 0 \qquad (5.12)$$

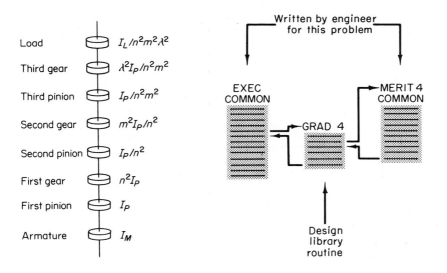

Load	$I_L/n^2 m^2 \lambda^2$
Third gear	$\lambda^2 I_P/n^2 m^2$
Third pinion	$I_P/n^2 m^2$
Second gear	$m^2 I_P/n^2$
Second pinion	I_P/n^2
First gear	$n^2 I_P$
First pinion	I_P
Armature	I_M

FIG. 81. The shish-kebab equivalent of all inertias reflected onto the motor armature shaft.

Written by engineer for this problem

EXEC COMMON   GRAD 4   MERIT 4 COMMON

Design library routine

FIG. 82. Example of program arrangement for solution of the gear-train problem using the IOWA CADET algorithm.

If there had been a fourth reduction, there would be three simultaneous equations similar to Eqs. (5.11) and (5.12) to be solved. We are clearly close to the limit of tractability of this form of solution.

A computer solution using the IOWA CADET algorithm would involve a search over the domain of n and m for the configuration of minimal equivalent inertia. We choose as the figure of merit the reciprocal of the equivalent inertia. We observe no functional constraint and declare the regional constraints to be

$$1 \leq n \leq 3$$
$$1 \leq m \leq 3$$

Inasmuch as there are no functional constraints to introduce "cliffs," a gradient search will be effective and we select the gradient search library subroutine GRAD4. According to the documentation it calls the subroutine MERIT4. The programs to solve this problem are structured as shown in Fig. 82. We begin by composing subroutine MERIT4, and then write the executive program. A listing of these programs follows.

```
C
C       EXECUTIVE PROGRAM FOR MINIMIZING THE INERTIA, AS SEEN BY MOTOR,
C       OF A MULTI-STEP DISK SPUR GEAR TRAIN, WITH OVERALL REDUCTION
C       RATIO SPECIFIED
C
C       I1=NUMBER OF GEAR REDUCTIONS IN TRAIN
C       RATIO=DESIRED OVERALL GEAR REDUCTION
C       XIM=ROTARY INERTIA OF MOTOR ARMATURE
C       XIP=ROTARY INERTIA OF PINIONS
C       XIL=ROTARY INERTIA OF LOAD ON LAST SHAFT
C
C       I2=CONVERGENCE MONITOR PRINT SIGNAL
C       I3=COMMENCE SEARCH LOCATION SIGNAL
C       DELTA=INITIAL EXPLORATION STEP SIZE
C       DMULT=STEPSIZE GROWTH MULTIPLIER
C       F=FRACTIONAL REDUCTION IN DOMAIN OF UNCERTAINTY DESIRED
C
C       EPS=SURVEY PATTERN INCREMENT
C       RLOW(I)=LOWER BOUNDS OF INTERVAL OF UNCERTAINTY
C       RHIGH(I)=UPPER BOUNDS OF INTERVAL OF UNCERTAINTY
C       X(I)=GEAR RATIOS FROM MOTOR TO LOAD
C
        COMMON I1,XIM,XIP,XIL,XIEQ,RATIO
        DIMENSION RLOW(9),RHIGH(9),X(9),P(9),Q(9)
C
C       ..... READ INPUT DATA .....
C
      9 READ(1,1)I1,RATIO,XIM,XIP,XIL
      1 FORMAT(I5,4F10.5)
        READ(1,2)I2,I3,DELTA,DMULT,EPS,F
      2 FORMAT(2I2,2F10.5,2F10.8)
        I1=I1-1
        DO 3 I=1,I1
        READ(1,4)XLOW,XHIGH
      4 FORMAT(2F10.5)
        RLOW(I)=XLOW
        RHIGH(I)=XHIGH
      3 CONTINUE
C
C       ..... INITIATE GRADIENT SEARCH FOR EXTREME FIGURE OF MERIT    .....
C       ..... WHICH IS THE RECIPROCAL OF THE EQUIVALENT INERTIA       .....
C       ..... AS SEEN ON THE MOTOR SHAFT.                             .....
C
        CALL GRAD4(I1,I2,I3,DELTA,DMULT,F,EPS,RLOW,RHIGH,Y,X,J3,J4,P,Q)
        I1=I1+1
C
C       ..... DOCUMENT SEARCH .....
C
        WRITE(3,5)I1,XIM,XIP,XIL,RATIO
      5 FORMAT('1EXECUTIVE PROGRAM OUTPUT FOR MINIMUM GEARTRAIN INERTIA'//
     1' INPUT DATA'//,
     2' NUMBER OF REDUCTION STEPS IN GEARTRAIN ................',I10  ,/,
     3' ROTARY INERTIA OF MOTOR ARMATURE, SLUG FT2, ..........',F10.5,/,
     4' ROTARY INERTIA OF MOTOR PINION, SLUG FT2, ............',F10.5,/,
     5' ROTARY INERTIA OF LOAD ON LAST SHAFT, SLUG FT2, ......',F10.5,/,
     6' OVERALL GEAR RATIO SPECIFIED .........................',F10.5,/)
```

130

```
      WRITE(3,6)XIEQ
6 FORMAT(/,' OUTPUT DATA',//,
  1' EQUIVALENT INERTIA OF OPTIMAL GEAR TRAIN,SLUG-FT2.....',F10.5,/,
  2' OPTIMAL GEAR RATIOS FROM MOTOR TO LOAD',/)
      DO 8 I=1,I1
      XX=X(I)
      WRITE(3,7)XX
7 FORMAT(' RATIO(S) ',45X,F10.5)
8 CONTINUE
      GO TO 9
      END

      SUBROUTINE MERIT4(X,Y)
      COMMON I1,XIM,XIP,XIL,XIEQ,RATIO
      DIMENSION X(9)
      N=I1
      PROD=1.
      SUM=0.
      BOTTOM=1.
      DO 2 I=1,N
      PROD=PROD*X(I)
2 CONTINUE
      X(N+1)=RATIO/PROD
      N=N+1
      DO 1 I=2,N
      TOP=1.+X(I)*X(I)
      BOTTOM=BOTTOM*X(I-1)*X(I-1)
      SUM=SUM+TOP/BOTTOM
1 CONTINUE
      XIEQ=XIM+XIP*(1.+X(1)*X(1))+XIP*SUM+XIL/(RATIO*RATIO)
      Y=1./XIEQ
      RETURN
      END
```

The following output was obtained using the data:

$$I1 = 3 \text{ dimensions}$$
$$R = RATIO = 10.$$
$$I_M = XIM = 10. \text{ slug ft}^2$$
$$I_P = XIP = 1. \text{ slug ft}^2$$
$$I2 = 1 \text{ convergence monitor print}$$
$$I3 = 1 \text{ commence search centrally}$$
$$DELTA = 0.1$$
$$DMULT = 1.2$$
$$EPS = 0.0001$$
$$F = 0.001$$
$$RLOW (1) = 1. \quad RHIGH (1) = 3.$$
$$RLOW (2) = 1. \quad RHIGH (2) = 3.$$

CONVERGENCE MONITOR SUBROUTINE GRAD4

N1	DELTA	Y	X(1)	X(2)	X(3)
3	0.100E 00	0.565E-01	0.200E 01	0.200E 01	0.250E 01
6	0.120E 00	0.571E-01	0.188E 01	0.200E 01	0.266E 01
9	0.144E 00	0.573E-01	0.174E 01	0.200E 01	0.289E 01
12	0.173E 00	0.571E-01	0.186E 01	0.212E 01	0.254E 01
15	0.173E-01	0.573E-01	0.172E 01	0.199E 01	0.292E 01
18	0.173E-02	0.573E-01	0.174E 01	0.200E 01	0.288E 01

```
 21    0.207E-02 0.573E-01 0.174E 01 0.200E 01 0.288E 01
 24    0.249E-02 0.573E-01 0.174E 01 0.200E 01 0.287E 01
 27    0.299E-02 0.573E-01 0.174E 01 0.201E 01 0.287E 01
 30    0.358E-02 0.573E-01 0.174E 01 0.201E 01 0.286E 01
 33    0.430E-02 0.573E-01 0.174E 01 0.201E 01 0.285E 01
 36    0.516E-02 0.573E-01 0.175E 01 0.201E 01 0.284E 01
 39    0.619E-02 0.573E-01 0.175E 01 0.202E 01 0.283E 01
 42    0.743E-02 0.573E-01 0.175E 01 0.202E 01 0.283E 01
 45    0.892E-02 0.573E-01 0.175E 01 0.202E 01 0.283E 01
 48    0.107E-01 0.573E-01 0.174E 01 0.202E 01 0.285E 01
 51    0.107E-02 0.573E-01 0.175E 01 0.202E 01 0.283E 01
 54    0.107E-03 0.573E-01 0.175E 01 0.202E 01 0.283E 01
```

```
LARGEST MERIT ORDINATE ......................... 0.57333771E-01
NUMBER OF FUNCTION EVALUATIONS .........................       60
FINAL SEARCH STEPSIZE ...............................  0.00010699
STEPSIZE GROWTH MULTIPLIER ...........................  1.19999981
SURVEY PATTERN INCREMENT ......................... 0.99999990E-04
FRACTIONAL REDUCTION IN INTERVAL OF UNCERTAINTY ......  0.00100000
SPECIE OF LARGEST MERIT ORDINATE ....................           1
```

```
X(  1)=   0.17486E 01    P(  1)=  -0.14901E-03    Q(  1)=  -0.10058E-03
X(  2)=   0.20209E 01    P(  2)=   0.10058E-03    Q(  2)=   0.10058E-03
```

```
MERIT EXTREME IS AN EXTREMUM
```

```
EXECUTIVE PROGRAM OUTPUT FOR MINIMUM GEARTRAIN INERTIA
```

```
INPUT DATA
```

```
NUMBER OF REDUCTION STEPS IN GEARTRAIN ................       3
ROTARY INERTIA OF MOTOR ARMATURE, SLUG FT2, ...........  10.00000
ROTARY INERTIA OF MOTOR PINION, SLUG FT2, .............   1.00000
ROTARY INERTIA OF LOAD ON LAST SHAFT, SLUG FT2, ...... 100.00000
OVERALL GEAR RATIO SPECIFIED .........................  10.00000
```

```
OUTPUT DATA
```

```
EQUIVALENT INERTIA OF OPTIMAL GEAR TRAIN,SLUG-FT2.....  17.44173
OPTIMAL GEAR RATIOS FROM MOTOR TO LOAD
```

```
RATIO(S)                                                 1.74862
RATIO(S)                                                 2.02090
RATIO(S)                                                 2.82983
```

The convergence monitor indicates the gradient search terminated in a region of very small slope. The forward slopes were

$$P(1) = -0.14901E - 03$$
$$P(2) = 0.10058E - 03$$

and the slopes in the negative abscissa directions were

$$Q(1) = -0.10058E - 03$$
$$Q(2) = +0.10058E - 03$$

Since the sign of the slope did not change when passing over the central ordinate to the merit surface, the search reported as terminating at an extreme rather than at a "domelike" summit. The extreme ordinate reported is very close to the summit ordinate as evidenced by the small slopes. The search reports the gear ratios as 1.74862, 2.02090, 2.82983, in that order from the motor shaft.

The following output is from the same program but considering I1 = 2 dimensions—i.e., a double reduction drive of the load. In this case the search terminated at a maximum reporting the proper gear ratios to be 2.42924 and 4.11651, in that order from the motor shaft. Note that the equivalent inertia has increased from 17.44173 slug ft² to 20.94221 slug ft² despite the removal of a pinion and gear from the train.

```
CONVERGENCE MONITOR SUBROUTINE GRAD4

  N1      DELTA      Y        X(1)      X(2)      X(3)

    2   0.100E 00 0.444E-01 0.200E 01 0.500E 01 0.283E 01
    4   0.120E 00 0.462E-01 0.212E 01 0.472E 01 0.283E 01
    6   0.144E 00 0.473E-01 0.226E 01 0.442E 01 0.283E 01
    8   0.173E 00 0.477E-01 0.244E 01 0.410E 01 0.283E 01
   10   0.207E 00 0.471E-01 0.223E 01 0.449E 01 0.283E 01
   12   0.207E-01 0.477E-01 0.246E 01 0.407E 01 0.283E 01
   14   0.207E-02 0.478E-01 0.243E 01 0.411E 01 0.283E 01
   16   0.249E-02 0.478E-01 0.243E 01 0.411E 01 0.283E 01
   18   0.299E-02 0.478E-01 0.243E 01 0.412E 01 0.283E 01
   20   0.358E-02 0.478E-01 0.243E 01 0.412E 01 0.283E 01
   22   0.358E-03 0.478E-01 0.243E 01 0.412E 01 0.283E 01

LARGEST MERIT ORDINATE ..................................... 0.47750439E-01
NUMBER OF FUNCTION EVALUATIONS .........................          26
FINAL SEARCH STEPSIZE .................................    0.00035832
STEPSIZE GROWTH MULTIPLIER .............................     1.19999981
SURVEY PATTERN INCREMENT ........................... 0.99999990E-04
FRACTIONAL REDUCTION IN INTERVAL OF UNCERTAINTY ......    0.00100000
SPECIE OF LARGEST MERIT ORDINATE ......................           2

X( 1)=   0.24292E 01    P( 1)=   -0.33528E-04    Q( 1)=    0.67055E-04

MERIT EXTREME IS A MAXIMUM


EXECUTIVE PROGRAM OUTPUT FOR MINIMUM GEARTRAIN INERTIA

INPUT DATA

NUMBER OF REDUCTION STEPS IN GEARTRAIN ...............            2
ROTARY INERTIA OF MOTOR ARMATURE, SLUG FT2, ..........    10.00000
ROTARY INERTIA OF MOTOR PINION, SLUG FT2, ............     1.00000
ROTARY INERTIA OF LOAD ON LAST SHAFT, SLUG FT2, ......   100.00000
OVERALL GEAR RATIO SPECIFIED .........................    10.00000


OUTPUT DATA

EQUIVALENT INERTIA OF OPTIMAL GEAR TRAIN,SLUG-FT2..... 20.94221
OPTIMAL GEAR RATIOS FROM MOTOR TO LOAD

RATIO(S)                                                 2.42924
RATIO(S)                                                 4.11651
```

This last exercise of the program could have been done using a golden section one-dimensional search.

5.6 A FUNCTION GENERATOR OF MAXIMUM ACCURACY

The natural input to an automatic control system is often either a mechanical rotation or a mechanical translation. It is a prudent concession to operators' tastes to provide control station input as a rotation of a knob scanning a *linear* scale, thereby providing both confidence in interpolation and ease of use. The necessary command input may be a translational movement, as in the compression of a coil spring, motion of a valve stem, motion of a hydraulic amplifier piston, the movement of an inductance core, etc. The necessary input command may be a rotational movement, as in a potentiometer shaft, condenser shaft, rotary valve stem, etc. In terms of the characteristics of the system under control, and of the automatic control itself, these inputs are not linear with the performance of the system. In order to provide a *linear* input dial it is necessary to interpose a mechanism that will accept a uniform angular displacement and convert it into a nonuniform translational or rotational response of appropriate characteristics—i.e., it is necessary to interpose a function generator between the operator and the "real" mechanical input command.

The problem reduces itself to the synthesis of the kinematic proportions of a mechanism to be used as a function generator. The simplest devices include the offset slider-crank mechanism, the flat-faced radial follower cam, and the flat-faced radial follower disk cam for rotational-input–translational-output function generators. The plane four-bar mechanism may be used as a rotational-input–rotational-output function generator.

As an illustration of the use of the digital computer and the IOWA CADET algorithm we shall consider the three-point synthesis of a four-bar mechanism to perform as a function generator in the command module of an automatic feedback control. The plane four-bar chain can accept a rotational input and provide a rotational output with approximate fidelity to a given functional relationship. The schematic of a four-bar function generator is shown in Fig. 83. Four configurations can be identified as illustrated in Fig. 84.

The linkage exists when the vector chain $\rho_1, \rho_2, \rho_3, \rho_4$ is closed—i.e., when

$$\rho_1 + \rho_2 + \rho_3 + \rho_4 = 0$$

In order to obtain relationships which involve link lengths and the angles α and β, the dot product $\rho_2 \cdot \rho_2$ is evaluated ($\rho_4 = -\hat{i}$).

$$\rho_2 \cdot \rho_2 = (\hat{i} - \rho_1 - \rho_3) \cdot (\hat{i} - \rho_1 - \rho_3)$$

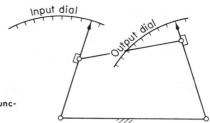

FIG. 83. The four-bar linkage as a function generator.

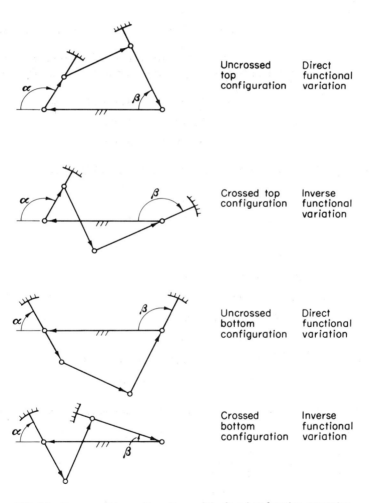

Uncrossed top configuration — Direct functional variation

Crossed top configuration — Inverse functional variation

Uncrossed bottom configuration — Direct functional variation

Crossed bottom configuration — Inverse functional variation

FIG. 84. Four possible configurations of the four-bar function generator.

135

This leads to the equation

$$\cos(\alpha - \beta) = \frac{(1 + \rho_1^2 - \rho_2^2 + \rho_3^2)}{2|\rho_1||\rho_3|} + \frac{1}{|\rho_3|}\cos\alpha - \frac{1}{|\rho_1|}\cos\beta \quad \text{(uncrossed top conf.)}$$

Denoting

$$\Delta_1 = \frac{1}{|\rho_1|}, \quad \Delta_2 = \frac{(1 + \rho_1^2 - \rho_2^2 + \rho_3^2)}{2|\rho_1||\rho_3|}, \quad \Delta_3 = \frac{1}{|\rho_3|}$$

it follows that

$$\cos(\alpha - \beta) = \Delta_3\cos\alpha - \Delta_1\cos\beta + \Delta_2 \quad \text{(uncrossed top)}$$

A three-precision-point synthesis will be undertaken. The angular coordinates of the points of precision (zero error) are denoted (α_1, β_1), (α_2, β_2), (α_3, β_3).

$$\cos(\alpha_1 - \beta_1) = \Delta_3\cos\alpha_1 - \Delta_1\cos\beta_1 + \Delta_2 \qquad (5.13)$$

$$\cos(\alpha_2 - \beta_2) = \Delta_3\cos\alpha_2 - \Delta_1\cos\beta_2 + \Delta_2 \qquad (5.14)$$

$$\cos(\alpha_3 - \beta_3) = \Delta_3\cos\alpha_3 - \Delta_1\cos\beta_3 + \Delta_2 \qquad (5.15)$$

Subtracting Eq. (5.14) from Eq. (5.13) and Eq. (5.15) from Eq. (5.13) yields

$$\delta_5 = \delta_1\Delta_3 - \delta_3\Delta_1$$
$$\delta_6 = \delta_2\Delta_3 - \delta_4\Delta_1$$

where

$$\delta_1 = \cos\alpha_1 - \cos\alpha_2$$
$$\delta_2 = \cos\alpha_1 - \cos\alpha_3$$
$$\delta_3 = \cos\beta_1 - \cos\beta_2$$
$$\delta_4 = \cos\beta_1 - \cos\beta_3$$
$$\delta_5 = \cos(\alpha_1 - \beta_1) - \cos(\alpha_2 - \beta_2)$$
$$\delta_6 = \cos(\alpha_1 - \beta_1) - \cos(\alpha_3 - \beta_3)$$

Solving the pair of simultaneous equations in Δ_1 and Δ_3 yields for the various configurations

Uncrossed top

$$\Delta_1 = \frac{\delta_2\delta_5 - \delta_1\delta_6}{\delta_1\delta_4 - \delta_2\delta_3}$$

$$\Delta_3 = \frac{\delta_4\delta_5 - \delta_3\delta_6}{\delta_1\delta_4 - \delta_2\delta_3}$$

$$\Delta_2 = \cos(\alpha_i - \beta_i) + \Delta_1\cos\beta_i - \Delta_3\cos\alpha_i, \quad i = 1, 2, 3$$

Uncrossed bottom	$\Delta_1 = \dfrac{\delta_1 \delta_6 - \delta_2 \delta_5}{\delta_1 \delta_4 - \delta_2 \delta_3}$

$$\Delta_3 = \frac{\delta_3 \delta_6 - \delta_4 \delta_5}{\delta_1 \delta_4 - \delta_2 \delta_3}$$

$$\Delta_2 = \cos(\alpha_i - \beta_i) - \Delta_1 \cos \beta_i + \Delta_3 \cos \alpha_i, \quad i = 1, 2, 3$$

For inverse functional variation the equations are

Crossed top	$\Delta_1 = \dfrac{\delta_2 \delta_5 - \delta_1 \delta_6}{\delta_1 \delta_4 - \delta_2 \delta_3}$

$$\Delta_3 = \frac{\delta_3 \delta_6 - \delta_4 \delta_5}{\delta_1 \delta_4 - \delta_2 \delta_3}$$

$$\Delta_2 = -\cos(\alpha_i - \beta_i) - \Delta_1 \cos \beta_i - \Delta_3 \cos \alpha_i, \quad i = 1, 2, 3$$

Crossed bottom	$\Delta_1 = \dfrac{\delta_1 \delta_6 - \delta_2 \delta_5}{\delta_1 \delta_4 - \delta_2 \delta_3}$

$$\Delta_3 = \frac{\delta_4 \delta_5 - \delta_3 \delta_6}{\delta_1 \delta_4 - \delta_2 \delta_3}$$

$$\Delta_2 = -\cos(\alpha_i - \beta_i) + \Delta_1 \cos \beta_i + \Delta_3 \cos \alpha_i, \quad i = 1, 2, 3$$

Configurations may be discerned by observing the algebraic signs of Δ_1 and Δ_3, both of which must be positive.

A suitable linkage may be synthesized by choosing precision points (α_1, β_1), (α_2, β_2), (α_3, β_3), evaluating δ's, discovering configuration by testing Δ_1 and Δ_3 for positiveness, solving appropriate equations for $\Delta_1, \Delta_2, \Delta_3$ from which ρ_1, ρ_2, and ρ_3 follow ($\rho_4 = 1$).

The four-bar linkage synthesized by the previously described method will be completely faithful to the function desired only at three precision points. Elsewhere, error will be detectable. Such built-in errors are referred to as *structural* errors. In this type of application we may be seeking that linkage in which the largest structural error has the least possible magnitude. A sketch of an error for a three-precision-point synthesis is shown as Fig. 85. Notice that the three precision points within the usable range of the device break the error curve into four domains, each of which contains an extremum. The largest extreme of error can be reduced by moving the flanking precision points toward each other or by moving a precision point toward a boundary. Although this change results in lessening the extreme between the precision points, the adjustment will increase the error on flanking domains. It is clear that the choice of precision points resulting in the largest error of least size is the one which creates extremes in each of the four domains which are equal in size.

Recognition of this idea is central to a strategy for uncovering the optimal positioning of precision points. We shall envision our merit space

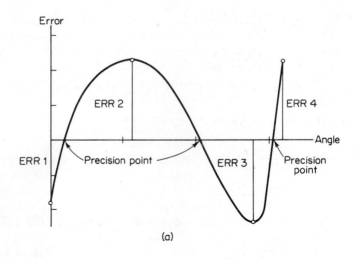

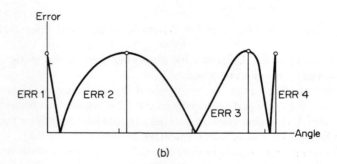

FIG. 85. Error curves for a three-point synthesis (a) unrectified and (b) rectified.

as having the independent coordinates which are the locations of the precision points (expressed conveniently as input dial readings) and use as the ordinate to the merit hypersurface the reciprocal of the largest structural error present in the mechanism.

In solving this problem we shall call upon several library routines already present in the IOWA CADET design library. These are ME0034, ME0035, and ME0036, which are documented in Appendix 2. The routine ME0034 accepts linkage configuration information, input dial angle, link lengths, and returns the output dial angle. ME0035 performs a three-point synthesis when given the input and output angles corresponding to the precision points, and returns the link lengths and the linkage configuration. ME0036 accepts the function values of the independent variable at the precision

138

points and sector angles of input and output dials, and returns the input and output angles corresponding to the precision points as well as the dependent variable values at the precision points. Another useful subroutine is YASORT, which orders a column vector placing the largest value of Y in the first entry, and subsequent entries are in descending order of magnitude. The associated abscissas are ordered to correspond to the new arrangement of the column vector Y.

The plan for using IOWA CADET is indicated in Fig. 86. Inasmuch as no ridges are expected and the summit of merit function will be domelike, a gradient search will be utilized. The gradient search plan selected will be GRAD4, and the necessary name of the merit subroutine (which is called by GRAD4) is MERIT4, as indicated in the documentation of GRAD4. The subroutine MERIT4 will first call ME0036 to obtain important angles to use in calling ME0035. The subroutine ME0035 will synthesize a linkage and return the link lengths. Since the left-hand and right-hand extremes of error will be at the ends of the dial intervals, a simple call to MERIT1 at an extreme will give the largest errors in the extreme domains outside the precision points. For determining the largest errors in the two interior domains (a one-dimensional search), it is necessary to call GOLD1, which manipulates MERIT1 and returns the largest errors in the interior domains. The four largest domain errors are placed in a column vector, and the largest is found by subroutine YASORT. The reciprocal of the largest structural error present in the current linkage is returned as the merit ordinate to gradient search GRAD4.

The subroutine MERIT1 determines the absolute value of the absolute structural error in a linkage. In doing this, MERIT1 calls ME0034 and another subroutine FUNCT, which defines the function to be generated and returns an ordinate for a tendered abscissa.

```
C
C       EXECUTIVE PROGRAM FOR OPTIMAL PROPORTIONS OF A FOURBAR LINKAGE
C       WITH THREE PRECISION POINTS TO ANALOGICALLY GENERATE A FUNCTION.
C       C. MISCHKE   IOWA STATE UNIVERSITY
C
C       A1=INPUT ANGLE AT FIRST PRECISION POINT, RAD
C       A2=INPUT ANGLE AT SECOND PRECISION POINT, RAD
C       A3=INPUT ANGLE AT THIRD PRECISION POINT, RAD
C       A4=INPUT ANGLE AT EXTREME LEFT OF DIAL, RAD
C       A5=INPUT ANGLE AT EXTREME RIGHT OF DIAL, RAD
C
C       B1=OUTPUT ANGLE AT FIRST PRECISION POINT, RAD
C       B2=OUTPUT ANGLE AT SECOND PRECISION POINT, RAD
C       B3=OUTPUT ANGLE AT THIRD PRECISION POINT, RAD
C       B4=OUTPUT ANGLE AT EXTREME LEFT OF DIAL, RAD
C       B5=OUTPUT ANGLE AT EXTREME RIGHT OF DIAL, RAD
C
C       X1=VALUE OF INDEPENDENT VARIABLE AT FIRST PRECISION POINT
C       X2=VALUE OF INDEPENDENT VARIABLE AT SECOND PRECISION POINT
C       X3=VALUE OF INDEPENDENT VARIABLE AT THIRD PRECISION POINT
C       X4=VALUE OF INDEPENDENT VARIABLE AT EXTREME LEFT OF INPUT DIAL
C       X5=VALUE OF INDEPENDENT VARIABLE AT EXTREME RIGHT OF INPUT DIAL
C
C       Y1=VALUE OF DEPENDENT VARIABLE AT FIRST PRECISION POINT
```

139

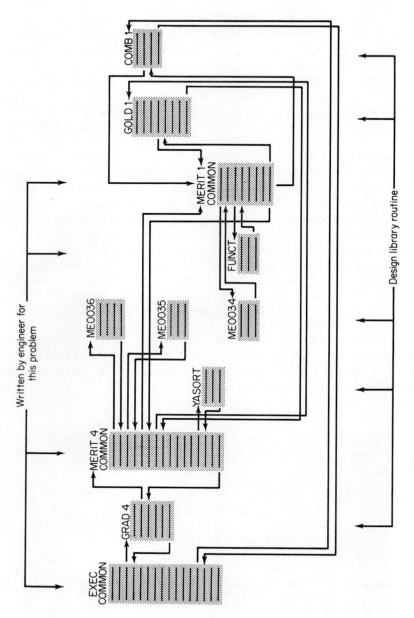

FIG. 86. Example of program arrangement for solution of the four-bar function generator problem using the IOWA CADET algorithm.

140

```
C       Y2=VALUE OF DEPENDENT VARIABLE AT SECOND PRECISION POINT
C       Y3=VALUE OF DEPENDENT VARIABLE AT THIRD PRECISION POINT
C       Y4= VALUE OF DEPENDENT VARIABLE AT EXTREME LEFT OF OUTPUT DIAL
C       Y5=VALUE OF DEPENDENT VARIABLE AT EXTREME RIGHT OF OUTPUT DIAL
C
C       XX=INDEPENDENT VARIABLE
C       YY=DEPENDENT VARIABLE
C       A=INPUT ANGLE CORRESPONDING TO XX
C       B=OUTPUT ANGLE CORRESPONDING TO YY
C
C       R1=LENGTH OF CRANK VECTOR
C       R2=LENGTH OF COUPLER VECTOR
C       R3=LENGTH OF FOLLOWER VECTOR
C       R4=LENGTH OF GROUNDED LINK VECTOR
C
        COMMON X4,X5,A4,A5,Y4,Y5,B4,B5,R1,R2,R3,R4,F,I4,J1
        DIMENSION XL(9),XR(9),X(9),P(9),Q(9),BB3(2001),BB4(2001),ABC(20)
      1 READ(1,2)A6,A7,B6,B7,X4,X5,Y4,Y5
      2 FORMAT(8F10.4)
        C=3.14159/180.
        A4=A6*C
        A5=A7*C
        B4=B6*C
        B5=B7*C
        READ(1,3)I1,I2,I3,DELTA,DMULT,EPS,F,I4
      3 FORMAT(3I2,2F10.5,2F10.8,I5)
        READ(1,4)(ABC(I),I=1,20)
      4 FORMAT(20A4)
        XL(1)=1.
        XL(2)=1.
        XL(3)=1.
        XR(1)=10.
        XR(2)=10.
        XR(3)=10.
        X(1)=1.1
        X(2)=7.
        X(3)=9.9
        CALL GRAD4(I1,I2,I3,DELTA,DMULT,F,EPS,XL,XR,RERR,X,K3,K4,P,Q)
        ERROR=1./RERR
        WRITE(3,5)(ABC(I),I=1,20),X4,X5,Y4,Y5,A6,A7,B6,B7
      5 FORMAT(1H1,'EXECUTIVE PROGRAM PRINTOUT',/,/,' INPUT DATA',//,20A4,
      1/,
      2' NUMBER APPEARING EXTREME LEFT OF INPUT DIAL ...........',F15.5,/,
      3' NUMBER APPEARING EXTREME RIGHT OF INPUT DIAL ..........',F15.5,/,
      4' NUMBER APPEARING EXTREME LEFT OF OUTPUT DIAL ..........',F15.5,/,
      5' NUMBER APPEARING EXTREME RIGHT OF OUTPUT DIAL .........',F15.5,/,
      6/,
      7' INPUT ANGLE ALPHA OF LOWEST INPUT DIAL READING .......',F15.5,/,
      8' INPUT ANGLE ALPHA OF HIGHEST INPUT DIAL READING ......',F15.5,/,
      9' OUTPUT ANGLE BETA OF LOWEST OUTPUT DIAL READING ......',F15.5,/,
      1' OUTPUT ANGLE BETA OF HIGHEST OUTPUT DIAL READING .....',F15.5)
        X1=X(1)
        X2=X(2)
        X3=X(3)
        CALL MEOO36(X1,X2,X3,X4,X5,Y4,Y5,A4,A5,B4,B5,
      1 A1,A2,A3,B1,B2,B3,Y1,Y2,Y3)
        CALL MEOO35(A1,B1,A2,B2,A3,B3,R1,R2,R3,R4,J1)
        WRITE(3,6)R1,R2,R3,R4
      6 FORMAT(/,' OUTPUT DATA',//,
      1' LENGTH OF CRANK VECTOR ...............................',E15.8,/,
      2' LENGTH OF COUPLER VECTOR .............................',E15.8,/,
      3' LENGTH OF FOLLOWER VECTOR ............................',E15.8,/,
      4' LENGTH OF GROUNDED LINK VECTOR .......................',E15.8)
        GO TO(7,9,11,13),J1
      7 WRITE(3,8)
      8 FORMAT(/,' LINKAGE CONFIGURATION UNCROSSED TOP')
        GO TO 15
      9 WRITE(3,10)
     10 FORMAT(/,' LINKAGE CONFIGURATION CROSSED TOP')
        GO TO 15
     11 WRITE(3,12)
     12 FORMAT(/,' LINKAGE CONFIGURATION UNCROSSED BOTTOM')
        GO TO 15
```

141

```
13 WRITE(3,14)
14 FORMAT(/,' LINKAGE CONFIGURATION CROSSED BOTTOM')
15 I=1
   FF=0.1
   CALL COMB1(I,A4,A5,FF,BB1,BB2,BB3,BB4,BB5,BB6,L)
   GO TO 1
   END

   SUBROUTINE MERIT4(X,Y)
   COMMON X4,X5,A4,A5,Y4,Y5,B4,B5,R1,R2,R3,R4,F,I4,J1
   DIMENSION U(100),WYE(100),X(9)
   X1=X(1)
   X2=X(2)
   X3=X(3)
   CALL ME0036(X1,X2,X3,X4,X5,Y4,Y5,A4,A5,B4,B5,
  1A1,A2,A3,B1,B2,B3,Y1,Y2,Y3)
   CALL ME0035(A1,B1,A2,B2,A3,B3,R1,R2,R3,R4,J1)
   CALL MERIT1(A4,ERR1)
   CALL GOLD1(I4,A1,A2,F,ERR2,XX2,XL2,XR2,J4)
   CALL GOLD1(I4,A2,A3,F,ERR3,XX3,XL3,XR3,J6)
   CALL MERIT1(A5,ERR4)
   WYE(1)=ERR1
   WYE(2)=ERR2
   WYE(3)=ERR3
   WYE(4)=ERR4
   N=4
   U(1)=XX1
   U(2)=XX2
   U(3)=XX3
   U(4)=XX4
   CALL YASORT(N,U,WYE)
   Y=1./WYE(1)
   RETURN
   END

   SUBRCUTINE MERIT1(A,ERROR)
   COMMON X4,X5,A4,A5,Y4,Y5,B4,B5,R1,R2,R3,R4,F,I4,J1
   CALL ME0034(J1,A,R1,R2,R3,R4,B)
   YGEN=Y5-(B5-B)*(Y5-Y4)/(B5-B4)
   XX=X5-(A5-A)*(X5-X4)/(A5-A4)
   CALL FUNCT(XX,YTRUE)
   ERROR=ABS(YGEN-YTRUE)
   RETURN
   END

   SUBROUTINE FUNCT(XX,YTRUE)
   YTRUE=XX*XX
   RETURN
   END
```

The following output was obtained from this program with input data

$A6 = 0.$ deg
$A7 = 90.$ deg
$B6 = 60.$ deg
$B7 = 180.$ deg
$X4 = 1.$
$X5 = 10.$
$Y4 = 1.$
$Y5 = 100.$
$I1 = 3$ dimensions
$I2 = 1$ convergence monitor print
$I3 = 4$ search start at initial value of column vector X, established
   by FORTRAN declarative statement in executive program

142

DELTA = 0.1
DMULT = 1.2
  EPS = 0.0001
    F = 0.01
   I4 = 0 GOLD1 convergence monitor do not print

The search began with the precision points located at input dial readings 1.1, 7.0, 9.9. The search terminated at an extreme due to the "lumpy" nature of the merit hypersurface. This surface cannot be examined too closely, since the merit ordinates used were established by golden section searches of not too fine a resolution. The proportions of the four-bar linkage were established as

$$\rho_1 = 0.77127433$$

$$\rho_2 = 0.16044645$$

$$\rho_3 = 0.39842039$$

$$\rho_4 = 1.00000000$$

but not to the number of significant figures implied by the computer output sheet. The linkage configuration is uncrossed top.

CONVERGENCE MONITOR SUBROUTINE GRAD4

N1	DELTA	Y	X(1)	X(2)	X(3)
4	0.100E 00	0.384E 00	0.110E 01	0.700E 01	0.990E 01
8	0.120E 00	0.389E 00	0.114E 01	0.689E 01	0.988E 01
12	0.144E 00	0.418E 00	0.122E 01	0.697E 01	0.978E 01
16	0.173E 00	0.444E 00	0.139E 01	0.694E 01	0.980E 01
20	0.2C7E 00	0.383E 00	0.141E 01	0.709E 01	0.966E 01
24	0.207E-01	0.436E 00	0.139E 01	0.694E 01	0.982E 01
28	0.207E-02	0.445E 00	0.139E 01	0.694E 01	0.980E 01
32	0.249E-02	0.445E 00	0.139E 01	0.694E 01	0.979E 01
36	0.299E-02	0.446E 00	0.139E 01	0.694E 01	0.979E 01
40	0.358E-02	0.446E 00	0.139E 01	0.694E 01	0.979E 01
44	0.430E-02	0.447E 00	0.139E 01	0.694E 01	0.979E 01
48	0.516E-02	0.448E 00	0.140E 01	0.693E 01	0.979E 01
52	0.619E-02	0.449E 00	0.140E 01	0.693E 01	0.979E 01
56	0.743E-02	0.449E 00	0.140E 01	0.693E 01	0.978E 01
60	0.892E-02	0.449E 00	0.140E 01	0.693E 01	0.978E 01
64	0.107E-01	0.452E 00	0.140E 01	0.693E 01	0.977E 01
68	0.128E-01	0.454E 00	0.141E 01	0.693E 01	0.977E 01
72	0.154E-01	0.454E 00	0.143E 01	0.692E 01	0.977E 01
76	0.154E-02	0.454E 00	0.141E 01	0.693E 01	0.977E 01

```
LARGEST MERIT ORDINATE ....................................... 0.45404536E 00
NUMBER OF FUNCTION EVALUATIONS ..........................                  84
FINAL SEARCH STEPSIZE ...................................        0.00154069
STEPSIZE GROWTH MULTIPLIER ..............................        1.19999981
SURVEY PATTERN INCREMENT ................................ 0.99999990E-04
FRACTIONAL REDUCTION IN INTERVAL OF UNCERTAINTY .......        0.00100000
SPECIE OF LARGEST MERIT ORDINATE ........................                 1
```

```
X(  1)=    0.14137E 01    P(  1)=    0.14350E 00    Q(  1)=    0.14032E 00
X(  2)=    0.69252E 01    P(  2)=   -0.20301E 00    Q(  2)=    0.94281E-01
X(  3)=    0.97692E 01    P(  3)=   -0.26008E 00    Q(  3)=   -0.13579E 00
```

MERIT EXTREME IS AN EXTREMUM

EXECUTIVE PROGRAM PRINTOUT

INPUT DATA

FUNCTION GENERATED IS Y=X*X
NUMBER APPEARING EXTREME LEFT OF INPUT DIAL 1.00000
NUMBER APPEARING EXTREME RIGHT OF INPUT DIAL 10.00000
NUMBER APPEARING EXTREME LEFT OF OUTPUT DIAL 1.00000
NUMBER APPEARING EXTREME RIGHT OF OUTPUT DIAL 100.00000

INPUT ANGLE ALPHA OF LOWEST INPUT DIAL READING 0.0
INPUT ANGLE ALPHA OF HIGHEST INPUT DIAL READING 90.00000
OUTPUT ANGLE BETA OF LOWEST OUTPUT DIAL READING 60.00000
OUTPUT ANGLE BETA OF HIGHEST OUTPUT DIAL READING 180.00000

OUTPUT DATA

LENGTH OF CRANK VECTOR 0.77127433E 00
LENGTH OF COUPLER VECTOR 0.16044645E 01
LENGTH OF FOLLOWER VECTOR 0.39842039E 00
LENGTH OF GROUNDED LINK VECTOR 0.10000000E 01

LINKAGE CONFIGURATION UNCROSSED TOP

CONVERGENCE MONITOR SUBROUTINE COMB1

ORDINATE	ABSCISSA	EXTREME
0.6261444E 00	0.0	-0.9999997E 51
0.8524799E-01	0.8267337E-01	0.6261444E 00
0.7083435E 00	0.1653467E 00	0.6261444E 00
0.1236617E 01	0.2480201E 00	0.7083435E 00
0.1660911E 01	0.3306935E 00	0.1236617E 01
0.1970069E 01	0.4133669E 00	0.1660911E 01
0.2153262E 01	0.4960402E 00	0.1970069E 01
0.2200516E 01	0.5787136E 00	0.2153262E 01
0.2105133E 01	0.6613870E 00	0.2200516E 01
0.1864670E 01	0.7440603E 00	0.2200516E 01
0.1482315E 01	0.8267337E 00	0.2200516E 01
0.9694214E 00	0.9094071E 00	0.2200516E 01
0.3475037E 00	0.9920805E 00	0.2200516E 01
0.3476715E 00	0.1074754E 01	0.2200516E 01
0.1059937E 01	0.1157427E 01	0.2200516E 01
0.1701859E 01	0.1240100E 01	0.2200516E 01
0.2132019E 01	0.1322773E 01	0.2200516E 01
0.2108536E 01	0.1405446E 01	0.2200516E 01
0.1160721E 01	0.1488119E 01	0.2200516E 01
0.1884399E 01	0.1570792E 01	0.2200516E 01

EXTREME ORDINATE FOUND IN EXHAUSTIVE SEARCH 0.2200516E 01
ABSCISSA CORRESPONDING TO EXTREME ORDINATE 0.5787136E 00
ORIGINAL LOWER BOUND ON INTERVAL OF UNCERTAINTY 0.0
ORIGINAL UPPER BOUND ON INTERVAL OF UNCERTAINTY 0.1570794E 01
FINAL LOWER BOUND ON INTERVAL OF UNCERTAINTY 0.4960402E 00
FINAL UPPER BOUND ON INTERVAL OF UNCERTAINTY 0.6613870E 00
FRACTIONAL REDUCTION IN INTERVAL OF UNCERTAINTY 0.9999996E-01
NUMBER OF FUNCTION EVALUATION EXPENDED   20

    The convergence monitor of subroutine COMB1 was allowed to print
out the error in the Y indication using the input dial angle as the abscissa.
The largest error in the Y indication occurs in the neighborhood of $\alpha =$
0.5787136 radians and is of magnitude 2.2200516. The next improvement can
result from the use of a relative error criterion rather than an absolute
error criterion in developing the merit ordinate.

    Further improvement in accuracy, using the input sector of 90° and

144

the output sector of 120°, can be sought by making A4 and B4 design variables in addition to the location of the precision points X(1), X(2), and X(3), raising the number of design variables to five.

5.7 A CURVED BEAM OF MINIMAL WEIGHT

A C clamp is to be designed to provide clearances as indicated in Fig. 87(a). The design load is to be 900 lbf with a design factor of 2, based upon ultimate strength as it relates to the stresses developed in the inner and outer fibers of the curved beam. The cross section is to be a "T" made of ASTM 40 cast iron. Because of casting limitations, the lower limit on the magnitude of the thickness dimensions x_2 and x_3 in Fig. 87(b) will be one quarter inch. The proportions of the tee section exhibiting the minimum weight are required.

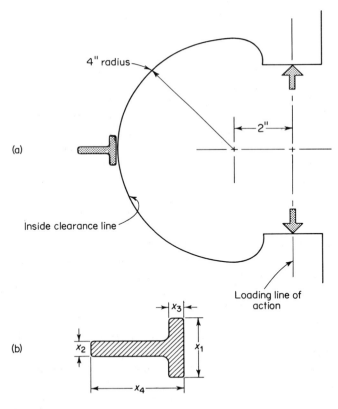

FIG. 87. The clearance geometry of a required C-clamp design and the geometry of the contemplated curved beam section.

Information on ASTM 40 cast iron is as follows:

Ultimate tensile stress   40,000 psi
Ultimate compressive stress   120,000 psi
Specific weight   0.26 lbf/in.^{3}

The question of the merit of alternatives will be considered first. The conditions in the statement of the problem limit the designer to finding the minimum weight configuration using a specified section and a stipulated material. In order to determine the weight of the toroidal curved beam, the distance from the center of curvature to the centroid of the cross section must be found. The figure of merit must be sensitive to the weight of the curved beam, and so the reciprocal of the beam weight is chosen to be the figure of merit. The regional constraints could be

$$0.25 \leq x_1 \leq 1.50$$

$$0.25 \leq x_2 \leq 0.50$$

$$0.25 \leq x_3 \leq 0.50$$

$$0.25 \leq x_4 \leq 3.00$$

The functional constraints involve the limiting stresses in the outermost fibers. The calculation of stresses from information on sectional geometry in a curved beam is straightforward, but the determination of geometry corresponding to a given stress level is very complex. Again, if the configuration tendered to the merit subroutine violates a functional constraint by exceeding a stress level, the merit ordinate will be penalized by calling subroutine PENAL. The functional constraints are

$$s_i \leq (s_t) \qquad \text{allowable}$$

$$s_o \leq (s_c) \qquad \text{allowable}$$

The problem becomes that of finding the configuration (specified by x_1, x_2, x_3, x_4) wherein the reciprocal of the beam weight is largest, subject to the regional and functional constraints. The problem geometry is five-dimensional with the four independent design variables of merit hyperspace being x_1, x_2, x_3, and x_4. If we could be certain that the minimum weight configuration is associated with $x_2 = x_3 = 0.25$, then we could operate in geometrically interpretable 3 space. Since this is not obviously true at this stage, we begin to program the problem for 5 space.

The IOWA CADET design library has a subroutine ME0053 which calculates the fiber stresses in a curved bar with a tee cross section. The documentation of this routine is in Appendix 2. We note that the subroutine has ten arguments in its call list, accepting seven and returning three. If

146

PP = load, lbf

RI = radius of curvature of inner fiber, in.

D = offset of center of curvature from load line of action, in.

BI = section-width at inner fiber, in.

BO = section-width at outer fiber, in.

C1 = thickness of cap of tee, in.

C2 = thickness of stem of tee, in.

SI = inner fiber stress, psi

SO = outer fiber stress, psi

R = radius of curvature of section centroidal locus, in.

then the proper call for the subroutine is

CALL ME0053 (PP, RI, D, BI, BO, C1, C2, SI, SO, R)

We are now in a position to construct the merit subroutine. Choosing grid-search library subroutine GRID4, we discover, from its documentation in Appendix 2, that it calls MERIT4 in searching for the extreme ordinate. The name of the merit subroutine is required to be MERIT4 (X, Y). Figure 88 reveals the structure of our strategy to solve the problem. The function of MERIT4 is to generate the figure of merit ordinate, with the assistance of subroutines ME0053 and PENAL, and respond to interrogations of GRID4 in its search for the extreme merit ordinate.

The executive program supplies data to GRID4 via its call list, and to

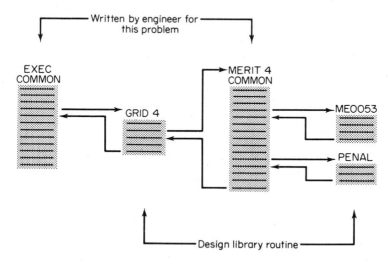

FIG. 88. Example of program arrangement for solution of the curved beam problem using the IOWA CADET algorithm.

147

MERIT4 via the COMMON declaration. Output information held by MERIT4 that cannot be passed back via GRAD4 is returned through the COMMON statement. We now write the MERIT4 subprogram and the executive program. A possible composition follows.

```
C      EXECUTIVE PROGRAM FOR C-CLAMP FRAME OF A 'T' SECTION OF
C      SMALLEST WEIGHT.
C
C      STATEMENT OF PROBLEM
C
C      A C-CLAMP IS TO BE DESIGNED HAVING A T-CROSSSECTION WITH CAP OF
C      THE T ON INSIDE OF FRAME. DEVISE A PROGRAM TO DETERMINE THE
C      PARAMETERS OF THE CONFIGURATION OF MINIMAL WEIGHT OF C-FRAME,
C      GIVEN ESSENTIAL GEOMETRY, MATERIAL SPECIFIC WEIGHT, ALLOWABLE
C      STRESSES IN TENSION AND COMPRESSION, LOAD, AND SUBJECT TO SECTION
C      MINIMUM THICKNESSES DUE TO CASTING CONSIDERATIONS
C
C      NOMENCLATURE
C
C      PP=FORCE ON C-CLAMP,POSITIVE OPENS 'C',LBF
C      D=DISTANCE BETWEEN CENTER OF CURVATURE AND LINE OF ACTION OF
C         FORCE PP, POSITIVE IF OUTSIDE, INCHES
C      RI=RADIUS OF CURVATURE OF INNER FIBER, INCHES
C      BI=SECTION WIDTH AT INNER FIBER, INCHES
C      BO=SECTION WIDTH AT OUTER FIBER, INCHES
C
C      C1=THICKNESS OF CAP OF 'T', INCHES
C      C2=LENGTH OF STEM OF 'T', INCHES
C      N=NUMBER OF INDEPENDENT VARIABLES IN OPTIMIZATION
C      I2=CONVERGENCE MONITOR PRINT SIGNAL
C      F=FRACTIONAL REDUCTION IN DOMAIN OF UNCERTAINTY DESIRED
C      R=FRACTIONAL REDUCTION IN GRID SIZE UTILIZED
C
C      XL(I)=LOWER BOUND OF SEARCH DOMAIN, COLUMN VECTOR
C      XR(I)=UPPER BOUND OF SEARCH DOMAIN, COLUMN VECTOR
C      GAMMA=SPECIFIC WEIGHT OF FRAME MATERIAL, LBF/IN3
C      GOOD=COLUMN VECTOR OF CROSS SECTION DIMENSIONS NOT VIOLATING
C      FUNCTIONAL CONSTRAINTS OF STRESS LEVEL AT OUTER AND INNER SURFACE.
C
       COMMON PP,D,RI,GAMMA,ST,SC,W,SI,SO,GOOD(9),N,XL(9),XR(9)
       DIMENSION X(9),IABC(20),XLOW(9),XHIGH(9)
C
C      ..... READ IN DATA .....
C
     1 READ(1,2)PP,D,RI,BI,BO,GAMMA
     2 FORMAT(6F10.5)
       READ(1,3)C1,C2,ST,SC,N
     3 FORMAT(2F10.5,2F10.0,I5)
       READ(1,4)I2,F,R
     4 FORMAT(I5,2F10.5)
       DO 6 I=1,N
       READ(1,5)XLO,XHI
     5 FORMAT(2F10.5)
       XL(I)=XLO
       XR(I)=XHI
     6 CONTINUE
       READ(1,9)(IABC(I),I=1,20)
     9 FORMAT(20A4)
       READ(1,10)(GOOD(I),I=1,4)
    10 FORMAT(4F10.5)
C
C      ..... INITIATE A GRID SEARCH TO FIND THE DIMENSIONS OF      .....
C      ..... LEAST WEIGHT SECTION.                                .....
C
       CALL GRID4(N,I2,XL,XR,F,R,Y,X,XLOW,XHIGH,NN)
C
C      ..... DOCUMENT SEARCH RESULTS .....
C
```

```
      WRITE(3,7)PP,D,RI,C1,BO,ST,SC,GAMMA,(IABC(I),I=1,20)
    7 FORMAT('1EXECUTIVE PROGRAM OUTPUT MINIMUM WEIGHT C-CLAMP FRAME',/,
     1' FORCE ON C-CLAMP (POSITIVE OPENS  C ), LBF ...........',F10.0,/,
     2' DISTANCE FROM LOA OF FORCE TO CENTER OF CURVATURE,IN..',F10.5,/,
     3' RADIUS OF CURVATURE OF INNER FIBER, INCHES ...........',F10.5,/,
     4' MINIMUM SECTION WIDTH IN CAP OF  T , INCHES ..........',F10.5,/,
     5' MINIMUM SECTION WIDTH IN STEM OF  T , INCHES .........',F10.5,/,
     6' MAXIMUM ALLOWABLE TENSILE STRESS, PSI ................',F10.0,/,
     7' MAXIMUM ALLOWABLE COMPRESSIVE STRESS, PSI ............',F10.0,/,
     8' SPECIFIC WEIGHT OF FRAME MATERIAL, LBF/IN3 ...........',F10.5,/,
     920A4)
      WRITE(3,8)W,(X(I),I=1,4),SI,SO
    8 FORMAT(//,' CHARACTERISTICS OF OPTIMAL CONFIGURATION',//,
     1' WEIGHT OF FRAME, LBF .................................',F1C.5,/,
     2' WIDTH OF SECTION AT INNER RADIUS,INCHES..............',F1C.5,/,
     3' WIDTH OF SECTION AT OUTER RADIUS,INCHES..............',F1C.5,/,
     4' THICKNESS OF CAP OF  T , INCHES......................',F10.5,/,
     5' RADIAL DEPTH OF SECTION, INCHES......................',F10.5,/,
     6' NORMAL STRESS AT INNER FIBER, PSI ...................',F1C.0,/,
     7' NORMAL STRESS AT OUTER  FIBER, PSI ..................',F1C.0)
      GO TO 1
      END


      SUBROUTINE MERIT4(X,Y)
      COMMON PP,D,RI,GAMMA,ST,SC,W,SI,SO,GOOD(9),N,XL(9),XR(9)
      DIMENSION X(9)
C
C     ..... CHECK TO SEE IF POINT VIOLATES ANY REGIONAL CONSTRAINT, ....
C     ..... IF SO, ASSIGN PENALTY ORDINATE AND RETURN.            ....
C
      DO 10 I=1,N
      IF(X(I)-XL(I))4,9,9
    9 IF(X(I)-XR(I))10,10,4
   10 CONTINUE
C
C     ..... INITIALIZE .....
C
      BI=X(1)
      BO=X(2)
      C1=X(3)
      C2=X(4)-X(3)
C
C     ..... CALL CURVED BEAM TEE-SECTION SUBROUTINE TO DETERMINE  .....
C     ..... STRESS LEVELS AT THE INNER AND OUTER SURFACES, AND TO .....
C     ..... DETERMINE THE RADIUS OF CURVATURE OF LOCUS OF THE CENTER....
C     ..... OF MASS OF CROSS SECTIONAL AREA.                      .....
C
      CALL ME0053(PP,RI,D,BI,BO,C1,C2,SI,SO,R)
C
C     ..... PREPARE MERIT ORDINATE .....
C
      A=BI*C1+BO*C2
      W=R*A*GAMMA*3.14159
      Y=1./W
C
C     ..... DETERMINE IF FUNCTIONAL CONSTRAINTS HAVE BEEN VIOLATED .....
C     ..... BY THIS PARTICULAR CROSS SECTIONAL CONFIGURATION, IF SO,....
C     ..... RETURN PENALTY ORDINATE; IF NOT, RETURN MERIT ORDINATE .....
C
      IF(SI)6,1,1
    1 IF(ABS(ST)-ABS(SI))4,2,2
    2 IF(ABS(SC)-ABS(SO))4,3,3
    6 IF(ABS(SC)-ABS(SI))4,7,7
    7 IF(ABS(ST)-ABS(SO))4,3,3
    4 CALL PENAL(N,GOOD,X,Y)
    3 RETURN
      END


      SUBROUTINE PENAL(N,GOOD,X,Y)
      DIMENSION GOOD(9),X(9)
```

```
      Y=0.
      DO 100 I=1,N
      Y=Y+(GOOD(I)-X(I))*(GOOD(I)-X(I))
100 CONTINUE
      Y=-Y
      RETURN
      END
```

When asymmetric cross sections are used for curved beams, the informed literature often points out that when materials are used that have different allowable fiber stresses in tension and compression, the opportunity is present to proportion the section so that the limiting stresses in tension and compression are reached simultaneously. One would believe that the weight of the section under these circumstances would be about as small as possible for that family of sections, since there is no "underworked" material present. The expectation of the outcome of this programming is, at this point, considered to be a set of section proportions which has the material working up to allowable limits on the outer and inner fibers.

In order to gain some confidence, advantage should be taken of the program flexibility to use data that would proportion a cross section for a material with equal allowable tensile and compressive stress limits. The first data used is for a hypothetical material with 20,000 psi working stress in tension and compression. The input data used will place the regional constraints as

$$0.50 \leq x_1 \leq 2.00$$
$$0.25 \leq x_2 \leq 0.50$$
$$0.25 \leq x_3 \leq 0.50$$
$$1.00 \leq x_4 \leq 3.00$$

because we feel certain that the solution lies within the above basis space. Since a point in feasible space must be provided for the orientation of the penalty hypersurface, the point chosen is the conservative location

$$x_1 = 2.00$$
$$x_2 = 0.50$$
$$x_3 = 0.50$$
$$x_4 = 2.00$$

The fractional reduction in the grid-search pattern was chosen as $r = 0.8$.

CONVERGENCE MONITOR SUBROUTINE GRID4

NN	SIDE	Y	X(1)	X(2)	X(3)	X(4)
17	0.100E 01	0.248E 00	0.100E 01	0.333E 00	0.333E 00	0.233E 01
25	0.800E 00	0.248E 00	0.100E 01	0.333E 00	0.333E 00	0.233E 01

```
 41  0.640E 00  0.308E 00  0.840E 00  0.307E 00  0.307E 00  0.212E 01
 49  0.512E 00  0.308E 00  0.840E 00  0.307E 00  0.307E 00  0.212E 01
 65  0.410E 00  0.315E 00  0.738E 00  0.290E 00  0.290E 00  0.226E 01
 73  0.328E 00  0.315E 00  0.738E 00  0.290E 00  0.290E 00  0.226E 01
 89  0.262E 00  0.333E 00  0.803E 00  0.279E 00  0.279E 00  0.217E 01
 97  0.210E 00  0.333E 00  0.803E 00  0.279E 00  0.279E 00  0.217E 01
113  0.168E 00  0.336E 00  0.761E 00  0.272E 00  0.272E 00  0.223E 01
121  0.134E 00  0.336E 00  0.761E 00  0.272E 00  0.272E 00  0.223E 01
137  0.107E 00  0.336E 00  0.761E 00  0.272E 00  0.272E 00  0.223E 01
145  0.859E-01  0.336E 00  0.761E 00  0.272E 00  0.272E 00  0.223E 01
161  0.687E-01  0.340E 00  0.778E 00  0.269E 00  0.275E 00  0.220E 01
169  0.550E-01  0.340E 00  0.778E 00  0.269E 00  0.275E 00  0.220E 01
185  0.440E-01  0.340E 00  0.778E 00  0.269E 00  0.275E 00  0.220E 01
193  0.352E-01  0.340E 00  0.778E 00  0.269E 00  0.275E 00  0.220E 01
209  0.281E-01  0.340E 00  0.771E 00  0.268E 00  0.276E 00  0.221E 01
217  0.225E-01  0.340E 00  0.771E 00  0.268E 00  0.276E 00  0.221E 01
233  0.180E-01  0.340E 00  0.771E 00  0.268E 00  0.276E 00  0.221E 01
241  0.144E-01  0.340E 00  0.771E 00  0.268E 00  0.276E 00  0.221E 01
257  0.115E-01  0.340E 00  0.771E 00  0.268E 00  0.276E 00  0.221E 01
265  0.922E-02  0.340E 00  0.771E 00  0.268E 00  0.276E 00  0.221E 01
281  0.738E-02  0.340E 00  0.771E 00  0.268E 00  0.276E 00  0.221E 01
289  0.590E-02  0.340E 00  0.771E 00  0.268E 00  0.276E 00  0.221E 01
305  0.472E-02  0.340E 00  0.771E 00  0.268E 00  0.276E 00  0.221E 01
313  0.378E-02  0.340E 00  0.771E 00  0.268E 00  0.276E 00  0.221E 01
329  0.302E-02  0.340E 00  0.771E 00  0.268E 00  0.276E 00  0.221E 01
337  0.242E-02  0.340E 00  0.771E 00  0.268E 00  0.276E 00  0.221E 01
353  0.193E-02  0.340E 00  0.771E 00  0.268E 00  0.276E 00  0.221E 01
361  0.155E-02  0.340E 00  0.771E 00  0.268E 00  0.276E 00  0.221E 01
377  0.124E-02  0.340E 00  0.771E 00  0.268E 00  0.276E 00  0.221E 01
```

```
LARGEST MERIT ORDINATE FOUND DURING SEARCH ........... 0.34038961E 00
NUMBER OF FUNCTION EVALUATIONS USED DURING SEARCH ....           386
FRACTIONAL REDUCTION IN INTERVAL OF UNCERTAINTY EXTANT 0.14854670E-02


XLOW(1)= 0.76983702E 00   X(1)= 0.77057981E 00   XHIGH(1)= 0.77132249E 00
XLOW(2)= 0.26740086E 00   X(2)= 0.26752466E 00   XHIGH(2)= 0.26764840E 00
XLOW(3)= 0.27572483E 00   X(3)= 0.27584863E 00   XHIGH(3)= 0.27597237E 00
XLOW(4)= 0.22115622E 01   X(4)= 0.22125530E 01   XHIGH(4)= 0.22135429E 01


EXECUTIVE PROGRAM OUTPUT MINIMUM WEIGHT C-CLAMP FRAME
FORCE ON C-CLAMP (POSITIVE OPENS  C ), LBF ...........        900.
DISTANCE FROM LOA OF FORCE TO CENTER OF CURVATURE,IN..     2.00000
RADIUS OF CURVATURE OF INNER FIBER, INCHES ...........     4.00000
MINIMUM SECTION WIDTH IN CAP OF  T , INCHES ..........     0.25000
MINIMUM SECTION WIDTH IN STEM OF  T , INCHES .........     0.25000
MAXIMUM ALLOWABLE TENSILE STRESS, PSI ................    20000.
MAXIMUM ALLOWABLE COMPRESSIVE STRESS, PSI ............   -20000.
SPECIFIC WEIGHT OF FRAME MATERIAL, LBF/IN3 ...........     0.26000
MATERIAL IS HYPOTHETICAL WITH EQUAL ALLOWABLE NORMAL STRESSES.


CHARACTERISTICS OF OPTIMAL CONFIGURATION

WEIGHT OF FRAME, LBF ....................................     2.93781
WIDTH OF SECTION AT INNER RADIUS,INCHES.................     0.77058
WIDTH OF SECTION AT OUTER RADIUS,INCHES.................     0.26752
THICKNESS OF CAP OF  T , INCHES ........................     0.27585
RADIAL DEPTH OF SECTION, INCHES.........................     2.21255
NORMAL STRESS AT INNER FIBER, PSI ......................    20000.
NORMAL STRESS AT OUTER  FIBER, PSI .....................   -18963.
```

Examination of the output for this data indicates that the optimal proportions are

$$x_1 = 0.77058 \text{ in.}$$
$$x_2 = 0.26752 \text{ in.}$$

$$x_3 = 0.27585 \text{ in.}$$
$$x_4 = 2.21255 \text{ in.}$$

Inspection of the convergence monitor of GRID4 indicates that the section thicknesses x_2 and x_3 are approaching nearly their smallest allowable value of $\frac{1}{4}$ in. The working stresses at the outer fibers are 20,000 psi and $-18,963$ psi. Notice also that x_2 and x_3 decreased nearly concurrently during the search. We are given to suspect that the optimal section configuration is one in which the section thicknesses are $\frac{1}{4}$ in. and the program could have been made for two independent design variables. Further work along this line may be considered.

The input data for the ASTM 40 cast iron is now supplied to the program. The basis space is defined as

$$0.50 \leq x_1 \leq 2.00$$
$$0.25 \leq x_2 \leq 0.50$$
$$0.25 \leq x_3 \leq 0.50$$
$$1.00 \leq x_4 \leq 3.00$$

The point in feasible space is retained as $x_1 = 2.00$, $x_2 = 0.5$, $x_3 = 0.5$, $x_4 = 2.00$, and the fractional reduction in the grid-search pattern is chosen as 0.7.

CONVERGENCE MONITOR SUBROUTINE GRID4

NN	SIDE	Y	X(1)	X(2)	X(3)	X(4)
17	0.100E 01	0.284E 00	0.150E 01	0.333E 00	0.333E 00	0.167E 01
25	0.700E 00	0.284E 00	0.150E 01	0.333E 00	0.333E 00	0.167E 01
41	0.490E 00	0.311E 00	0.162E 01	0.313E 00	0.313E 00	0.150E 01
49	0.343E 00	0.311E 00	0.162E 01	0.313E 00	0.313E 00	0.150E 01
65	0.240E 00	0.315E 00	0.156E 01	0.303E 00	0.303E 00	0.158E 01
73	0.168E 00	0.347E 00	0.139E 01	0.275E 00	0.275E 00	0.170E 01
89	0.118E 00	0.355E 00	0.142E 01	0.270E 00	0.270E 00	0.166E 01
97	0.824E-01	0.355E 00	0.142E 01	0.270E 00	0.270E 00	0.166E 01
113	0.576E-01	0.359E 00	0.144E 01	0.268E 00	0.268E 00	0.164E 01
121	0.404E-01	0.359E 00	0.144E 01	0.268E 00	0.268E 00	0.164E 01
137	0.282E-01	0.360E 00	0.143E 01	0.266E 00	0.266E 00	0.165E 01
145	0.198E-01	0.360E 00	0.143E 01	0.266E 00	0.266E 00	0.165E 01
161	0.138E-01	0.361E 00	0.143E 01	0.266E 00	0.266E 00	0.164E 01
169	0.969E-02	0.361E 00	0.143E 01	0.266E 00	0.266E 00	0.164E 01
185	0.678E-02	0.362E 00	0.144E 01	0.266E 00	0.266E 00	0.164E 01
193	0.475E-02	0.362E 00	0.144E 01	0.266E 00	0.266E 00	0.164E 01
209	0.332E-02	0.362E 00	0.144E 01	0.265E 00	0.266E 00	0.164E 01
217	0.233E-02	0.362E 00	0.144E 01	0.265E 00	0.266E 00	0.164E 01
233	0.163E-02	0.362E 00	0.144E 01	0.265E 00	0.266E 00	0.164E 01
241	0.114E-02	0.362E 00	0.144E 01	0.265E 00	0.266E 00	0.164E 01

LARGEST MERIT ORDINATE FOUND DURING SEARCH 0.36198169E 00
NUMBER OF FUNCTION EVALUATIONS USED DURING SEARCH 258
FRACTIONAL REDUCTION IN INTERVAL OF UNCERTAINTY EXTANT 0.59795380E-03

XLOW(1)= 0.14371367E 01   X(1)= 0.14373341E 01   XHIGH(1)= 0.14377346E 01
XLOW(2)= 0.26532203E 00   X(2)= 0.26538855E 00   XHIGH(2)= 0.26542181E 00
XLOW(3)= 0.26569873E 00   X(3)= 0.26573193E 00   XHIGH(3)= 0.26579845E 00
XLOW(4)= 0.16376114E 01   X(4)= 0.16381435E 01   XHIGH(4)= 0.16384096E 01

```
EXECUTIVE PROGRAM OUTPUT MINIMUM WEIGHT C-CLAMP FRAME
FORCE ON C-CLAMP (POSITIVE OPENS  C ), LBF ...........      900.
DISTANCE FROM LOA OF FORCE TO CENTER OF CURVATURE,IN..    2.00000
RADIUS OF CURVATURE OF INNER FIBER, INCHES ...........    4.00000
MINIMUM SECTION WIDTH IN CAP OF  T , INCHES ..........    0.25000
MINIMUM SECTION WIDTH IN STEM OF  T , INCHES .........    0.25000
MAXIMUM ALLOWABLE TENSILE STRESS, PSI ................   20000.
MAXIMUM ALLOWABLE COMPRESSIVE STRESS, PSI ............  -60000.
SPECIFIC WEIGHT OF FRAME MATERIAL, LBF/IN3 ...........    0.26000
MATERIAL IS ASTM 40 CAST IRON WITH DESIGN FACTOR OF TWO ON ULTIMATE.


CHARACTERISTICS OF OPTIMAL CONFIGURATION

WEIGHT OF FRAME, LBF .................................    2.76257
WIDTH OF SECTION AT INNER RADIUS,INCHES...............    1.43733
WIDTH OF SECTION AT OUTER RADIUS,INCHES...............    0.26539
THICKNESS OF CAP OF  T , INCHES ......................    0.26573
RADIAL DEPTH OF SECTION, INCHES.......................    1.63814
NORMAL STRESS AT INNER FIBER, PSI ....................   19998.
NORMAL STRESS AT OUTER  FIBER, PSI ...................  -30760.
```

The program using ASTM 40 stress limits surprisingly does not return a
set of sectional proportions which works the material up to both its tensile
and compressive stress levels of 20,000 psi and $-60,000$ psi, but reports
intensities of 19,998 psi and $-30,760$ psi. The proportions reported are

$$x_1 = 1.43733 \text{ in.}$$

$$x_2 = 0.26539 \text{ in.}$$

$$x_3 = 0.26573 \text{ in.}$$

$$x_4 = 1.63814 \text{ in.}$$

and again we note that the section thicknesses x_2 and x_3 are close to the
minimal allowable value of $\frac{1}{4}$ in. We are led to expect that the problem
may have only two independent design variables. Since we are puzzled by
the low value of the compressive stress at the outer fiber, $-30,760$ instead
of $-60,000$, in the optimal section, we will now undertake the necessary
work to modify the program we have for two independent design variables.
This will place the problem in 3 space and visualization as well as geometric
interpretation will be possible.

In reprogramming, the design variable x_1 will now become the width
of the section at the inner radius and x_2 will become the radial depth of the
section. This is necessary because the column vectors in the library grid-
search routine will be only two deep. With this thought in mind, the existing
program is modified the small amount that is necessary.

```
C      EXECUTIVE PROGRAM FOR C-CLAMP FRAME OF A 'T' SECTION OF
C      SMALLEST WEIGHT.
C
C      STATEMENT OF PROBLEM
C
C      A C-CLAMP IS TO BE DESIGNED HAVING A T-CROSSSECTION WITH CAP OF
C      THE T ON INSIDE OF FRAME. DEVISE A PROGRAM TO DETERMINE THE
C      PARAMETERS OF THE CONFIGURATION OF MINIMAL WEIGHT OF C-FRAME,
C      GIVEN ESSENTIAL GEOMETRY, MATERIAL SPECIFIC WEIGHT, ALLOWABLE
```

```
C      STRESSES IN TENSION AND COMPRESSION, LOAD, AND SUBJECT TO SECTION
C      MINIMUM THICKNESSES DUE TO CASTING CONSIDERATIONS
C
C      NOMENCLATURE
C
C      PP=FORCE ON C-CLAMP,POSITIVE OPENS 'C',LBF
C      D=DISTANCE BETWEEN CENTER OF CURVATURE AND LINE OF ACTION OF
C         FORCE PP, POSITIVE IF OUTSIDE, INCHES
C      RI=RADIUS OF CURVATURE OF INNER FIBER, INCHES
C      BI=SECTION WIDTH AT INNER FIBER, INCHES
C      BO=SECTION WIDTH AT OUTER FIBER, INCHES
C
C      C1=THICKNESS OF CAP OF 'T', INCHES
C      C2=LENGTH OF STEM OF 'T', INCHES
C      N=NUMBER OF INDEPENDENT VARIABLES IN OPTIMIZATION
C      I2=CONVERGENCE MONITOR PRINT SIGNAL
C      F=FRACTIONAL REDUCTION IN DOMAIN OF UNCERTAINTY DESIRED
C      R=FRACTIONAL REDUCTION IN GRID SIZE UTILIZED
C
C      X(1)=INTERNAL WIDTH OF SECTION, IN.
C      X(2)=RADIAL DEPTH OF SECTION, IN.
C      XL(I)=LOWER BOUND OF SEARCH DOMAIN, COLUMN VECTOR
C      XR(I)=UPPER BOUND OF SEARCH DOMAIN, COLUMN VECTOR
C      GAMMA=SPECIFIC WEIGHT OF FRAME MATERIAL, LBF/IN3
C      GOOD=COLUMN VECTOR OF CROSS SECTION DIMENSIONS NOT VIOLATING
C      FUNCTIONAL CONSTRAINTS OF STRESS LEVEL AT OUTER AND INNER SURFACE.
C
       COMMON PP,D,RI,GAMMA,ST,SC,W,SI,SO,GOOD(9),N,XL(9),XR(9),T
       DIMENSION X(9),IABC(20),XLOW(9),XHIGH(9)
C
C      ..... READ IN DATA .....
C
     1 READ(1,2)PP,D,RI,BI,BO,GAMMA
     2 FORMAT(6F10.5)
       READ(1,3)C1,C2,ST,SC,N
     3 FORMAT(2F10.5,2F10.0,I5)
       READ(1,4)I2,F,R
     4 FORMAT(I5,2F10.5)
       DO 6 I=1,N
       READ(1,5)XLO,XHI
     5 FORMAT(2F10.5)
       XL(I)=XLO
       XR(I)=XHI
     6 CONTINUE
       READ(1,9)(IABC(I),I=1,20)
     9 FORMAT(20A4)
       READ(1,10)(GOOD(I),I=1,2)
    10 FORMAT(2F10.5)
       T=BO
C
C      ..... INITIATE A GRID SEARCH TO FIND THE DIMENSIONS OF      .....
C      ..... LEAST WEIGHT SECTION.                                 .....
C
       CALL GRID4(N,I2,XL,XR,F,R,Y,X,XLOW,XHIGH,NN)
C
C      ..... DOCUMENT SEARCH RESULTS .....
C
       WRITE(3,7)PP,D,RI,C1,BO,ST,SC,GAMMA,(IABC(I),I=1,20)
     7 FORMAT('1EXECUTIVE PROGRAM OUTPUT MINIMUM WEIGHT C-CLAMP FRAME',/,
      1' FORCE ON C-CLAMP (POSITIVE OPENS  C ), LBF ............',F10.0,/,
      2' DISTANCE FROM LOA OF FORCE TO CENTER OF CURVATURE,IN..',F10.5,/,
      3' RADIUS OF CURVATURE OF INNER FIBER, INCHES ............',F10.5,/,
      4' MINIMUM SECTION WIDTH IN CAP OF  T , INCHES ..........',F10.5,/,
      5' MINIMUM SECTION WIDTH IN STEM OF  T , INCHES ..........',F10.5,/,
      6' MAXIMUM ALLOWABLE TENSILE STRESS, PSI ................',F10.0,/,
      7' MAXIMUM ALLOWABLE COMPRESSIVE STRESS, PSI ............',F10.0,/,
      8' SPECIFIC WEIGHT OF FRAME MATERIAL, LBF/IN3 ............',F10.5,/,
      920A4)
       WRITE(3,8)W,X(1),BO,C1,X(2),SI,SO
     8 FORMAT(//,' CHARACTERISTICS OF OPTIMAL CONFIGURATION',//,
      1' WEIGHT OF FRAME, LBF ................................',F10.5,/,
      2' WIDTH OF SECTION AT INNER RADIUS,INCHES.................',F10.5,/,
      3' WIDTH OF SECTION AT OUTER RADIUS,INCHES.................',F10.5,/,
```

154

```
   4' THICKNESS OF CAP OF  T , INCHES .....................',F10.5,/,
   5' RADIAL DEPTH OF SECTION, INCHES.....................',F10.5,/,
   6' NORMAL STRESS AT INNER FIBER, PSI ..................',F10.0,/,
   7' NORMAL STRESS AT OUTER  FIBER, PSI ..................',F10.0)
     GO TO 1
     END

     SUBROUTINE MERIT4(X,Y)
     COMMON PP,D,RI,GAMMA,ST,SC,W,SI,SO,GOOD(9),N,XL(9),XR(9),T
     DIMENSION X(9)
C
C     ..... CHECK TO SEE IF POINT VIOLATES ANY REGIONAL CONSTRAINT, ....
C     ..... IF SO, ASSIGN PENALTY ORDINATE AND RETURN.            ....
C
     DO 10 I=1,N
     IF(X(I)-XL(I))4,9,9
   9 IF(X(I)-XR(I))10,10,4
  10 CONTINUE
C
C     ..... INITIALIZE .....
C
     BI=X(1)
     BO=T
     C1=T
     C2=X(2)-T
C
C     ..... CALL CURVED BEAM TEE-SECTION SUBROUTINE TO DETERMINE   .....
C     ..... STRESS LEVELS AT THE INNER AND OUTER SURFACES, AND TO  .....
C     ..... DETERMINE THE RADIUS OF CURVATURE OF LOCUS OF THE CENTER....
C     ..... OF MASS OF CROSS SECTIONAL AREA.                       .....
C
     CALL ME0053(PP,RI,D,BI,BO,C1,C2,SI,SO,R)
C
C     ..... PREPARE MERIT ORDINATE .....
C
     A=BI*C1+BO*C2
     W=R*A*GAMMA*3.14159
     Y=1./W
C
C     ..... DETERMINE IF FUNCTIONAL CONSTRAINTS HAVE BEEN VIOLATED .....
C     ..... BY THIS PARTICULAR CROSS SECTIONAL CONFIGURATION, IF SO,....
C     ..... RETURN PENALTY ORDINATE; IF NOT, RETURN MERIT ORDINATE .....
C
     IF(SI)6,1,1
   1 IF(ABS(ST)-ABS(SI))4,2,2
   2 IF(ABS(SC)-ABS(SO))4,3,3
   6 IF(ABS(SC)-ABS(SI))4,7,7
   7 IF(ABS(ST)-ABS(SO))4,3,3
   4 CALL PENAL(N,GOOD,X,Y)
   3 RETURN
     END

     SUBROUTINE PENAL(N,GOOD,X,Y)
     DIMENSION GOOD(9),X(9)
     Y=0.
     DO 100 I=1,N
     Y=Y+(GOOD(I)-X(I))*(GOOD(I)-X(I))
 100 CONTINUE
     Y=-Y
     RETURN
     END


CONVERGENCE MONITOR SUBROUTINE GRID4

   NN    SIDE      Y       X(1)      X(2)

    5 0.100E 01 0.323E 00 0.100E 01 0.233E 01
    9 0.800E 00 0.323E 00 0.100E 01 0.233E 01
   13 0.640E 00 0.323E 00 0.100E 01 0.233E 01
   17 0.512E 00 0.323E 00 0.100E 01 0.233E 01
   21 0.410E 00 0.353E 00 0.898E 00 0.220E 01
```

```
 25  0.328E 00  0.353E 00  0.898E 00  0.220E 01
 29  0.262E 00  0.353E 00  0.898E 00  0.220E 01
 33  0.210E 00  0.353E 00  0.898E 0C  0.220E 01
 37  0.168E 00  0.353E 00  0.898E 00  0.220E 01
 41  0.134E 00  0.353E C0  0.898E 00  0.220E 01
 45  0.107E 00  0.353E 00  0.898E 00  0.220E 01
 49  0.859E-01  0.353E 00  0.898E 00  0.220E 01
 53  0.687E-01  0.353E 00  0.898E 00  0.220E 01
 57  0.550E-01  0.353E 00  0.898E 00  0.220E 01
 61  0.440E-01  0.354E 00  0.909E 00  0.218E 01
 65  0.352E-01  0.354E 00  0.909E 00  0.218E 01
 69  0.281E-01  0.354E 00  0.909E 00  0.218E 01
 73  0.225E-01  0.354E 00  0.909E 00  0.218E 01
 77  0.180E-01  0.354E C0  0.909E 00  0.218E 01
 81  0.144E-01  0.354E C0  0.894E 00  0.219E 01
 85  0.115E-01  0.355E 00  0.891E 00  0.219E 01
 89  0.922E-02  0.355E 00  0.891E 00  0.219E 01
 93  0.738E-02  0.356E 00  0.889E 00  0.219E 01
 97  0.590E-02  0.356E 00  0.884E 00  0.219E 01
101  0.472E-02  0.356E 00  0.882E 00  0.219E 01
105  0.378E-02  0.356E 00  0.879E 00  0.219E 01
109  0.302E-02  0.356E 00  0.878E 00  0.219E 01
113  0.242E-02  0.356E 00  0.878E 00  0.219E 01
117  0.193E-02  0.356E 00  0.877E 00  0.219E 01
121  0.155E-02  0.356E 00  0.877E 00  0.219E 01
125  0.124E-02  0.356E 00  0.877E 00  0.219E 01
```

```
LARGEST MERIT ORDINATE FOUND DURING SEARCH ........... 0.35647225E 00
NUMBER OF FUNCTION EVALUATIONS USED DURING SEARCH ....        130
FRACTIONAL REDUCTION IN INTERVAL OF UNCERTAINTY EXTANT 0.14854670E-02


XLOW(1)= 0.87661237E 00  X(1)= 0.87735516E 00  XHIGH(1)= 0.87809783E 00
XLOW(2)= 0.21876745E 01  X(2)= 0.21886654E 01  XHIGH(2)= 0.21896553E 01


EXECUTIVE PROGRAM OUTPUT MINIMUM WEIGHT C-CLAMP FRAME
FORCE ON C-CLAMP (POSITIVE OPENS  C ), LBF ...........        900.
DISTANCE FROM LOA OF FORCE TO CENTER OF CURVATURE,IN..    2.00000
RADIUS OF CURVATURE OF INNER FIBER, INCHES ...........    4.00000
MINIMUM SECTION WIDTH IN CAP OF  T , INCHES ..........    0.25000
MINIMUM SECTION WIDTH IN STEM OF  T , INCHES .........    0.25000
MAXIMUM ALLOWABLE TENSILE STRESS, PSI ...............     20000.
MAXIMUM ALLOWABLE COMPRESSIVE STRESS, PSI ............    -20000.
SPECIFIC WEIGHT OF FRAME MATERIAL, LBF/IN3 ...........    0.26000
MATERIAL IS HYPOTHETICAL WITH EQUAL ALLOWABLE NORMAL STRESSES.


CHARACTERISTICS OF OPTIMAL CONFIGURATION

WEIGHT OF FRAME, LBF .................................    2.80527
WIDTH OF SECTION AT INNER RADIUS,INCHES...............    0.87736
WIDTH OF SECTION AT OUTER RADIUS,INCHES...............    0.25000
THICKNESS OF CAP OF  T , INCHES ......................    0.25000
RADIAL DEPTH OF SECTION, INCHES.......................    2.18867
NORMAL STRESS AT INNER FIBER, PSI ....................     19674.
NORMAL STRESS AT OUTER  FIBER, PSI ...................    -19998.
```

The first trial of the two-independent-variable program is with the equal allowable stress material using the basis plane defined by

$$0.50 \leq x_1 \leq 2.00$$
$$1.00 \leq x_2 \leq 3.00$$

and the point in the feasible area as $x_1 = 2.00$, $x_2 = 2.00$. The fractional reduction in the grid-search pattern size is chosen as $r = 0.8$. The optimal configuration reported in the 3 space entertains an inner-fiber stress of

19,674 psi and an outer-fiber stress of $-19,998$ psi. The width of the inner section and the radial depth of the section of $\frac{1}{4}$-in. thicknesses are reported as

$$x_1 = 0.87736 \text{ in.}$$
$$x_2 = 2.18867 \text{ in.}$$

The section weight reported with the two-independent-variable program was 2.80527 lbf and with the four-independent variable program 2.93781 in the case of the equal-strength model. One is led to believe that the optimal configuration is indeed the one with the $\frac{1}{4}$-in. section thicknesses. The irregularities in the pattern-search results may be due to the adverse effects of dimensionality and the higher incidence of false moves.

```
CONVERGENCE MONITOR SUBROUTINE GRID4

    NN    SIDE       Y        X(1)       X(2)

     5  0.100E 01  0.371E 00  0.150E 01  0.167E 01
     9  0.800E 00  0.371E 00  0.150E 01  0.167E 01
    13  0.640E 00  0.371E 00  0.150E 01  0.167E 01
    17  0.512E 00  0.371E 00  0.150E 01  0.167E 01
    21  0.410E 00  0.371E 00  0.150E 01  0.167E 01
    25  0.328E 00  0.373E 00  0.117E 01  0.189E 01
    29  0.262E 00  0.373E 00  0.117E 01  0.189E 01
    33  0.210E 00  0.373E 00  0.117E 01  0.189E 01
    37  0.168E 00  0.373E 00  0.117E 01  0.189E 01
    41  0.134E 00  0.373E 00  0.117E 01  0.189E 01
    45  0.107E 00  0.376E 00  0.120E 01  0.185E 01
    49  0.859E-01  0.376E 00  0.120E 01  0.185E 01
    53  0.687E-01  0.376E 00  0.120E 01  0.185E 01
    57  0.550E-01  0.376E 00  0.120E 01  0.185E 01
    61  0.440E-01  0.376E 00  0.120E 01  0.185E 01
    65  0.352E-01  0.376E 00  0.120E 01  0.185E 01
    69  0.281E-01  0.377E 00  0.121E 01  0.184E 01
    73  0.225E-01  0.377E 00  0.121E 01  0.184E 01
    77  0.180E-01  0.377E 00  0.121E 01  0.184E 01
    81  0.144E-01  0.377E 00  0.121E 01  0.184E 01
    85  0.115E-01  0.377E 00  0.121E 01  0.184E 01
    89  0.922E-02  0.377E 00  0.121E 01  0.184E 01
    93  0.738E-02  0.377E 00  0.121E 01  0.184E 01
    97  0.590E-02  0.377E 00  0.120E 01  0.184E 01
   101  0.472E-02  0.377E 00  0.120E 01  0.184E 01
   105  0.378E-02  0.377E 00  0.120E 01  0.184E 01
   109  0.302E-02  0.377E 00  0.120E 01  0.184E 01
   113  0.242E-02  0.377E 00  0.120E 01  0.184E 01
   117  0.193E-02  0.377E 00  0.120E 01  0.184E 01
   121  0.155E-02  0.377E 00  0.120E 01  0.184E 01
   125  0.124E-02  0.377E 00  0.120E 01  0.184E 01

LARGEST MERIT ORDINATE FOUND DURING SEARCH ...........  0.37683195E 00
NUMBER OF FUNCTION EVALUATIONS USED DURING SEARCH ....          130
FRACTIONAL REDUCTION IN INTERVAL OF UNCERTAINTY EXTANT 0.14848709E-02


XLOW(1)= 0.11995468E 01   X(1)= 0.12002897E 01   XHIGH(1)= 0.12010317E 01
XLOW(2)= 0.18428879E 01   X(2)= 0.18438787E 01   XHIGH(2)= 0.18448687E 01


EXECUTIVE PROGRAM OUTPUT MINIMUM WEIGHT C-CLAMP FRAME
FORCE ON C-CLAMP (POSITIVE OPENS  C ), LBF ............       900.
DISTANCE FROM LOA OF FORCE TO CENTER OF CURVATURE,IN..    2.00000
RADIUS OF CURVATURE OF INNER FIBER, INCHES ...........    4.00000
MINIMUM SECTION WIDTH IN CAP OF  T , INCHES ..........    0.25000
MINIMUM SECTION WIDTH IN STEM OF  T , INCHES .........    0.25000
```

```
MAXIMUM ALLOWABLE TENSILE STRESS, PSI .................    20000.
MAXIMUM ALLOWABLE COMPRESSIVE STRESS, PSI .............   -60000.
SPECIFIC WEIGHT OF FRAME MATERIAL, LBF/IN3 ............    0.26000
MATERIAL IS ASTM 40 CAST IRON WITH DESIGN FACTOR OF TWO ON ULTIMATE.


CHARACTERISTICS OF OPTIMAL CONFIGURATION

WEIGHT OF FRAME, LBF ...................................    2.65370
WIDTH OF SECTION AT INNER RADIUS,INCHES................    1.20029
WIDTH OF SECTION AT OUTER RADIUS,INCHES................    0.25000
THICKNESS OF CAP OF  T , INCHES .......................    0.25000
RADIAL DEPTH OF SECTION, INCHES........................    1.84388
NORMAL STRESS AT INNER FIBER, PSI .....................    20000.
NORMAL STRESS AT OUTER  FIBER, PSI ....................   -26339.
```

The second trial of the two-independent-variable program for ASTM 40 cast iron was made with the basis plane defined by

$$0.5 \leq x_1 \leq 2.00$$
$$1.00 \leq x_2 \leq 3.00$$

and the point in the feasible area as $x_1 = 2.00$, $x_2 = 2.00$. The fractional reduction in the grid-size pattern was chosen as $r = 0.8$. The optimal configuration reported entertained an inner-fiber stress of 20,000 psi and an outer-fiber stress of $-26,339$ psi. The weight of the section was reported as 2.65370 lbf as compared to the previous report of 2.76257 lbf for ASTM 40. "Underworked" material is still present, but now the geometry is sufficiently simple so as to encourage a little more investigation.

Figure 89 shows some inner- and outer-stress loci traced upon the basis plane. Displayed also are contours of constant beam weight. The functional constraints on the problem are such as to confine the feasible points to lying above the limiting outer-fiber stress locus and above the limiting inner-fiber stress locus. In the case of the equal-strength material feasible points lie above the $-20,000$ psi locus and above the 20,000 psi locus. A point moving in the direction of decreasing weight of section is moving toward the lower-left-hand corner of the figure. The minimum-weight configuration is found at the intersection of the dashed $-20,000$ psi locus and the solid 20,000 psi locus.

In the case of the ASTM 40 cast iron, feasible points must lie above the dashed $-60,000$ psi locus and above the solid 20,000 psi locus. These loci intersect somewhere off the figure to the right. Clearly this intersection is not the one of minimal weight. The section working the material to its tensile and compressive limits is wide at the inner radius and of small radial depth. The optimal weight section is narrower at the inner radius and of greater depth. This is due to the curvature. These results also suggest that the tee section is not the best section to choose for this design if the very least possible beam weight is desired. However the statement of the problem limited our consideration to just the tee section.

158

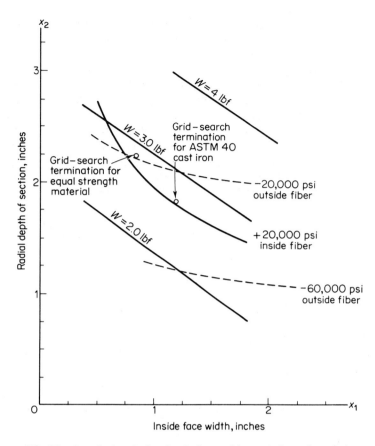

FIG. 89. Search domain for the C clamp with two independent design variables.

Note also from Fig. 89 that in the case of ASTM 40 how much the configuration can change in moving a point along the 20,000 psi stress locus without materially affecting the section weight. It would take a very sensitive searching technique to terminate on the constrained optimum. As an engineering solution the results are useful. Why?

5.8 EPILOGUE

This brief excursion into a part of the world of computer-aided design was planned, with the reader's cooperation and involvement, to acquaint him with the nature, triumphs, and frustrations associated with such sorties. The reader should now have an appreciation of the potential aid that the

159

computer is capable of providing, and that its contribution is limited only by the resourcefulness, imagination, creativeness, boldness, and determination that he brings to the experience.

That only little is known and that pioneering work is still being done should neither surprise nor deter the engineer. This volume concerns itself with engineer-machine interaction as exemplified by the IOWA CADET algorithm. A list of references and additional reading in the general area of machine computation is provided in Appendix 4. Reading can begin in topical areas of immediate interest or need and broaden from that point.

The computer will make some dramatic changes in the engineer's world. Be alert to recognize them in their early stages so that you can incorporate additional skills and concepts into your professional knowledge.

appendix

1

PROBLEMS

1. A right circular cylindrical container is to be fabricated from sheet steel by crimping and soldering seams. Management specifies that it wants the cheapest quart can that can be made from 0.020-in. tin-plated sheet steel stock. Specify the tactical function of merit by identifying all of the variables and parameters of which it is a function. How many of these are under the designer's control? Identify the functional constraints. Identify the regional constraints.

2. A pipeline company desires to establish a pipeline to pump gasoline between a Texas port and an inland Midwestern city. It has options on thirty parcels of land which could be used for construction of pumping stations. Management specifies that it wants to know the route which could be used to locate those pumping stations which result in the least cost per barrel delivered at the Midwest city over the next twenty years. Specify the tactical function of merit by identifying the variables and parameters of which it is a function. How many are under the designer's control? Identify the regional constraints. Identify the functional constraints.

3. A pipe carrying high-temperature, high-pressure gases has to be insulated so that it is safe for a human to touch. It is essential that the complex (pipe plus insulation layers) be as light as possible. Specify the tactical function of merit by identifying all variables and parameters of which it is a function. How many of these are under the designer's control? Identify the functional constraints. Identify the regional constraints.

4. A horizontal electrical conductor cannot operate with its surface temperature in excess of T_s degrees Fahrenheit. Its geometry is fixed by other considerations. It is desired to have it carry as large a direct current as possible without exceeding the T_s surface temperature limit. The addition of "insulation" for electrical and heat-transfer reasons is being considered. Specify the tactical figure of merit function by identifying all of the variables and parameters of which it is a function. How many are under the designer's control? Identify the functional constraints. Identify the regional constraints.

161

5. A steam-power plant turbine operates upon a Rankine cycle and has one closed regenerative feed water heater fed by steam bled from the turbine at some intermediate pressure between throttle pressure and condenser pressure. Considering the case of ideal components, it is desired to maximize the cycle efficiency by choosing the proper bleed pressure. Specify the tactical figure of merit function by identifying all the variables and parameters of which it is a function. How many of these are under the designer's control? Identify the functional constraints. Identify the regional constraints.

6. Most parachutists would agree that, having bailed out of an airplane, the time to pull the ripcord is when you are moving at your slowest air speed during free fall. In a specific problem to determine the best time to open the parachute, what would be a suitable tactical figure of merit function? Identify all the variables and parameters of which it is a function. Identify the functional constraints. Identify the regional constraints.

7. A right circular cylinder is in double transverse shear. Because of other considerations its diameter and length are established, and only the composition of the material from which it is fabricated can be varied to meet the load requirements. At its critical cross section the pin is subjected to a shearing load corresponding to a shearing stress of 45,000 ± 5,000 psi. The load-induced stress is completely random in the range of 40,000 to 50,000 psi. The material for the pin is available with an ultimate shearing strength of $S_{ult} \pm 5{,}000$ psi. The material is available with ultimate shearing strengths ranging from 20,000 to 60,000 psi. A sample of material shows the distribution of the shearing ultimate strength to be completely random in a range of 5,000 psi on either side of the mean. The cost of the material is a function of the ultimate shearing stress specified and is, per pin,

$$\$ = 0.15 \qquad\qquad\qquad\qquad 20{,}000 \leq S_{ult} \leq 40{,}000$$

$$\$ = 0.15 + 0.00017\left[\frac{S_{ult} - 40{,}000}{1{,}000}\right]^3 \qquad 40{,}000 \leq S_{ult} \leq 60{,}000$$

The cost of machining the pin is related to its ultimate shearing strength. The cost, per pin, is given by

$$\$ = 0.00002\,S_{ult} + 1.25$$

The cost of failures becomes increasingly severe as the number of failures increases. The cost of failures, exclusive of the cost of replacement pins, is

$$\$ = 1.00n^{1.5}$$

where n is the number of failures. The project engineer has assigned you the task of determining the material specification so that the total cost of filling a thousand holes satisfactorily is a minimum. Specify the tactical figure of merit function. Specify the functional constraints. Specify the regional constraints. (If this problem is programmed for computer, answer the following questions: Does it disturb you to encounter failures when the design factor exceeds unity? Why or why not?)

8. A speed limit is to be selected for a straight, limited-access highway heavily used by commuters. Suggest a candidate to a tactical figure of merit function. If there are differences within the class, debate the different candidates. Could agreement be reached?

9. The "best" straight line is to be passed through some data points. What could the tactical figure of merit function be? Is there agreement within the class? Could the disagreements be resolved?

10. A steel skeleton is to be designed for a large building. What could the tactical figure of merit function be? Is there agreement within the class? Could the disagreements be resolved?

11. Develop a working program that will read a card in FORMAT (3F10.5), thereby sensing the three sides of a proposed triangle. Have the program ascertain whether or not a triangle is possible using these specified sides. Have the program print out the sides and whether or not a triangle is possible.

12. Determine to your satisfaction the internal machine representation of the alphabetic characters A, B, C, D, E, and "blank." (Hint: Punch the characters into "column one" of six data cards. Read the contents of column one with an integer variable using an A1 format. Print out the variable using an I15 format. Prove to yourself that these are valid by preparing data cards with the integers, read them, and print out the alphabetic characters.)

13. Using your experience with Prob. 12, write a program that will scan a card and discover whether or not it is blank.

14. Write a program that will read a line of less than eighty characters of any sort of "text" and write out the same line on the printer. Can you plan your program in such a way so that without modification it will read and print any number of cards?

15. Use your experience with Probs. 12, 13, and 14 to write a program which will read and copy a program deck making any specified number of copies. Blank cards can be used as control cards to separate subroutines, and two blank cards can be used to detect the end of the material to be read. This is a useful program for obtaining an *exact* copy of a program for inclusion in reports. The copy is accurate, clean, and free of machine-specific processing printing.

16. Write a program that will read a one-dimensional array (a column vector) of five numbers. On the same sheet of output paper have your program print them out in (a) a horizontal line in F format; (b) a horizontal line in E format; (c) a vertical column, single-spaced in F format; and (d) a vertical column double-spaced in E format.

17. Take the program developed as a solution to Prob. 11 and rewrite it as a subroutine. This subroutine is to accept and return all necessary information via the call list. Have it accept the three side lengths and return a coded integer that will tell the main program which situation prevails—i.e., there is a triangle, there is a degenerate straight line, or that no triangle is possible. Accomplish all the reading and writing in the main program and allow the subroutine to do neither.

18. Take the subroutine developed as a solution to Prob. 17 and modify it so that there is no call list, and all values are transferred to and from the subroutine via a COMMON declaration.

19. Check with your instructor on how to obtain a machine language (object deck) at your computational facility. Obtain object decks for the subroutine developed for Probs. 17 and 18. Use these instead of the FORTRAN subroutine decks to see if they are in working order. Exchange decks with another class member and use his subroutine. What problems did you encounter? What problems could you have encountered? How might these problems be eased?

20. Write a subroutine to accept the side lengths of a triangle and to calculate and return the area of the triangle. Write a main program to read in side lengths, use this and previous subroutines to determine if a triangle is possible, and, if so, determine its area. Have the main program print out the side lengths, whether or not a triangle is possible, and, if so, the area of the triangle. You are now learning that a very useful division of labor in programming is to write an executive program to read in information and write out information. Specialized subroutines are called to do the technical manipulation. In this way subroutines are not rewritten for every problem. Only the executive program is problem-specific.

21. In the problems you have already solved by writing computer programs insert COMMENT cards (a) to explain the use of the program to yourself and any potential borrower; and (b) to explain the macroprogramming.

22. Examine the subroutines you have written. Are there places where variables outside a certain range can give invalid results? Are there places where division by zero or occurrence of a negative argument in the SQRT operator can abort your program from the computer? Devise protection in your program for these contingencies and allow the subroutine to write an error message before the blow falls. This will greatly help the user identify the cause of the trouble.

23. Document all the subroutines you have written according to Sec. 3.5.

24. Write a FORTRAN subprogram to implement an exhaustive search over a one-dimensional interval of a function. Test your subroutine.

25. Write a FORTRAN subprogram to implement an interval-halving search over a one-dimensional unimodal function. Test your subroutine and check its performance with Table 4.2.

26. Write a FORTRAN subprogram to implement a dichotomous search over a one-dimensional interval of a unimodal function. Test your subroutine and check its performance with Table 4.3.

27. Write a FORTRAN subprogram to implement a golden-section search over a one-dimensional interval of a unimodal function. Test your subroutine and check its performance with Table 4.4.

28. Write a FORTRAN subprogram to implement a random search over a multidimensional function. Test your subroutine and check its performance with the prediction equation of Sec. 4.5.

29. Write a FORTRAN subprogram to implement a sequential linear search. Test it with a function that has a domelike maximum and with a function that has a ridge (such as a triangular pyramid).

30. Write a FORTRAN subprogram to implement an area-elimination routine on a two-dimensional basis plane.

31. Write a FORTRAN subprogram to implement a gradient search. Test the subroutine with a function having a domelike maximum and a function with a clifflike ridge such as in Fig. 25.

32. Devise a scheme whereby a gradient search recognizes a constraint which produces a cliff, and can orient itself to steer a path along the edge of the cliff.

33. Write a FORTRAN subprogram to implement a pattern search. Test the routine with functions of varying complexity.

34. Write a FORTRAN subprogram utilizing a random search in the locale of the highest point on the merit surface discovered by an exhaustive search.

35. In the can problem of Sec. 5.2 determine the proportions of a can of minimum cost (for a given gauge of sheet metal) and include in the consideration the cost of punching, seaming, soldering, and reclaiming of scrap from the punching sheets.

36. For the rapid transit car problem of Sec. 5.3, improve the integration programming which finds the time from start to stop.

37. For the rapid transit car problem of Sec. 5.3, reprogram as necessary to deal with a straight level line of tangent track but with several stations with variable distances. Determine the gear ratio for minimum schedule time over the entire run.

38. For the rapid transit car problem of Sec. 5.3, reprogram as necessary to allow equipment to be run in trains of from one to ten cars, including trailers. The Davis formula for drag resistance in lbf per ton of car weight for a car other than the first car is

$$r = 1.3 + \frac{29}{W} + 0.03\,V + 0.00034\frac{A\,V^2}{wn}$$

The symbols are defined in Sec. 5.3.

39. Under the direction of your instructor, with a division of labor devise a program that will allow track grade, curvature, speed restrictions, etc. to be so incorporated into the programming that an actual line may be simulated.

40. Obtain some actual traction motor data from an equipment manufacturer and write a subroutine such as TMOTOR.

41. Obtain some braking data on passenger equipment with mechanical brakes and write the BRAKE subroutine for such circumstances.

42. Obtain some data on dynamic braking of electrically propelled equipment that is "blended with air" and write a BRAKE subroutine for such circumstances.

43. For a computational cam with an offset roller follower which follows a linear path, develop the equations which will establish the cam contour. Solve the problem of Sec. 5.4 using the roller follower instead of the knifeedge follower.

44. Write a subroutine that will establish the cam torque necessary to overcome a force exerted on the follower.

45. Hertsian stresses due to rolling cylindrical surfaces are important in cam design. Write a subroutine that can be called to give the local radius of curvature of the cam. Write also a subroutine that will calculate the principal stresses and the maximum shear stress due to contact.

46. Write a program to map on an x_1x_2 plane, for the problem in Sec 5.4, a locus of values of a and b having constant maximum-pressure angle. Examine the output in specific cases for functions of your choice and comment on how this information dovetails with your expectations.

47. Determine if the program presented in Sec. 5.5 is suitable with any number of gear reductions.

48. Develop an expression for the equivalent inertia of a gear train with k reductions.

49. Write a program to show how the gear reduction for minimal inertia is a function of the overall reduction R. Determine the influence of the motor-armature inertia I_M and the load I_L inertia.

50. In a function generator such as that described in Sec. 5.6, the position of the input sector on the input shaft and the positioning of the output sector on the output

shaft are arbitrary. The scanning pointers can be indexed relative to the links by merely using a set-screw adjustment. In response to this observation, treat both the input angle A4 corresponding to the input dial's initial position and the angle B4 corresponding to the initial position of the output dial as design variables. This brings the number of design variables to five. Determine the linkage with minimum structural error and compare the error obtained to the ordinary three-point synthesis for several functions of your choice.

51. It is sometimes asserted that structural errors are smaller for four-bar function generators developing odd functions than is found in those developing even functions. As a class project, investigate this assertion.

52. If one views a steering linkage on a tractor or automobile as a function generator, what function must be generated for nonskid steering?

53. As a class project, write subroutines for different cross sections of the curved beams of Sec. 5.7. Exercise the programs with the general programs of Sec. 5.7 and discover what cross sections are more effective in producing a minimal-weight configuration in this circumstance.

54. For the problem of Sec. 5.7, introduce the additional constraint that the outer radius cannot exceed 5.5 inches. Using some programs developed for Prob. 53, find a minimal-weight configuration.

55. As the outer-radius constraint is varied on the problem in Sec. 5.7, the cross section that will produce the minimum weight of all minimal-weight configurations may change. As a class project, develop data that will enable you to plot minimal weights versus outer-radius limitation. Is the resulting information display a surprise, or is it a confirmation of your intuitive estimate of the situation? All the cross sections for which subroutines were prepared for Prob. 55 should be used here. If the results suggest a section that has not been programmed, investigate such a fruitful lead.

The following problem may be solved in its entirety at the end of the course or all subroutines developed as the course progresses. The subroutine problems are numbered 57–72.

56. Depicted in Fig. P-56 is a linkage and hydraulic cylinder being considered for use in lifting an outrigger, on a piece of agricultural machinery, from a horizontal working position to a vertical transport position. The pivot points labeled A, B, C, and D are anchored to the frame and their positions are invariable during the lifting operation. Although the system is completely symmetrical, one side will complete its motion before the other side commences its movement. The points labeled E, F, G, H, I, and J move. The following information is given: Maximum hydraulic cylinder working pressure: 1,800 psi; maximum usable piston stroke for one side: 5.5 in.; BH = 8.0 in., BD = 57.6 in., BK = 15.54 in., CGH = 37.5 in., CGV = 3.0 in., KL = 8.08 in., GH = 17.750 in., GL = 20.50 in., and the initial value of important angles is $\theta_1 = 86.1°$, $\theta_2 = 163.8°$, and $\theta_3 = 69.9°$. The final values of these angles are $\theta_1 \leq 121°$, $\theta_2 = 73.8°$, and $\theta_3 \leq 105°$.

(a) Subject to the above conditions, proportion a four-bar linkage which will raise the outriggers to the transport position minimizing the cylinder pressure required.

(b) Can a superior system be designed by allowing BH to be chosen differently along with $(\theta_3)_{initial}$?

(c) During the process of determining the proper linkage proportions, discover the largest value of the pin reactions and maximum bending moments induced in the crank and follower.

166

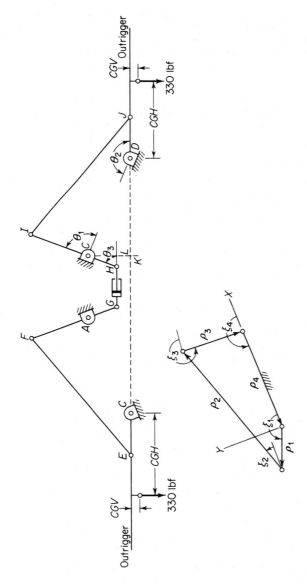

FIG. P-56. Schematic diagram of the lifting mechanism to raise a pair of outriggers from the operating to the transport position on an agricultural machinery vehicle.

167

57. Conceive, test, and document a subroutine VADD that will accept the magnitude and abscissa angles of two vectors and return the magnitude and abscissa angle of the vector sum.

58. Conceive, test, and document a subroutine that will determine the moment of a force (in a planer-force system) about a point. The subroutine is to accept the magnitude and abscissa angle of the position vector of any convenient point on the line of action of the force relative to the point about which the moment is desired. The subroutine is to accept the magnitude of the force and its abscissa angle and return the moment as an algebraic scalar ($ccw+$). The name of the subroutine could be MOMENT.

59. Conceive, test, and document a subroutine that will perform the inverse of that required in Prob. 58—i.e., determine the magnitude of a force, given the moment and displacement vector of a convenient point on the line of action of the force and an angle describing the LOA. Be certain that the subroutine corrects the angle describing the LOA of the force to an abscissa angle of the force, if such correction is necessary. The name of the subroutine might be FDUEM.

60. Conceive, test, and document a subroutine that will determine the direction of the third LOA in a three-force concurrent planer-force system when the other two LOA directions are known. Use as input information the position vectors of three convenient points on the individual lines of action. The name of the subroutine might be LOA3.

61. Conceive, test, and document a subroutine called FORCE2 which will determine the magnitudes and abscissa angles of the other two forces when given the magnitude and abscissa angle of a force and angles describing the LOAs of the other two forces.

62. Conceive, test, and document a subroutine to carry out a plane coordinate transformation from a global coordinate system to a local Cartesian coordinate system. The subroutine PLOCAL should accept the position vector of the origin of local reference frame xy as seen in global reference frame XY, the abscissa angle of the x axis as seen in XY, the global coordinates, and return the coordinates of the point in the xy frame.

63. Conceive, test, and document a subroutine to carry out a plane transformation from a local coordinate system to a global Cartesian coordinate system. The subroutine PGLOBE should accept the position vector of the origin of xy as seen in XY, the abscissa angle of the x axis as seen in XY, the local coordinates, and return the coordinates of the point in the XY frame.

64. Conceive, test, and document a subroutine ALOCAL that will accept the abscissa angle of the x axis, the abscissa angle as seen in global XY frame, and return an abscissa angle as seen in the local xy frame. Prepare a subroutine AGLOBE that will perform the converse of ALOCAL.

65. Conceive, test, and document a subroutine PVECT that will establish the position vector of a point (x, y) when tendered its Cartesian coordinates. Prepare a subroutine POINT that will perform the converse of PVECT.

66. Conceive, test, and document a subroutine VMINUS that will accept the magnitude and abscissa angle of a vector and return the magnitude and abscissa angle of the negative of the vector. Be sure abscissa angles are maintained in the range $0 \leq \theta < 2\pi$.

67. Conceive, test, and document a subroutine TEST4 which will accept four link lengths

168

and ascertain whether or not they can be assembled into a four-bar plane linkage, returning the coded integer I = 1 if yes, I = 2 if no.

68. Conceive, test, and document a subroutine **FANGLE** which, for a plane four-bar linkage, will accept a coded integer, I = 1 for uncrossed configuration and I = 2 for crossed configuration, the abscissa angle of the crank vector, the four link lengths, and return the abscissa angles of the coupler vector and the follower vector. [Reference can be made to Charles R. Mischke, *Elements of Mechanical Analysis* (Reading, Mass.: Addison-Wesley Publishing Co., Inc., 1963), pp. 100 ff.]

69. Conceive, test, and document a subroutine **AINT4**, for a four-bar planer linkage that will accept a coded integer for configuration, abscissa angle of the crank vector, the four link lengths, and return the interior angles of the linkage polygon.

70. Conceive, test, and document a subroutine **SMOM** which will, for a four-bar planer linkage, accept a coded integer expressing configuration, the four link lengths, the abscissa angle of the crank and follower vectors, and return the ratio of the moment on the follower shaft to the moment on the crank shaft.

71. Probs. 57–71 represent a fine class project early in the course to prepare for the solution later in the course of Prob. 56. If Probs. 57–71 are not done in detail, a useful exercise is to write the **MERIT** program in terms of the subroutines represented in these problems. Notice that all the above subroutines are useful, independent of this problem.

72. A problem-specific subroutine is required to determine the line of action of the thruster for various orientations of the linkages. Conceive, test, and document a subroutine **THRUST** which will accomplish the determination of this important angle.

2

DOCUMENTATION OF IOWA CADET SUBROUTINES USED IN ILLUSTRATIVE PROBLEMS IN CHAPTER 5

ONE-DIMENSIONAL EXHAUSTIVE SEARCH
COMB1 (I1, A2, A3, A4, B1, B2, B3, B4, B5, B6, J7)

```
ONE-DIMENSIONAL EXHAUSTIVE SEARCH
COMB1(I1,A2,A3,A4,B1,B2,B3,B4,B5,B6,J7)
C
THIS SUBROUTINE CONDUCTS AN EXHAUSTIVE SEARCH OVER A ONE-DIMENSIONAL
FUNCTION RETURNING THE EXTREME ORDINATE, ITS ABSCISSA, ALL
ORDINATES AND ABSCISSAS EVALUATED, NEW LOWER AND UPPER BOUNDS
OF INTERVAL OF UNCERTAINTY, AND THE NUMBER OF FUNCTION
EVALUATIONS UTILIZED DURING THE SEARCH.
C
THE SUBROUTINE REQUIRES THE SPECIFICATION OF THE LOWER AND
UPPER BOUNDS ON THE INITIAL INTERVAL OF UNCERTAINTY AND THE
FRACTIONAL REDUCTION IN THIS INTERVAL DESIRED.  DO NOT ALLOW
LIST VARIABLE A4 TO BE LESS THAN 0.001.
C
C     CALLING PROGRAM REQUIREMENTS
C
C     PROVIDE A DIMENSION DECLARATION AS FOLLOWS:
C
C         DIMENSION B3(2001),B4(2001)
C
      PROVIDE A SUBROUTINE MERIT1(X,Y) WHEREIN Y IS THE ORDINATE
      RETURNED UPON SPECIFICATION OF THE ABSCISSA X.
C
C     VARIABLES
C
      I1=0 CONVERGENCE MONITOR WILL NOT PRINT.
      I1=1 CONVERGENCE MONITOR WILL PRINT.
      A2=LOWER INITIAL BOUND ON INTERVAL OF UNCERTAINTY.
      A3=UPPER INITIAL BOUND ON INTERVAL OF UNCERTAINTY.
      A4=FRACTIONAL REDUCTION OF INTERVAL OF UNCERTAINTY DESIRED.
C
      B1=EXTREME ORDINATE DISCOVERED DURING SEARCH.
      B2=ABSCISSA CORRESPONDING TO EXTREME ORDINATE.
      B3=ALL ORDINATES EVALUATED DURING SEARCH, COLUMN VECTOR.
      B4=ABSCISSAS OF EVALUATED ORDINATES, COLUMN VECTOR.
      B5=NEW LOWER BOUND ON INTERVAL OF UNCERTAINTY.
      B6=NEW UPPER BOUND ON INTERVAL OF UNCERTAINTY.
      J7=NUMBER OF FUNCTION EVALUATIONS EXPENDED DURING SEARCH.
```

ONE-DIMENSIONAL GOLDEN SECTION SEARCH
GOLD1 (I1, A2, A3, A4, B1, B2, B3, B4, J5)

```
      ONE-DIMENSIONAL GOLDEN SECTION SEARCH
      GOLD1(I1,A2,A3,A4,B1,B2,B3,B4,J5)
C
      THIS SUBROUTINE WILL SEARCH OVER A ONE-DIMENSIONAL UNIMODAL
      FUNCTION AND REPORT THE EXTREME ORDINATE FOUND, ITS ABSCISSA,
      FINAL ABSCISSAS BOUNDING THE INTERVAL OF UNCERTAINTY, AND THE
      NUMBER OF FUNCTION EVALUATIONS EXPENDED DURING THE SEARCH.
C
      THE SUBROUTINE REQUIRES THE SPECIFICATION OF THE PRESENT INTERVAL
      OF UNCERTAINTY, FRACTIONAL REDUCTION REQUIRED IN THE INTERVAL
      OF UNCERTAINTY, AND WHETHER OR NOT A CONVERGENCE MONITOR PRINTOUT
      IS DESIRED.
C
      CALLING PROGRAM REQUIREMENTS
C
      PROVIDE A SUBROUTINE MERIT1(X,Y) WHICH RETURNS THE ORDINATE Y
      WHEN THE ABSCISSA X IS TENDERED.
C
      VARIABLES
C
      I1=0 CONVERGENCE MONITOR WILL NOT PRINT.
      I1=1 CONVERGENCE MONITOR WILL PRINT.
      A2=ORIGINAL LEFTHAND ABSCISSA OF INTERVAL OF UNCERTAINTY.
      A3=ORIGINAL RIGHTHAND ABSCISSA OF INTERVAL OF UNCERTAINTY.
      A4=FRACTIONAL REDUCTION IN INTERVAL OF UNCERTAINTY DESIRED.
      B1=EXTREME ORDINATE DISCOVERED DURING SEARCH.
      B2=ABSCISSA OF EXTREME ORDINATE.
      B3=FINAL LEFTHAND ABSCISSA OF INTERVAL OF UNCERTAINTY.
      B4=FINAL RIGHTHAND ABSCISSA OF INTERVAL OF UNCERTAINTY.
      J5=NUMBER OF FUNCTION EVALUATIONS EXPENDED DURING SEARCH.
```

ONE-DIMENSIONAL GOLDEN SECTION SEARCH
GOLD2 (I1, A2, A3, A4, B1, B2, B3, B4, J5)

```
      ONE-DIMENSIONAL GOLDEN SECTION SEARCH
      GOLD2(I1,A2,A3,A4,B1,B2,B3,B4,J5)
C
      THIS SUBROUTINE WILL SEARCH OVER A ONE-DIMENSIONAL UNIMODAL
      FUNCTION AND REPORT THE EXTREME ORDINATE FOUND, ITS ABSCISSA,
      FINAL ABSCISSAS BOUNDING THE INTERVAL OF UNCERTAINTY, AND THE
      NUMBER OF FUNCTION EVALUATIONS EXPENDED DURING THE SEARCH.
C
      THE SUBROUTINE REQUIRES THE SPECIFICATION OF THE PRESENT INTERVAL
      OF UNCERTAINTY, THE FRACTIONAL REDUCTION REQUIRED IN THE INTERVAL
      OF UNCERTAINTY, AND WHETHER OR NOT A CONVERGENCE MONITOR PRINTOUT
      IS DESIRED.
C
      CALLING PROGRAM REQUIREMENTS
C
      PROVIDE A SUBROUTINE MERIT2(X,Y) WHICH RETURNS THE ORDINATE Y
      WHEN THE ABSCISSA X IS TENDERED.
C
      VARIABLES
C
      I1=0 CONVERGENCE MONITOR WILL NOT PRINT.
      I1=1 CONVERGENCE MONITOR WILL PRINT.
      A2=ORIGINAL LEFTHAND ABSCISSA OF INTERVAL OF UNCERTAINTY.
      A3=ORIGINAL RIGHTHAND ABSCISSA OF INTERVAL OF UNCERTAINTY.
      A4=FRACTIONAL REDUCTION IN INTERVAL OF UNCERTAINTY DESIRED.
      B1=EXTREME ORDINATE DISCOVERED DURING SEARCH.
      B2=ABSCISSA OF EXTREME ORDINATE.
      B3=FINAL LEFTHAND ABSCISSA OF INTERVAL OF UNCERTAINTY.
      B4=FINAL RIGHTHAND ABSCISSA OF INTERVAL OF UNCERTAINTY.
      J5=NUMBER OF FUNCTION EVALUATIONS EXPENDED DURING SEARCH.
```

172

GRADIENT SEARCH FOR EXTREME ORDINATE
GRAD4 (I1, I2, I3, A4, A5, A6, A7, A8, A9, B1, B2, J3, J4, B5, B6)

```
      GRADIENT SEARCH FOR EXTREME ORDINATE
C     GRAD4(I1,I2,I3,A4,A5,A6,A7,A8,A9,B1,B2,J3,J4,B5,B6)

      THIS SUBROUTINE DETERMINES THE EXTREME ORDINATE OF A UNIMODAL
      HYPERSURFACE OF UP TO EIGHT INDEPENDENT VARIABLES.  THE
      SUBROUTINE WILL TERMINATE SEARCH AFTER 100 TIMES THE NUMBER OF
      INDEPENDENT VARIABLES EVALUATIONS OF THE MERIT ORDINATE.  IF
      SEARCH HAS NOT BEEN CARRIED TO CONCLUSION AND HYPERSURFACE
      ABNORMALITIES ARE NOT RETARDING SEARCH, THE SUBROUTINE GRAD4 CAN
      BE RECALLED BY USING SEARCH OPTION FOUR.
C
      CALLING PROGRAM REQUIREMENTS
C
      PROVIDE A DIMENSION DECLARATION AS FOLLOWS:
C
      DIMENSION A8(9),A9(9),B2(9),B5(9),B6(9)
C
      PROVIDE A SUBROUTINE MERIT4(X,Y) FROM WHICH AN ORDINATE Y IS RETURNED
      WHEN COLUMN VECTOR OF ABSCISSA X IS TENDERED.
C
      VARIABLES
C
      I1=NUMBER OF INDEPENDENT VARIABLES IN SEARCH (8 OR LESS).
      I2=0 CONVERGENCE MONITOR WILL NOT PRINT.
      I2=1 CONVERGENCE MONITOR PRINT EVERY 1ST SURVEY STEP.
      I2=2 CONVERGENCE MONITOR PRINT EVERY 2ND SURVEY STEP.
C       .
C       .
C       .
      I3=1 COMMENCE SEARCH CENTRALLY IN DOMAIN OF UNCERTAINTY.
      I3=2 COMMENCE SEARCH IN"LOWER CORNER" OF DOMAIN OF UNCERTAINTY.
      I3=3 COMMENCE SEARCH IN "UPPER CORNER" OF DOMAIN OF UNCERTAINTY.
      I3=4 COMMENCE SEARCH AT LOCATION SPECIFIED IN COLUMN VECTOR B2.
      A4=INITIAL EXPLORATION STEP SIZE.
      A5=STEP-SIZE GROWTH MULTIPLIER ( A LITTLE MORE THAN UNITY).
      A6=FRACTIONAL REDUCTION IN DOMAIN OF UNCERTAINTY DESIRED.
      A7=SURVEY PATTERN INCREMENT.
      A8=LOWER BOUND OF SEARCH DOMAIN, COLUMN VECTOR.
      A9=UPPER BOUND OF SEARCH DOMAIN, COLUMN VECTOR.
C
      B1=EXTREME ORDINATE FOUND DURING SEARCH.
      B2=COLUMN VECTOR OF ABSCISSAS CORRESPONDING TO EXTREME ORDINATE.
      J3=1 LARGEST ORDINATE IS AN EXTREMUM.
      J3=2 LARGEST ORDINATE IS A MAXIMUM.
      J3=3 LARGEST ORDINATE IS IN A PLATEAU.
      J3=4 ERROR RETURN, SEARCH TRUNCATED.
      J4=NUMBER OF FUNCTION EVALUATIONS EXPENDED DURING SEARCH.
      B5=COLUMN VECTOR OF FORWARD SLOPES OF HYPERSURFACE AT EXTREMUM.
      B6=COLUMN VECTOR OF BACKWARD SLOPES OF HYPERSURFACE AT EXTREMUM.
```

GRID SEARCH
GRID4 (I1, I2, A3, A4, A5, A6, B1, B2, B3, B4, J5)

```
      GRID SEARCH
C     GRID4(I1,I2,A3,A4,A5,A6,B1,B2,B3,B4,J5)

      THIS SUBROUTINE CONDUCTS A GRID-TYPE SEARCH WITHIN REGIONAL
      CONSTRAINTS IN A HYPERSPACE OF UP TO EIGHT INDEPENDENT VARIABLES.
      THE FRACTIONAL REDUCTION OF GRID SIZE MUST BE GREATER THAN 2/3 BUT
      LESS THAN ONE.
C
      THE SEARCH PATTERN ALTERNATES BETWEEN A HYPERCUBE AND A
```

173

HYPERSTAR ORIENTED ABOUT A CENTRAL POINT. FOR ADDITIONAL DETAILS
SEE "AN INTRODUCTION TO COMPUTER-AIDED DESIGN", MISCHKE,
PRENTICE-HALL INC.

C

CALLING PROGRAM REQUIREMENTS

C

PROVIDE A DIMENSION DECLARATION EQUIVALENT TO THE FOLLOWING:

C
C
C

      DIMENSION A3(9),A4(9),B2(9),B3(9),B4(9)

PROVIDE A SUBPROGRAM MERIT4(X,Y) WHICH WILL RETURN TO GRID4
AN ORDINATE Y CORRESPONDING TO THE COLUMN VECTOR OF
ABSCISSAS, X.

C

VARIABLES

C

I1=NUMBER OF INDEPENDENT DESIGN VARIABLES PRESENT, INTEGER.
I2=0 CONVERGENCE MONITOR WILL NOT PRINT.
I2=1 CONVERGENCE MONITOR WILL PRINT EACH NEW GRID CENTER.
A3=COLUMN VECTOR OF INITIAL LOWER EXTREMITIES OF INTERVAL.
A4=COLUMN VECTOR OF INITIAL UPPER EXTREMITIES OF INTERVAL.
A5=FRACTIONAL REDUCTION OF INTERVAL OF UNCERTAINTY DESIRED.
A6=FRACTIONAL REDUCTION IN GRID SIZE DESIRED (BETWEEN 2/3 AND 1.).
B1=LARGEST MERIT ORDINATE DISCOVERED DURING GRID SEARCH.
B2=COLUMN VECTOR OF ABSCISSAS CORRESPONDING TO LARGEST ORDINATE.
B3=COLUMN VECTOR OF FINAL LOWER EXTREMITY OF INTERVAL.
B4=COLUMN VECTOR OF FINAL UPPER EXTREMITY OF INTERVAL.
J5=NUMBER OF FUNCTION EVALUATIONS EXPENDED DURING SEARCH.

FOURBAR FUNCTION GENERATOR INPUT ANGLE-OUTPUT ANGLE
ME0034 (I1, A2, A3, A4, A5, A6, B1)

FOURBAR FUNCTION GENERATOR INPUT ANGLE-OUTPUT ANGLE
ME0034(I1,A2,A3,A4,A5,A6,B1)

C

THIS SUBROUTINE ACCEPTS LINKAGE CONFIGURATION INFORMATION,
INPUT DIAL ANGLE, LINK LENGTHS AND RETURNS THE OUTPUT DIAL
ANGLE. THE ANGLES ARE MEASURED CLOCKWISE. ADDITIONAL
INFORMATION CONTAINED IN SUPPLEMENTS P38 AND P39 OF
"COMPUTERS IN ENGINEERING DESIGN EDUCATION", 1 APRIL 1966,
PUBLICATIONS DISTRIBUTION OFFICE, UNIVERSITY OF MICHIGAN,
ANN ARBOR.

C

CALLING PROGRAM REQUIREMENTS

C

NONE.

C

VARIABLES

C

I1=1 UNCROSSED TOP CONFIGURATION.
I1=2 CROSSED TOP CONFIGURATION.
I1=3 UNCROSSED BOTTOM CONFIGURATION.
I1=4 CROSSED BOTTOM CONFIGURATION.
A2=INPUT DIAL ANGLE ALPHA, RADIANS, MEASURED CLOCKWISE.
A3=CRANK VECTOR LENGTH.
A4=COUPLER VECTOR LENGTH.
A5=FOLLOWER VECTOR LENGTH.
A6=GROUNDED LINK VECTOR LENGTH.
B1=OUTPUT DIAL ANGLE BETA, RADIANS, MEASURED CLOCKWISE.

174

FOURBAR FUNCTION GENERATOR THREE POINT SYNTHESIS
ME0035 (A1, A2, A3, A4, A5, A6, B1, B2, B3, B4, J5)

```
     FOURBAR FUNCTION GENERATOR THREE POINT SYNTHESIS
     ME0035(A1,A2,A3,A4,A5,A6,B1,B2,B3,B4,J5)
C
     THIS SUBROUTINE PERFORMS A THREE-POINT SYNTHESIS OF A FOURBAR
     FUNCTION GENERATOR REPORTING LINK LENGTHS AND LINKAGE CONFIGURATION.
C
     THE METHOD UTILIZED IS EXPLAINED IN SECTION 4-2, P. 100,
     "ELEMENTS OF MECHANICAL ANALYSIS", MISCHKE, ADDISON-WESLEY PUB. CO.
C
     CALLING PROGRAM REQUIREMENTS
C
     NONE.
C
     VARIABLES
C
     A1=INPUT ANGLE ALPHA OF FIRST PRECISION POINT, RAD.
     A2=OUTPUT ANGLE BETA OF FIRST PRECISION POINT, RAD.
     A3=INPUT ANGLE ALPHA OF SECOND PRECISION POINT, RAD.
     A4=OUTPUT ANGLE BETA OF SECOND PRECISION POINT, RAD.
     A5=INPUT ANGLE ALPHA OF THIRD PRECISION POINT, RAD.
     A6=OUTPUT ANGLE BETA OF THIRD PRECISION POINT, RAD.

     B1=LENGTH OF CRANK VECTOR, IN.
     B2=LENGTH OF COUPLER VECTOR, IN.
     B3=LENGTH OF FOLLOWER VECTOR, IN.
     B4=LENGTH OF GROUNDED VECTOR, UNITY, IN.
     J5=1 UNCROSSED TOP CONFIGUATION.
     J5=2 CROSSED TOP CONFIGURATION.
     J5=3 UNCROSSED BOTTOM CONFIGURATION.
     J5=4 CROSSED BOTTOM CONFIGURATION.
```

FUNCTION GENERATOR ANGLE-FUNCTION RELATIONS
ME0036 (A1, A2, A3, A4, A5, A6, A7, A8, A9, A10, A11, B1, B2, B3, B4, B5,
1 B6, B7, B8, B9)

```
     FUNCTION GENERATOR ANGLE-FUNCTION RELATIONS
     ME0036(A1,A2,A3,A4,A5,A6,A7,A8,A9,A10,A11,B1,B2,B3,B4,B5,B6,B7,B8,B9)
C
     THIS SUBROUTINE COMPUTES THE INPUT ANGLE AND OUTPUT ANGLE OR
     DISPLACEMENT CORRESPONDING TO THE PRECISION POINTS OF A FOURBAR
     LINKAGE OR A SLIDER-CRANK FUNCTION GENERATOR.  IT ALSO PROVIDES
     THE VALUES OF THE DEPENDENT VARIABLE Y1,Y2,Y3 AT THE
     PRECISION POINTS.
C
     CALLING PROGRAM REQUIREMENTS
C
     PROVIDE A SUBROUTINE FUNCT(X,Y) WHERE X IS THE INDEPENDENT
     VARIABLE OF THE FUNCTION TO BE GENERATED, AND Y IS THE DEPENDENT
     VARIABLE OF THE FUNCTION TO BE GENERATED.
C
     VARIABLES
C
     A1=VALUE OF THE INDEPENDENT VARIABLE X1 AT FIRST PRECISION POINT.
     A2=VALUE OF THE INDEPENDENT VARIABLE X2 AT SECOND PRECISION POINT.
     A3=VALUE OF THE INDEPENDENT VARIABLE X3 AT THIRD PRECISION POINT.
     A4=VALUE OF THE INDEPENDENT VARIABLE AT EXTREME LEFT OF INPUT DIAL.
     A5=VALUE OF THE INDEPENDENT VARIABLE AT EXTREME RIGHT OF INPUT DIAL.
     A6=VALUE OF DEPENDENT VARIABLE AT EXTREME LEFT OF OUTPUT SCALE.
     A7=VALUE OF DEPENDENT VARIABLE AT EXTREME RIGHT OF OUTPUT SCALE.
     A8=INPUT ANGLE CORRESPONDING TO A4, RAD.
     A9=INPUT ANGLE CORRESPONDING TO A5, RAD.
```

```
                  A10=OUTPUT ANGLE CORRESPONDING TO A6, RAD.
                  A11=OUTPUT ANGLE CORRESPONDING TO A7, RAD.
C
                  B1=INPUT ANGLE CORRESPONDING TO A1, RAD.
                  B2=INPUT ANGLE CORRESPONDING TO A2, RAD.
                  B3=INPUT ANGLE CORRESPONDING TO A3, RAD.
                  B4=OUTPUT ANGLE OF DISTANCE CORRESPONDING TO A1, RAD. OR IN.
                  B5=OUTPUT ANGLE OR DISTANCE CORRESPONDING TO A2, RAD. OR IN.
                  B6=OUTPUT ANGLE OR DISTANCE CORRESPONDING TO A3, RAD. OR IN.
                  B7=VALUE OF THE DEPENDENT VARIABLE Y1 CORRESPONDING TO A1
                  B8=VALUE OF THE DEPENDENT VARIABLE Y2 CORRESPONDING TO A2
                  B9=VALUE OF THE DEPENDENT VARIABLE Y3 CORRESPONDING TO A3.
```

CURVED BEAM TEE SECTION IN FLEXURE
ME0053 (A1, A2, A3, A4, A5, A6, A7, B1, B2, B3)

```
                  CURVED BEAM TEE SECTION IN FLEXURE
                  ME0053(A1,A2,A3,A4,A5,A6,A7,B1,B2,B3)
C
                  THIS SUBROUTINE CALCULATES THE BENDING STRESS AT THE INNER AND
                  OUTER FIBER OF A TEE-SECTION CURVED BEAM AND REPORTS THE RADIUS OF
                  CURVATURE OF THE CENTROIDAL LOCUS.
C
                  THE SECTION IS DIAGRAMMED AND DOCUMENTED IN "MECHANICAL ENGINEERING
                  DESIGN", SHIGLEY, P. 46.
C
                  CALLING PROGRAM REQUIREMENTS
C
                  NONE.
C
                  VARIABLES
C
                  A1=CURVED BEAM LOAD, POSITIVE LOAD PRODUCES INNER FIBER TENSION, LBF.
                  A2=RADIUS OF CURVATURE OF INNER FIBER, IN.
                  A3=DISTANCE BETWEEN CENTER OF CURVATURE OF BEAM FIBERS AND THE LINE
C                    OF ACTION OF FORCE A1, POSITIVE IF LINE OF ACTION DOES NOT
C                    INTERSECT RADIUS OF CURVATURE LINE SEGMENT WHEN THEY ARE
C                    PERPENDICULAR, IN.
                  A4=SECTION SIDTH AT INNER FIBER RADIUS, IN.
                  A5=SECTION WIDTH AT OUTER FIBER RADIUS, IN.
                  A6=THICKNESS IF CAP OF TEE, IN.
                  A7=THICKNESS OF STEM OF TEE, IN.
C
                  B1=NORMAL FLEXURE STRESS AT INNER FIBER, POSITIVE IF TENSION, PSI.
                  B2=NORMAL FLEXURE STRESS AT OUTER FIBER, POSITIVE IF TENSION, PSI.
                  B3=RADIUS OF CURVATURE OF CENTROIDAL LOCUS, IN.
```

ROOT FINDER
ROOT1 (I1, A2, A3, A4, B1, B2, B3, B4, J5, J6)

```
                  ROOT FINDER
                  ROOT1(I1,A2,A3,A4,B1,B2,B3,B4,J5,J6)
C
                  THIS SUBROUTINE DETERMINES THE ZERO PLACES OF A FUNCTION.  SINCE THE
                  SUBROUTINE DOES NOT UTILIZE ANY FUNCTION DERIVATIVES, IT CAN PERFORM
                  ROOTFINDING ON BOUNDED SINGLE-VALUED FUNCTIONS.  THE SUBROUTINE
                  REQUIRES SPECIFICATION OF THE PRESENT LIMITS OF THE INTERVAL OF
                  UNCERTAINTY, AND THE FRACTIONAL REDUCTION IN THE INTERVAL DESIRED.
C
                  IT RETURNS THE ABSCISSA OF THE ZERO PLACE (SMALLEST ROOT), NEW
                  LIMITS ON THE INTERVAL OF UNCERTAINTY, LOCALE OF NEXT HIGHER
                  ROOT, IF PRESENT, THE NUMBER OF ROOTS SUSPECTED, AND AN ERROR SIGNAL.
```

176

```
C                A CONVERGENCE MONITOR CAN BE PRINTED, IF DESIRED.
C
C                MORE THAN FIVE ROOTS IN THE INTERVAL COULD CONFUSE THE SUBROUTINE.
C
C                CALLING PROGRAM REQUIREMENTS
C
                 PROVIDE A SUBROUTINE EQUAT1(X,Y) WHICH WILL BE CALLED BY ROOT1.
                 EQUAT1 RETURNS AN ORDINATE Y FOR A TENDERED ABSCISSA X.
C
                 VARIABLES
C
                 I1=0 CONVERGENCE MONITOR DOES NOT PRINT.
                 I1=1 CONVERGENCE MONITOR WILL PRINT.
                 A2=INITIAL LOWER LIMIT OF INTERVAL OF UNCERTAINTY.
                 A3=INITIAL UPPER LIMIT OF INTERVAL OF UNCERTAINTY.
                 A4=FRACTIONAL REDUCTION IN INTERVAL OF UNCERTAINTY DESIRED.
                 B1=ABSCISSA OF SMALLEST ZERO PLACE OF FUNCTION EQUAT1.
                 B2=FINAL LOWER LIMIT OF INTERVAL OF UNCERTAINTY.
                 B3=FINAL UPPER LIMIT OF INTERVAL OF UNCERTAINTY.
                 B4=LOCALE OF NEXT LARGER ROOT, IF PRESENT.  IF ONLY ONE ROOT LIES
C                   IN THE INTERVAL, THIS VARIABLE WILL BE EQUAL TO B1.
                 J5=0 NO ROOTS IN THE INTERVAL OF UNCERTAINTY SPECIFIED.
                 J5=1 ONE ROOT IN THE INTERVAL OF UNCERTAINTY SPECIFIED.
                 J5=2 TWO ROOTS IN THE INTERVAL OF UNCERTAINTY SPECIFIED.
C                   .
C                   .
C                   .
                 J6=0 ERROR RETURN SIGNAL, NO ERROR.
                 J6=1 ERROR RETURN SIGNAL, DEFECTIVE CALL, MESSAGE PRINTED.
                 J6=2 ERROR RETURN SIGNAL, SUBROUTINE HIT A MAXIMUM FIVE TIMES.
                 J6=3 ERROR RETURN SIGNAL, EITHER EXACT ROOT FOUND OR FUNCTION
C                   HAS PLATEAU ON THE ABSCISSA, INVESTIGATE.
```

ASCENDING SORT OF COLUMN VECTOR
YASORT (I1, A2, A3)

```
                 ASCENDING SORT OF COLUMN VECTOR
                 YASORT(I1,A2,A3)
C
                 THIS SUBROUTINE WILL SCAN A COLUMN VECTOR AND ARRANGE IT SO THAT
                 THE FIRST ENTRY OF A3 IS THE LARGEST NUMBER PRESENT IN A3.  THE
                 COLUMN VECTOR A2 CAN BE USED FOR CORRESPONDING VALUES OF THE
                 A3-A2 PAIR.  THE LENGTH OF THE COLUMN VECTOR CANNOT EXCEED 100 ENTRIES.
C
C                CALLING PROGRAM REQUIREMENTS
C
C                PROVIDE A DIMENSION DECLARATION OF THE FOLLOWING FORM:
C
                 DIMENSION A2(100),A3(100)
C
C                VARIABLES
C
                 I1=NUMBER OF ENTRIES IN COLUMN VECTOR TO BE ORDERED (NOT MORE THAN 100).
                 A2=COLUMN VECTOR OF ASSOCIATED VALUES TO A3.
                 A3=COLUMN VECTOR TO BE ARRANGED FROM LARGEST FIRST TO SMALLEST LAST.
```

PENALTY MERIT ORDINATE SUBROUTINE
PENAL (I1, A2, A3, B1)

```
                 PENALTY MERIT ORDINATE SUBROUTINE
                 PENAL(I1,A2,A3,B1)
```

```
C
        THIS SUBROUTINE SUBSTITUTES A MERIT SURFACE OF NEGATIVE
        ORDINATE AND HAVING SLOPES APPROPRIATE TO LEAD A GRADIENT
        SEARCH BACK INTO FEASIBLE SPACE WITH UP TO NINE INDEPENDENT VARIABLES.
C
        CALLING PROGRAM REQUIREMENTS
C
        PROVIDE A DIMENSION DECLARATION AS FOLLOWS:
C
        DIMENSION A2(9),A3(9)
C
        VARIABLES
C
        I1=NUMBER OF INDEPENDENT VARIABLES IN MERIT HYPERSPACE.
        A2=COORDINATES OF A POINT IN FEASIBLE SPACE, COLUMN VECTOR.
        A3=TENDERED COORDINATES, COLUMN VECTOR.
        B1=PENALTY ORDINATE CORRESPONDING TO TENDERED COORDINATES, A3.
```

a p p e n d i x

3

LISTINGS OF
IOWA CADET SUBROUTINES
USED IN
ILLUSTRATIVE PROBLEMS
IN CHAPTER 5

SUBROUTINE COMB1

```
      SUBROUTINE COMB1(K,XL,XR,F,YBIG,XBIG,Y,X,XL1,XR1,N)
      DIMENSION X(2001),Y(2001)
      GO TO 100
  111 IF(K)21,21,22
   22 WRITE(3,23)
   23 FORMAT('1CONVERGENCE MONITOR SUBROUTINE COMB1',//,
     1'      ORDINATE           ABSCISSA           EXTREME',//)
   21 N=0
      YBIG=-10.E50
      XN=2./F-1.
      NN=XN+1.5
      DELTA=(XR-XL)/XN
      X(1)=XL
      IF(NN-2000)30,30,31
   31 NN=2000
   30 DO 20 I=1,NN
      XX=X(I)
      CALL MERIT1(XX,YY)
      N=N+1
      Y(I)=YY
      IF(YBIG-YY)1,2,2
    1 YBIG=YY
      XBIG=X(I)
    2 IF(K)7,7,25
   25 WRITE(3,26)Y(I),X(I),YBIG.
   26 FORMAT(3(1X,E15.7))
    7 X(I+1)=X(I)+DELTA
   20 CONTINUE
      XL1=XBIG-DELTA
      XR1=XBIG+DELTA
      IF(XR1-XR)4,4,3
    3 XR1=XR
    4 IF(XL1-XL)8,9,9
    8 XL1=XL
    9 IF(K)5,5,6
    6 WRITE(3,27)YBIG,XBIG,XL,XR,XL1,XR1,F,N
   27 FORMAT(//,
     1' EXTREME ORDINATE FOUND IN EXHAUSTIVE SEARCH ..........',E15.7,/,
```

```
2' ABSCISSA CORRESPONDING TO EXTREME ORDINATE ............',E15.7,/,
3' ORIGINAL LOWER BOUND ON INTERVAL OF UNCERTAINTY .......',E15.7,/,
4' ORIGINAL UPPER BOUND ON INTERVAL OF UNCERTAINTY .......',E15.7,/,
5' FINAL LOWER BOUND ON INTERVAL OF UNCERTAINTY ..........',E15.7,/,
6' FINAL UPPER BOUND ON INTERVAL OF UNCERTAINTY ..........',E15.7,/,
7' FRACTIONAL REDUCTION IN INTERVAL OF UNCERTAINTY .......',E15.7,/,
8' NUMBER OF FUNCTION EVALUATION EXPENDED ................',I15)
5 RETURN
C
C     ..... PROTECTION .....
C
100 IF(K)102,101,101
101 IF(K-1)104,104,102
102 WRITE(3,103)K
103 FORMAT(' *****ERROR MESSAGE SUBROUTINE COMB1*****',/,
  1'        I1,',',I15,' IS NOT 0 OR 1')
    RETURN
104 IF(XR-XL)105,105,107
105 WRITE(3,106)XL,XR
106 FORMAT(' *****ERROR MESSAGE SUBROUTINE COMB1*****',/,
  1'        A2,',',E15.7,' NOT SMALLER THAN A3,',E15.7)
    RETURN
107 IF(F-0.001)109,108,108
108 IF(F-1.)111,109,109
109 WRITE(3,110)F
110 FORMAT(' *****ERROR MESSAGE SUBROUTINE COMB1*****',/,
  1'        A4,'E15.7,' DOES NOT LIE BETWEEN 0.001 AND 1.')
    RETURN
    END
```

SUBROUTINE GOLD1

```
    SUBROUTINE GOLD1(K,XL,XR,F,YBIG,XBIG,XL1,XR1,N)
    GO TO 100
C
C     ..... PRINT CONVERGENCE MONITOR HEADINGS IF REQUIRED .....
C
111 IF(K)32,31,32
 32 WRITE(3,33)
 33 FORMAT('1CONVERGENCE MONITOR SUBROUTINE GOLD1',//,
  1'     N        Y1           Y2           X1           X2'//)
C
C     ..... INITIALIZE .....
C
 31 N=0
    XLEFT=XL
    XRIGHT=XR
 13 SPAN=XR-XL
    DELTA=ABS(SPAN)
 14 X1=XL+0.381966*DELTA
    X2=XL+0.618034*DELTA
    CALL MERIT1(X1,Y1)
    CALL MERIT1(X2,Y2)
    N=N+2
C
C     ..... PRINT CONVERGENCE MONITOR IF REQUIRED .....
C
 3 IF(K)34,9,34
 34 WRITE(3,35)N,Y1,Y2,X1,X2
 35 FORMAT(I5,4(1X,E15.7))
C
C     ..... IS SEARCH COMPLETE? .....
C
 9 IF(ABS(XL-XR)-ABS(F*SPAN))4,4,8
C
C     ..... CONTINUE GOLDEN SECTION SEARCH .....
C
 8 DELTA=0.618034*DELTA
    IF(Y1-Y2)1,10,2
 1 XL=X1
    X1=X2
```

180

```
        Y1=Y2
        X2=XL+0.618034*DELTA
        CALL MERIT1(X2,Y2)
        N=N+1
        GO TO 3
      2 XR=X2
        Y2=Y1
        X2=X1
        X1=XL+0.381966*DELTA
        CALL MERIT1(X1,Y1)
        N=N+1
        GO TO 3
      4 IF(Y2-Y1)5,5,6
      5 YBIG=Y1
        XBIG=X1
        GO TO 7
      6 YBIG=Y2
        XBIG=X2
      7 XL1=XL
        XR1=XR
        GO TO 39
     10 XL=X1
        XR=X2
        DELTA=XR-XL
        GO TO 14
C
C
C       ..... IF CONVERGENCE MONITOR PRINT REQUIRED, PRINT SUMMARY .....
C
     39 IF(K)40,40,37
     37 WRITE(3,38)XLEFT,XRIGHT,F,YBIG,XBIG,XL1,XR1,N
     38 FORMAT(//,
       1' LEFTHAND ABSCISSA OF INTERVAL OF UNCERTAINTY ..........',E15.7,/,
       2' RIGHTHAND ABSCISSA OF INTERVAL OF UNCERTAINTY .........',E15.7,/,
       3' FRACTIONAL REDUCTION OF INTERVAL OF UNCERTAINTY .......',E15.7,/,
       4' EXTREME ORDINATE DISCOVERED DURING SEARCH .............',E15.7,/,
       5' ABSCISSA OF EXTREME ORDINATE ..........................',E15.7,/,
       6' NEW LEFTHAND ABSCISSA OF INTERVAL OF UNCERTAINTY ......',E15.7,/,
       7' NEW RIGHTHAND ABSCISSA OF INTERVAL OF UNCERTAINTY .....',E15.7,/,
       8' NUMBER OF FUNCTION EVALUATIONS EXPENDED IN SEARCH ....',I15,//)
     40 XL=XLEFT
        XR=XRIGHT
        RETURN
C
C
C       ..... PROTECTION .....
C
    100 IF(K)102,101,101
    101 IF(K-1)104,104,102
    102 WRITE(3,103)K
    103 FORMAT(' *****ERROR MESSAGE SUBROUTINE GOLD1*****',/,
       1'        I1,',',I15,' IS NOT 0 OR 1')
        RETURN
    104 IF(XR-XL)105,107,107
    105 WRITE(3,106)XL,XR
    106 FORMAT(' *****ERROR MESSAGE SUBROUTINE GOLD1*****',/,
       1'        A2,',E15.7,' NOT SMALLER THAN A3,',E15.7)
        RETURN
    107 IF(F)109,109,108
    108 IF(F-1.)111,109,109
    109 WRITE(3,110)F
    110 FORMAT(' *****ERROR MESSAGE SUBROUTINE GOLD1*****',/,
       1'        A4,',E15.7,' DOES NOT LIE BETWEEN 0. AND 1.')
        RETURN
        END
```

SUBROUTINE GRAD4

```
        SUBROUTINE GRAD4(N,NC,NS,DELTA,DMULT,F,EPS,XL,XR,Y,X,K,N1,P,Q)
C
C       DELTA=INITIAL EXPLORATION STEPSIZE
C       DMULT=STEPSIZE GROWTH MULTIPLIER
C       EPS=SURVEY PATTERN INCREMENT
```

181

```
C        F=FRACTIONAL REDUCTION IN INTERVAL OF UNCERTAINTY DESIRED
C        K=1   LARGEST ORDINATE EXTREME
C         =2   MAXIMUM ORDINATE EXTREME
C         =3   PLATEAU EXTREME
C        N=NUMBER OF INDEPENDENT VARIABLES
C        NC=CONVERGENCE MONITOR PRINT EVERY NC-TH EVALUATION
C        NS=1   START SEARCH CENTRALLY
C          =2   START SEARCH LOWER CORNER
C          =3   START SEARCH UPPER CORNER
C          =4   START SEARCH AT POSITION X, COLUMN VECTOR
C        N1=NUMBER OF MERIT FUNCTION EVALUATIONS
C        N2=COUNTING VARIABLE
C        N5=COUNTING VARIABLE
C        XL=LOWER BOUND OF SEARCH INTERVAL
C        XR=UPPER BOUND OF SEARCH INTERVAL
C        Y=ORDINATE OF EXTREME OF MERIT FUNCTION
C        X=ABSCISSAS OF EXTREME OF MERIT FUNCTION
         DIMENSION XL(9),XR(9),SPANX(9),X(9),P(9),YY(9),DELX(9),Q(9),SAVEX(
        19)
         N1=0
         N2=0
         NN=0
         DO 3 I=1,N
         SPANX(I)=XR(I)-XL(I)
       3 CONTINUE
C
C        ..... IS CONVERGENCE MONITOR REQUIRED .....
C
         IF(NC)2,2,1
       1 WRITE(3,5)
       5 FORMAT('1CONVERGENCE MONITOR SUBROUTINE GRAD4',//,
        1'     N1        DELTA       Y        X(1)      X(2)      X(3)        X(
        24)      X(5)      X(6)      X(7)      X(8)  BIGGEST Y',//)
C
C        ..... SEARCH START SPECIFICATION .....
C
         GO TO (200,201,202,2),NS
     200 DO 33 I=1,N
         X(I)=(XL(I)+XR(I))/2.
      33 CONTINUE
         GO TO 2
     201 DO 34 I=1,N
         X(I)=XL(I)
      34 CONTINUE
         GO TO 2
     202 DO 35 I=1,N
         X(I)=XR(I)
      35 CONTINUE
       2 YOLD=-10.**10.
         SAVEY=YOLD
C
C        ..... CONDUCT LOCAL SURVEY .....
C
       6 SUM=0.0
         IF(N1-100*N)503,503,504
     504 WRITE(3,505)
     505 FORMAT(//,' ***** ERROR MESSAGE SUBROUTINE GRAD4 *****',//,
        1' NUMBER OF FUNCTION EVALUATIONS EXCEEDED 100 TIMES THE NUMBER',/,
        2' OF INDEPENDENT VARIABLES. THERE MAY BE A MERIT4 HYPERSURFACE',/,
        3' COMPLEXITY RESPONSIBLE FOR THIS. RECOMMEND INVESTIGATION.',/,
        4' SUBROUTINE RETURN IS MADE ARBITRARILY AT THIS POINT IN ',/,
        5' SEARCH. STATE OF SEARCH IS INDICATED BY RETURNED VALUES.',/,
        6' TO CONTINUE FROM THIS POINT CALL GRAD4 AGAIN EXERCISING ',/,
        7' SEARCH OPTION 4.',/)
         K=4
         Y=SAVEY
         DO 506 I=1,N
         X(I)=SAVEX(I)
     506 CONTINUE
         GO TO 116
     503 J=0
         N5=0
         CALL MERIT4(X,Y)
```

182

```
      N1=N1+1
      IF(SAVEY-Y)500,502,502
  500 SAVEY=Y
      DO 501 I=1,N
      SAVEX(I)=X(I)
  501 CONTINUE
  502 DO 10 I=1,N
      X(I)=X(I)+EPS
      CALL MERIT4(X,YYY)
      N1=N1+1
      YY(I)=YYY
      P(I)=(YY(I)-Y)/EPS
      SUM=SUM+P(I)*P(I)
      X(I)=X(I)-EPS
   10 CONTINUE
      X(9)=SAVEY
C
C     ..... CONVERGENCE MONITOR PRINT IF REQUIRED .....
C
      IF(NC)4,22,4
    4 N2=N2+1
      IF(N2-NC)22,23,22
   23 WRITE(3,7)N1,DELTA,Y,(X(I),I=1,9)
    7 FORMAT(I7,3X,11E10.3)
      N2=0
C
C     ..... WAS LAST STEP A CLIMBING STEP ?????
C
   22 IF(YOLD-Y)100,101,101
C
C     ..... LAST STEP WAS A CLIMBING STEP, INCREMENT .....
C
  100 DELTA=DELTA*DMULT
  109 IF(SUM)108,110,108
C
C     ..... POSSIBLE PLATEAU, DECREASE DELTA .....
C
  110 IF(NN)431,430,431
C
C     ..... PERTURB ONCE TO DETECT FALSE PLATEAU .....
C     ..... BEING CAREFUL TO STAY WITHIN BOUNDS .....
C
  430 X(1)=X(1)+EPS
      IF(X(1)-XR(1))432,432,433
  433 X(1)=X(1)-2.*EPS
  432 GO TO 6
C
C     ..... PROBABLY A PLATEAU, DECREASE DELTA .....
C
  431 J7=0
      DO 111 I=1,N
      IF(ABS(DELTA)-ABS(F*SPANX(I)/2.))113,112,112
  112 J7=J7+1
  113 DELX(I)=EPS
  111 CONTINUE
C
C     ..... IS DELTA SMALL ENOUGH TO TERMINATE SEARCH ?????
C
      IF(J7)117,116,117
C
C     ..... CONTAIN NEXT SURVEY POINT WITHIN BOUNDS .....
C
  108 DENOM=SQRT(SUM)
      DO 20 I=1,N
      DELX(I)=P(I)*DELTA/DENOM
      X(I)=X(I)+DELX(I)
   20 CONTINUE
      YOLD=Y
      DO 36 I=1,N
      IF(X(I)-XL(I))102,103,103
  102 N5=N5+1
      X(I)=XL(I)
  103 IF(X(I)-XR(I))105,105,104
```

```
      104 N5=N5+1
          X(I)=XR(I)
      105 CONTINUE
       36 CONTINUE
          GO TO 6
C
C         ..... LAST STEP WAS NOT A CLIMBING STEP. CHECK PRESENT
C         ..... INTERVAL OF UNCERTAINTY WITH REQUIREMENTS .....
C
      101 J6=0
          YOLD=SAVEY
          Y=SAVEY
          DO 421 I=1,N
          X(I)=SAVEX(I)
      421 CONTINUE
          DO 42 I=1,N
          IF(ABS(DELTA   )-ABS(F*SPANX(I)/2.))130,131,131
      131 J6=J6+1
      130 CONTINUE
       42 CONTINUE
C
C         ..... IS INTERVAL OF UNCERTAINTY SUFFICIENTLY REDUCED .....
C
          IF(J6)117,116,117
C
C         ..... INTERVAL OF UNCERTAINTY NOT SUFFICIENTLY REDUCED.
C         ..... DECREMENT AND SEARCH AGAIN .....
C
      117 DELTA=DELTA/10.
          GO TO 109
C
C         ..... INTERVAL OF UNCERTAINTY SUFFICIENTLY REDUCED.
C         ..... OBTAIN A FINAL SURVEY .....
C
      116 IF(Y-SAVEY)511,513,513
      511 Y=SAVEY
          DO 512 I=1,N
          X(I)=SAVEX(I)
      512 CONTINUE
      513 CALL MERIT4(X,Y)
          N1=N1+1
      426 DO 40 I=1,N
          B=F*SPANX(I)/2.
          X(I)=X(I)+B
          CALL MERIT4(X,YPLUS)
          N1=N1+1
          P(I)=(YPLUS-Y)/B
          X(I)=X(I)-B
       40 CONTINUE
          DO 400 I=1,N
          X(I)=X(I)-B
          CALL MERIT4(X,YMINUS)
          N1=N1+1
          Q(I)=(Y-YMINUS)/B
          X(I)=X(I)+B
      400 CONTINUE
          IF(4-K)510,151,510
      510 N8=0
          N9=0
          DO 401 I=1,N
          IF(P(I))404,402,403
      404 N8=N8+1
          GO TO 403
      402 N9=N9+1
      403 CONTINUE
      401 CONTINUE
          DO 410 I=1,N
          IF(Q(I))407,406,405
      405 N8=N8+1
          GO TO 407
      406 N9=N9+1
      407 CONTINUE
      410 CONTINUE
```

184

```
C
C      ..... DO WE HAVE A MAXIMUM, AN EXTREME, OR A PLATEAU .....
C
       IF(N9-2*N)411,182,411
   411 IF(N8-2*N)183,123,183
C
C      ..... WE HAVE A MAXIMUM .....
C
   123 K=2
       GO TO 151
C
C      ..... WE HAVE A PLATEAU .....
C
   182 K=3
       GO TO 151
C
C      ..... WE HAVE AN EXTREME .....
C
   183 K=1
   151 CALL MERIT4(X,Y)
       N1=N1+1
       IF(NC)124,125,124
   124 WRITE(3,24)Y,N1,DELTA,DMULT,EPS,F,K
    24 FORMAT(/,
      1' LARGEST MERIT ORDINATE ................................',E15.8,/,
      2' NUMBER OF FUNCTION EVALUATIONS ........................',I15,/,
      3' FINAL SEARCH STEPSIZE .................................',F15.8,/,
      4' STEPSIZE GROWTH MULTIPLIER ............................',F15.8,/,
      5' SURVEY PATTERN INCREMENT ..............................',E15.8,/,
      6' FRACTIONAL REDUCTION IN INTERVAL OF UNCERTAINTY .......',F15.8,/,
      7' SPECIE OF LARGEST MERIT ORDINATE ......................',I15,/)
       JJ=0
       DO 41 I=1,N
       JJ=JJ+1
       Z=X(I)
       ZZ=P(I)
       ZZZ=Q(I)
       WRITE(3,128)JJ,Z,JJ,ZZ,JJ,ZZZ
   128 FORMAT(' X(',I3,')=',E15.5,5X,'P(',I3,')='E15.5,
      15X,'Q(',I3,')=',E15.5)
    41 CONTINUE
       GO TO(184,186,188),K
   184 WRITE(3,185)
   185 FORMAT(/,' MERIT EXTREME IS AN EXTREMUM')
   125 RETURN
   186 WRITE(3,187)
   187 FORMAT(/,' MERIT EXTREME IS A MAXIMUM')
       RETURN
   188 WRITE(3,189)
   189 FORMAT(/,' MERIT EXTREME IS A PLATEAU')
       RETURN
       END
```

SUBROUTINE GRID4

```
       SUBROUTINE GRID4(N,MPRINT,XL,XR,F,R,Y,X,XLOW,XHIGH,NN)
C
C      GRID SEARCH
C
C      THIS SUBROUTINE EXERCISES A GRID SEARCH IN A MERIT HYPERSURFACE
C      OF UP TO EIGHT DIMENSIONS BY CALLING SUBROUTINE MERIT4(X,Y)
C
C      CALLING PROGRAM REQUIREMENTS
C
C      PROVIDE A DIMENSION STATEMENT AS FOLLOWS;
C
C          DIMENSION XL(9),XR(9),XLOW(9),XHIGH(9),X(9)
C
C      NOMENCLATURE
```

```
C     N=NUMBER OF INDEPENDENT VARIABLES
C     MPRINT=0 CONVERGENCE MONITOR DOES NOT PRINT
C           =1 CONVERGENCE MONITOR WILL PRINT
C     XL=ORIGINAL LOWER EXTREMITY OF INTERVAL OF UNCERTAINTY
C     XR=ORIGINAL UPPER EXTREMITY OF INTERVAL OF UNCERTAINTY
C     F=FRACTIONAL REDUCTION IN INTERVAL OF UNCERTAINTY DESIRED
C     R=FRACTIONAL GRID REDUCTION UTILIZED
C     Y=EXTREME ORDINATE TO MERIT SURFACE DISCOVERED BY GRID SEARCH
C     X=COLUMN VECTOR OF ABSCISSAS CORRESPONDING TO Y
C     XLOW=FINAL LOWER EXTREMITY OF INTERVAL OF UNCERTAINTY
C     XHIGH=FINAL UPPER EXTREMITY OF INTERVAL OF UNCERTAINTY
C     NN=NUMBER OF FUNCTION EVALUATIONS EXPENDED IN GRID SEARCH
C
      DIMENSION XL(9),XR(9),X(9),XLOW(9),XHIGH(9),CENTER(9),SAVEX(9)
C
C     ..... PROTECTION .....
C
      IF(N-8)11,11,12
   12 WRITE(3,13)N
   13 FORMAT(' *****ERROR MESSAGE SUBROUTINE GRID4*****'/,
     1'        I1='I3' GREATER THAN 8.')
      RETURN
   11 IF(F-1.)14,14,15
   15 WRITE(3,16)F
   16 FORMAT(' *****ERROR MESSAGE SUBROUTINE GRID4*****',/,
     1'        A5='E15.8' GREATER THAN 1.')
      RETURN
   14 DO 50 I=1,N
      IF(XR(I)-XL(I))51,51,50
   51 XRR=XR(I)
      XLL=XL(I)
      WRITE(3,52)I,XLL,I,XRR
   52 FORMAT(' *****ERROR MESSAGE SUBROUTINE GRID4*****',/,
     1'        A3('I1')='E15.8'GREATER THAN A4('I1')='E15.8)
      RETURN
   50 CONTINUE
      IF(R-2./3.)53,54,54
   54 IF(R-1.)58,58,53
   53 WRITE(3,55)R
   55 FORMAT(' *****ERROR MESSAGE SUBROUTINE GRID4*****',/,
     1'        A6=',E15.8,' DOES NOT LIE BETWEEN 2/3 AND 1.')
      RETURN
C
C     ..... INITIALIZE .....
C
   58 NN=0
      SIDE=1.
      IF(MPRINT)1,3,1
    1 WRITE(3,2)
    2 FORMAT('1CONVERGENCE MONITOR SUBROUTINE GRID4',//,
     1'    NN    SIDE      Y      X(1)      X(2)      X(3)      X(4)
     2  X(5)      X(6)      X(7)      X(8)      BIGGEST Y'/)
    3 DO 4 I=1,N
      CENTER(I)=0.5
    4 CONTINUE
      JJ=0
C
C     ..... DETERMINE CENTRAL MERIT ORDINATE .....
C
      CALL UNNORM(N,XL,XR,CENTER)
      CALL REGION(N,XL,XR,CENTER)
      CALL MERIT4(CENTER,YMID)
      NN=NN+1
      CALL NORMAL(N,XL,XR,CENTER)
      DO 5 I=1,N
      XLOW(I)=0.
    5 CONTINUE
      YBIG=YMID
C
C     ..... DETERMINE MERIT ORDINATES IN GRID, NOTE LARGEST .....
C
   10 STEP=SIDE/3.
```

```
C
C       ..... AT EVERY GRID REDUCTION OCCASION, ALTERNATE BETWEEN A    .....
C       ..... SQUARE SURVEY PATTERN AND A STAR SURVEY PATTERN,         .....
C       ..... DEPENDING ON ODDNESS OR EVENNESS OF JJ.                  .....
C
        IF(JJ/2*2-JJ)600,510,600
C
C       ..... SQUARE GRID SURVEY.                                      .....
C
  510 DO 500 I=1,N
      X(I)=XLOW(I)
  500 CONTINUE
      GO TO (71,72,73,74,75,76,77,78),N
   78 DO 178 I8=1,2
      X(8)=X(8)+STEP
   77 DO 177 I7=1,2
      X(7)=X(7)+STEP
   76 DO 176 I6=1,2
      X(6)=X(6)+STEP
   75 DO 175 I5=1,2
      X(5)=X(5)+STEP
   74 DO 174 I4=1,2
      X(4)=X(4)+STEP
   73 DO 173 I3=1,2
      X(3)=X(3)+STEP
   72 DO 172 I2=1,2
      X(2)=X(2)+STEP
   71 DO 171 I1=1,2
      X(1)=X(1)+STEP
      CALL UNNORM(N,XL,XR,X)
      CALL REGION(N,XL,XR,X)
      CALL MERIT4(X,Y1)
      NN=NN+1
      CALL NORMAL(N,XL,XR.X)

      IF(Y1-YBIG)171,171,6
    6 YBIG=Y1
      DO 30 K=1,N
      SAVEX(K)=X(K)
   30 CONTINUE
  171 CONTINUE
      X(1)=XLOW(1)
      IF(N-1)501,501,172
  172 CONTINUE
      X(2)=XLOW(2)
      IF(N-2)501,501,173
  173 CONTINUE
      X(3)=XLOW(3)
      IF(N-3)501,501,174
  174 CONTINUE
      X(4)=XLOW(4)
      IF(N-4)501,501,175
  175 CONTINUE
      X(5)=XLOW(5)
      IF(N-5)501,501,176
  176 CONTINUE
      X(6)=XLOW(6)
      IF(N-6)501,501,177
  177 CONTINUE
      X(7)=XLOW(7)
      IF(N-7)501,501,178
  178 CONTINUE
      X(8)=XLOW(8)
      GO TO 501
C
C       ..... STAR SURVEY PATTERN.....
C
  600 DO 601 I=1,N
      X(I)=CENTER(I)
  601 CONTINUE
      DO 620 I=1,N
      X(I)=CENTER(I)+STEP
      CALL UNNORM(N,XL,XR,X)
      CALL REGION(N,XL,XR,X)
```

```
          CALL MERIT4(X,YPLUS)
          NN=NN+1
          CALL NORMAL(N,XL,XR,X)
          IF(YPLUS-YBIG)611,611,610
     610  YBIG=YPLUS
          DO 612 K=1,N
          SAVEX(K)=X(K)
     612  CONTINUE
     611  X(I)=CENTER(I)-STEP
          CALL UNNORM(N,XL,XR,X)
          CALL REGION(N,XL,XR,X)
          CALL MERIT4(X,YMINUS)
          NN=NN+1
          CALL NORMAL(N,XL,XR,X)
          IF(YMINUS-YBIG)614,614,613
     613  YBIG=YMINUS
          DO 615 K=1,N
          SAVEX(K)=X(K)
     615  CONTINUE
     614  CONTINUE
          X(I)=CENTER(I)
     620  CONTINUE
C
C         ..... CHECK TO SEE IF GRID SIZE IS SMALL ENOUGH .....
C
     501  JJ=JJ+1
          IF(F-SIDE)32,45,45
C
C         ..... GRID SIZE NOT SUFFICIENTLY SMALL, SELECT LARGEST .....
C         ..... ORDINATE LOCATION FROM GRID AND CENTER NEXT       .....
C         ..... SMALLER GRID ABOUT THIS POINT.                    .....
C
      32  IF(YBIG-YMID)44,44,33
      33  YMID=YBIG
          DO 40 K=1,N
          CENTER(K)=SAVEX(K)
      40  CONTINUE
C
C         ..... IF PRINTING OF CONVERGENCE MONITOR IS REQUIRED, DO SO .....
C
      44  IF(MPRINT)41,43,41
      41  CALL UNNORM(N,XL,XR,CENTER)
          WRITE(3,42)NN,SIDE,YMID,(CENTER(I),I=1,8),YBIG
      42  FORMAT(1X,I5,11E10.3)
          CALL NORMAL(N,XL,XR,CENTER)
C
C         ..... REDUCE SIZE OF GRID AND CONTINUE SEARCH .....
C
      43  SIDE=SIDE*R
          DO 502 I=1,N
          XLOW(I)=CENTER(I)-SIDE/2.
          XHIGH(I)=CENTER(I)+SIDE/2.
     502  CONTINUE
          CALL UNNORM(N,XL,XR,XLOW)
          CALL UNNORM(N,XL,XR,XHIGH)
          CALL REGION(N,XL,XR,XLOW)
          CALL REGION(N,XL,XR,XHIGH)
          CALL NORMAL(N,XL,XR,XLOW)
          CALL NORMAL(N,XL,XR,XHIGH)
          GO TO 10
C
C         ..... GRID SIZE SUFFICIENTLY SMALL, EXIT FROM SEARCH .....
C
      45  CALL UNNORM(N,XL,XR,SAVEX)
          CALL REGION(N,XL,XR,SAVEX)
          CALL MERIT4(SAVEX,Y)
          NN=NN+1
          CALL NORMAL(N,XL,XR,SAVEX)
          DO 46 K=1,N
          X(K)=SAVEX(K)
          IF(CENTER(K)-SAVEX(K))60,61,62
      60  XLOW(K)=CENTER(K)
```

```
      XHIGH(K)=CENTER(K)+SIDE/2.
      GO TO 46
   61 XLOW(K)=CENTER(K)-SIDE/2.
      XHIGH(K)=CENTER(K)+SIDE/2.
      GO TO 46
   62 XLOW(K)=CENTER(K)-SIDE/2.
      XHIGH(K)=CENTER(K)
   46 CONTINUE
      CALL UNNORM(N,XL,XR,XLOW)
      CALL UNNORM(N,XL,XR,XHIGH)
      CALL UNNORM(N,XL,XR,SAVEX)
      CALL UNNORM(N,XL,XR,X)
      IF(MPRINT)47,49,47
   47 FF=SIDE
      WRITE(3,48)Y,NN,FF
   48 FORMAT(/,
     1' LARGEST MERIT ORDINATE FOUND DURING SEARCH ...........',E15.8,/,
     2' NUMBER OF FUNCTION EVALUATIONS USED DURING SEARCH ....',I15,/,
     3' FRACTIONAL REDUCTION IN INTERVAL OF UNCERTAINTY EXTANT',E15.8//)
      DO 100 I=1,N
      X1=XLOW(I)
      X2=SAVEX(I)
      X3=XHIGH(I)
      WRITE(3,101)I,X1,I,X2,I,X3
  101 FORMAT(1X,'XLOW(',I1,')=',E15.8,2X,
     1'X(',I1,')=',E15.8,2X,'XHIGH(',I1,')=',E15.8)
  100 CONTINUE
   49 RETURN
      END




      SUBROUTINE NORMAL(N,XL,XR,XNORM)
      DIMENSION XL(9),XR(9),XNORM(9)
      DO 1 I=1,N
      XNORM(I)=(XNORM(I)-XL(I))/(XR(I)-XL(I))
    1 CONTINUE
      RETURN
      END




      SUBROUTINE UNNORM(N,XL,XR,EX)
      DIMENSION XL(9),XR(9),EX(9)
      DO 1 I=1,N
      EX(I)=XL(I)+EX(I)*(XR(I)-XL(I))
    1 CONTINUE
      RETURN
      END




      SUBROUTINE REGION(N,XL,XR,X)
      DIMENSION XL(9),XR(9),X(9)
      DO 4 I=1,N
      IF(XL(I)-X(I))2,2,1
    1 X(I)=XL(I)
      GO TO 4
    2 IF(XR(I)-X(I))3,4,4
    3 X(I)=XR(I)
    4 CONTINUE
      RETURN
      END
```

SUBROUTINE ME0034

```
      SUBROUTINE ME0034(I,A,RHO1,RHO2,RHO3,RHO4,B)

C
C         FOURBAR FUNCTION GENERATOR INPUT-OUTPUT ANGLE PROGRAM
C         ME0034(I1,A2,A3,A4,A5,A6,B1)                            MISCHKE
C              THIS SUBROUTINE ACCEPTS LINKAGE CONFIGURATION, INPUT DIAL
C              ANGLE, LINK LENGTHS, AND RETURNS OUTPUT DIAL ANGLE(CW).
C         CALLING PROGRAM REQUIREMENTS
C              NONE
C         CALL LIST VARIABLES
C              I1=1 UNCROSSED TOP CONFIGURATION
C                =2 CROSSED TOP CONFIGRUATION
C                =3 UNCROSSED BOTTOM CONFIGURATION
C                =4 CROSSED BOTTOM CONFIGURATION
C                =5 ERROR SIGNAL, I1 OUT OF RANGE
C                =6 ERROR SIGNAL, A2 GREATER THAN TWO PI RADIANS
C                =7 ERROR SIGNAL, A3,A4,A5,OR A6 NEGATIVE
C              A2=INPUT ANGLE ALPHA, RAD MEASURED CLOCKWISE
C              A3=CRANK VECTOR LENGTH
C              A4=COUPLER VECTOR LENGTH
C              A5=FOLLOWER VECTOR LENGTH
C              A6=GROUNDED VECTOR LENGTH
C              B1=OUTPUT DIAL ANGLE BETA, RAD MEASURED CLOCKWISE
C
      IF(I)10,10,12
   12 IF(I-4)9,9,10
   10 WRITE(3,11)I
   11 FORMAT(' *****ERROR MESSAGE SUBROUTINE ME0034*****',/,
     1' VALUE OF I1,',I2,', LIES OUTSIDE ALLOWABLE RANGE 1 THRU 4.')
      I=5
      RETURN
    9 IF(A-2.*3.1416)15,15,13
   13 WRITE(3,14)A
   14 FORMAT(' *****ERROR MESSAGE SUBROUTINE ME0034*****',/,
     1' VALUE OF A2,',E15.7,', EXCEEDS TWO PI RADIANS.')
      I=6
      RETURN
   15 IF(RHO1)16,17,17
   17 IF(RHO2)16,18,18
   18 IF(RHO3)16,19,19
   19 IF(RHO4)16,20,20
   16 WRITE(3,21)RHO1,RHO2,RHO3,RHO4
   21 FORMAT(' *****ERROR MESSAGE SUBROUTINE ME0034*****',/,
     1' ONE OR MORE OF A3,A4,A5,OR A6,',4(1X,E10.3),', NEGATIVE.')
      I=7
      RETURN
   20 GO TO(1,1,2,2),I
    1 RHO=SQRT(ABS(RHO1*RHO1+RHO4*RHO4+2.*RHO1*RHO4*COS(A)))
      GO TO 3
    2 RHO=SQRT(ABS(RHO1*RHO1+RHO4*RHO4-2.*RHO1*RHO4*COS(A)))
    3 ARG1=RHO1*SIN(A)/RHO
      ARG2=(RHO*RHO+RHO4*RHO4-RHO1*RHO1)/(2.*RHO*RHO4)
      CALL AQUAD(ARG1,ARG2,GAMMA)
      ARG4=(RHO*RHO+RHO3*RHO3-RHO2*RHO2)/(2.*RHO*RHO3)
      PSI=ATAN(SQRT(ABS(1.-ARG4*ARG4))/ABS(ARG4))
      IF(ARG4)4,5,5
    4 PSI=3.14159  -PSI
    5 GO TO(6,7,8,30),I
    6 B=PSI+GAMMA
      GO TO 31
    7 B=3.14159  -PSI+GAMMA
      GO TO 31
    8 B=3.14159  -PSI-GAMMA
      GO TO 31
```

```
30 B=PSI-GAMMA
31 IF(B)32,33,33
32 B=B+2.*3.14159
34 RETURN
33 IF(B-2.*3.14159   )34,35,35
35 B=B-2.*3.14159
   RETURN
   END




   SUBROUTINE AQUAD(S,C,A)
   A=ATAN(ABS(S/C))
   IF(S)2,1,1
 1 IF(C)3,4,4
 3 A=3.14159-A
 4 RETURN
 2 IF(C)5,5,6
 5 A=3.14159+A
   RETURN
 6 A=2.*3.14159-A
   RETURN
   END
```

SUBROUTINE ME0035

```
   SUBROUTINE ME0035(A1,B1,A2,B2,A3,B3,RHO1,RHO2,RHO3,RHO4,J)
C  FOURBAR FUNCTION GENERATOR THREE POINT SYNTHESIS
C  ME0035(A1,A2,A3,A4,A5,A6,B1,B2,B3,B4,J5)
C
C  THIS SUBROUTINE PERFORMS A THREE POINT SYNTHESIS OF A FOURBAR
C  FUNCTION GENERATOR, REPORTING LINK LENGTHS AND CONFIGURATION.
C  THE METHOD USED IS EXPLAINED IN SECTION 4-2, P100,
C  "ELEMENTS OF MECHANICAL ANALYSIS", MISCHKE, ADDISON-WESLEY PUB CO.
C
C  CALL LIST VARIABLES
C
C  A1=INPUT ANGLE ALPHA OF FIRST PRECISION POINT,RAD
C  A2=OUTPUT ANGLE BETA OF FIRST PRECISION POINT,RAD
C  A3=INPUT ANGLE ALPHA OF SECOND PRECISION POINT, RAD
C  A4=OUTPUT ANGLE BETA OF SECOND PRECISION POINT, RAD
C  A5=INPUT ANGLE ALPHA OF THIRD  PRECISION POINT, RAD
C
C  A6=OUTPUT ANGLE BETA OF THIRD  PRECISION POINT, RAD
C  B1=CRANK VECTOR LENGTH
C  B2=COUPLER VECTOR LENGTH
C  B3=FOLLOWER VECTOR LENGTH
C  B4=GROUNDED LINK VECTOR LENGTH, UNITY
C  J5=1   UNCROSSED TOP CONFIGURATION
C    =2   CROSSED TOP CONFIGURATION
C    =3   UNCROSSED BOTTOM CONFIGURATION
C    =4   CROSSED BOTTOM CONFIGURATION
C
   DEL1=COS(A1)-COS(A2)
   DEL2=COS(A1)-COS(A3)
```

```
      DEL3=COS(B1)-COS(B2)
      DEL4=COS(B1)-COS(B3)
      DEL5=COS(A1-B1)-COS(A2-B2)
      DEL6=COS(A1-B1)-COS(A3-B3)
      DDEL1=(DEL2*DEL5-DEL1*DEL6)/(DEL1*DEL4-DEL2*DEL3)
      DDEL3=(DEL4*DEL5-DEL3*DEL6)/(DEL1*DEL4-DEL2*DEL3)
      IF(DDEL1)4,1,1
    1 IF(DDEL3)3,2,2
    2 J=1
      DDEL2=COS(A1-B1)+DDEL1*COS(B1)-DDEL3*COS(A1)
      GO TO 7
    3 J=2
      DDEL3=-DDEL3
      DDEL2=-COS(A1-B1)-DDEL1*COS(B1)-DDEL3*COS(A1)
      GO TO 7
    4 IF(DDEL3)6,5,5
    5 J=4
      DDEL1=-DDEL1
      DDEL2=-COS(A1-B1)+DDEL1*COS(B1)+DDEL3*COS(A1)
      GO TO 7
    6 J=3
      DDEL1=-DDEL1
      DDEL3=-DDEL3
      DDEL2=COS(A1-B1)-DDEL1*COS(B1)+DDEL3*COS(A1)
    7 RHO1=1./DDEL1
      RHO3=1./DDEL3
      RHO2=SQRT(ABS(1.+RHO1*RHO1+RHO3*RHO3-2.*RHO1*RHO3*DDEL2))
      RHO4=1.
      RETURN
      END
```

SUBROUTINE ME0036

```
      SUBROUTINE ME0036(X1,X2,X3,X4,X5,Y4,Y5,A4,A5,B4,B5,
     1A1,A2,A3,B1,B2,B3,Y1,Y2,Y3)
C
C     ANGLE-FUNCTION RELATIONS FOR FUNCTION GENERATORS
C     ME0036(A1,A2,A3,A4,A5,A6,A7,A8,A9,A10,A11,
C     B1,B2,B3,B4,B5,B6,B7,B8,B9)                          MISCHKE
C     THIS SUBROUTINE COMPUTES THE INPUT ANGLE AND OUTPUT ANGLE OR
C     DISPLACEMENT CORRESPONDING TO THE PRECISION POINTS, AND PROVIDES
C     THE VALUES OF THE DEPENDENT VARIABLE Y1,Y2,Y3 AT PRECISION POINTS.
C     IT ALSO PROVIDES THE VALUES OF THE DEPENDENT VARIABLE Y1,Y2,Y3
C     AT THE PRECISION POINTS. ADDITIONAL INFORMATION CONTAINED IN
C     SUPPLEMENTS P38 AND P39 OF "COMPUTERS IN ENGINEERING DESIGN
C     EDUCATION", 1 APRIL 1966, PUBLICATIONS DISTRIBUTION OFFICE,
C     UNIVERSITY OF MICHIGAN, ANN ARBOR.
C
C     CALLING PROGRAM REQUIREMENTS
C
C     PROVIDE A SUBROUTINE FUNCT(X,Y) WHERE X IS THE INDEPENDENT
C     VARIABLE OF FUNCTION TO BE GENERATED AND Y IS THE DEPENDENT
C     VARIABLE OF FUNCTION TO BE GENERATED.
C
C     CALL LIST VARIABLES
C     A1=VALUE OF INDEPENDENT VARIABLE X1 AT FIRST PRECISION POINT
C     A2=VALUE OF INDEPENDENT VARIABLE X2 AT SECOND PRECISION POINT
C     A3=VALUE OF INDEPENDENT VARIABLE X3 AT THIRD PRECISION POINT
C     A4=VALUE OF INDEPENDENT VARIABLE AT EXTREME LEFT OF INPUT DIAL
C     A5=VALUE OF INDEPENDENT VARIABLE AT EXTREME RIGHT OF INPUT DIAL
C
C     A6=VALUE OF DEPENDENT VARIABLE AT EXTREME LEFT OF OUTPUT SCALE
C     A7=VALUE OF DEPENDENT VARIABLE AT EXTREME RIGHT OF OUTPUT SCALE
C     A8=INPUT ANGLE CORRESPONDING TO A4
C     A9=INPUT ANGLE CORRESPONDING TO A5
C     A10=OUTPUT VARIABLE CORRESPONDING TO A6
C     A11=OUTPUT VARIABLE CORRESPONDING TO A7
```

192

```
C
C      B1=INPUT ANGLE CORRESPONDING TO A1
C      B2=INPUT ANGLE CORRESPONDING TO A2
C      B3=INPUT ANGLE CORRESPONDING TO A3
C      B4=OUTPUT VARIABLE CORRESPONDING TO A1
C      B5=OUTPUT VARIABLE CORRESPONDING TO A2
C
C      B6=OUTPUT VARIABLE CORRESPONDING TO A3
C      B7=VALUE OF DEPENDENT VARIABLE Y1 CORRESPONDING TO A1
C      B8=VALUE OF DEPENDENT VARIABLE Y2 CORRESPONDING TO A2
C      B9=VALUE OF DEPENDENT VARIABLE Y3 CORRESPONDING TO A3
C
       CALL FUNCT(X1,Y1)
       CALL FUNCT(X2,Y2)
       CALL FUNCT(X3,Y3)
       A1=A5-(A5-A4)*(X5-X1)/(X5-X4)
       A2=A5-(A5-A4)*(X5-X2)/(X5-X4)
       A3=A5-(A5-A4)*(X5-X3)/(X5-X4)
       B1=B5-(B5-B4)*(Y5-Y1)/(Y5-Y4)
       B2=B5-(B5-B4)*(Y5-Y2)/(Y5-Y4)
       B3=B5-(B5-B4)*(Y5-Y3)/(Y5-Y4)
       RETURN
       END
```

SUBROUTINE ME0053

```
       SUBROUTINE ME0053(P,RI,D,BI,BO,C1,C2,SI,SO,R)
       R=RI+(BI*C1*C1+2.*BO*C1*C2+BO*C2*C2)/(2.*(BO*C2+BI*C1))
       RO=RI+C1+C2
       A=BI*C1+BO*C2
       DENOM=BI*ALOG((RI+C1)/RI)+BO*ALOG(RO/(RI+C1))
       RR=(BI*C1+BO*C2)/DENOM
       E=R-RR
       HO=RO-RR
       HI=RR-RI
       SI=P/A+P*(R+D)*HI/(A*E*RI)
       SO=P/A-P*(R+D)*HO/(A*E*RO)
       RETURN
       END
```

SUBROUTINE ROOT1

```
       SUBROUTINE ROOT1(I,XLEFT,XRIGHT,FF,XX,XL,XR,ROOT,K,L)
C
C      ROOTFINDING BY INTERVAL HALVING
C      ROOT1(I1,A2,A3,A4,B1,B2,B3,B4,J5,J6)
C          THIS SUBROUTINE DETERMINES THE ZERO PLACE OF A FUNCTION USING
C          THE INTERVAL HALVING METHOD. IT REQUIRES SPECIFICATION OF
C          PRESENT LIMITS OF INTERVAL OF UNCERTAINTY AND FRACTIONAL
C          REDUCTION OF INTERVAL DESIRED. IT RETURNS THE ABSCISSA OF THE
C          ZERO PLACE, NEW LIMITS ON INTERVAL OF UNCERTAINTY, LOCALE OF
C          SECOND ROOT IF PRESENT, NUMBER OF ROOTS SUSPECTED, AND AN
C          ERROR SIGNAL. A CONVERGENCE MONITOR CAN BE PRINTED IF DESIRED.
C          THE SUBROUTINE SEARCHES THE VICINITY OF THE SMALLEST ROOT.
C          MORE THAN FIVE ROOTS IN INTERVAL COULD CONFUSE THIS SUBROUTINE.
C      CALLING PROGRAM REQUIREMENTS
C          PROVIDE A SUBROUTINE EQUAT1(X,Y) WHICH IS CALLED BY ROOT1,
C          RETURNING AN ORDINATE Y CORRESPONDING TO ABSCISSA X.
C
C      CALL LIST VARIABLES
C
C          I1=0 CONVERGENCE MONITOR DOES NOT PRINT
C            =1 CONVERGENCE MONITOR WILL PRINT
C          A2=INITIAL LOWER LIMIT OF INTERVAL OF UNCERTAINTY
```

```
C          A3=INITIAL UPPER LIMIT OF INTERVAL OF UNCERTAINTY
C          A4=FRACTIONAL REDUCTION IN INTERVAL OF UNCERTAINTY DESIRED
C
C          B1=ABSCISSA OF SMALLEST ZERO PLACE OF EQUAT1
C          B2=FINAL LOWER LIMIT OF INTERVAL OF UNCERTAINTY
C          B3=FINAL UPPER LIMIT OF INTERVAL OF UNCERTAINTY
C          B4=LOCALE OF ANOTHER ROOT IF SUSPECTED
C          J5=0  NO ROOTS IN INITIAL INTERVAL
C            =1  ONE ROOT IN INITIAL INTERVAL
C            =2  TWO ROOTS IN INITIAL INTERVAL
C            .
C            .
C            .
C          J6=1  ERROR RETURN SIGNAL, DEFECTIVE CALL,MESSAGE PRINTED
C            =2  ERROR RETURN SIGNAL, SUBROUTINE HIT MAXIMUM FIVE TIMES
C            =3  ERROR RETURN SIGNAL, EXACT ROOT FOUND
C
C     ..... INITIALIZE .....
C
      DIMENSION X(22),Y(11),ROOTS(11)
      NN=0
      L=0
      N=0
      K=0
      DO 100 J=1,11
      ROOTS(J)=0.
      X(J+1)=0.
      Y(J)=0.
      X(J)=0.
  100 CONTINUE
C
C     ..... TEST THAT SECOND AND THIRD ARGUMENTS ARE PROPER .....
C
      IF(XRIGHT-XLEFT)5,5,7
    5 WRITE(3,6)
    6 FORMAT(' *****ERROR MESSAGE SUBROUTINE ROOT1*****',/,
     1' A3 IS NOT GREATER THAN A2')
      L=1
      RETURN
C
C     ..... TEST THAT FOURTH ARGUMENT IS PROPER .....
C
    7 IF(FF-1.)10,80,80
   10 IF(FF)80,80,11
   80 WRITE(3,9)FF
    9 FORMAT(' *****ERROR MESSAGE SUBROUTINE ROOT1*****',/,
     1' VALUE OF A4,',E15.7,', IS NOT WITHIN RANGE 0 TO 1')
      L=1
      RETURN
C
C     ..... TEST THAT FIRST ARGUMENT IS PROPER .....
C
   11 IF(I)1,2,2
    2 IF(I-1)8,8,1
    1 WRITE(3,4)I
    4 FORMAT(' *****ERROR MESSAGE SUBROUTINE ROOT1*****',/,
     1' VALUE OF I1,',I3,', IS NOT 0 OR 1')
      L=1
      RETURN
C
C     ..... EVALUATE FUNCTION AT ELEVEN ORDINATES .....
C
    8 DELTA=(XRIGHT-XLEFT)/10.
      XL=XLEFT
      XR=XRIGHT
      XX=XLEFT
      X(1)=XLEFT
      CALL EQUAT1(XX,YY)
      NN=NN+1
      IF(YY)30,31,30
   31 K=K+1
      X2=XX
      XL=XX
```

194

```
          XR=XX
          FFF=0.
          L=3
          X(K+11)=XX
          GO TO 52
   30     Y(1)=YY
          DO 20 J=1,10
          XX=XX+DELTA
          CALL EQUAT1(XX,YY)
          NN=NN+1
          X(J+1)=XX
          Y(J+1)=YY
C
C         ..... EVERY CHANGE IN SIGN IS AT LEAST ONE ROOT .....
C
          IF(Y(J+1))21,22,23
   21     M=-1
          GO TO 24
   22     K=K+1
          X(K+11)=XX
          X2=XX
          XL=XX
          XR=XX
          FFF=0.
          L=3
          GO TO 52
   23     M=1
   24     IF(Y(J))25,27,27
   25     M=M-1
          GO TO 28
   27     M=M+1
   28     IF(M)20,26,20
   26     K=K+1
          IF(K-1)61,60,61
   60     XL=X(J)
          XR=X(J+1)
   61     ROOTS(K)=X(J)-(Y(J)*X(J+1)-Y(J)*X(J))/(Y(J+1)-Y(J))
   20     CONTINUE
C
C         ..... IF THERE ARE NO ROOTS, RETURN .....
C
          IF(K)32,32,33
   32     RETURN
   33     IF(I-1)103,104,104
C
C         ..... WRITE CONVERGENCE MONITOR HEADING, DISPLAY COARSE SURVEY.....
C
  104     WRITE(3,50)(X(J),J=1,11),(Y(J),J=1,11)
   50     FORMAT('1CONVERGENCE MONITOR SUBROUTINE ROOT1',//,
         1' COARSE SURVEY OF FUNCTION',//,
         2' X ',11E11.3,/,
         3' Y ',11E11.3,//,
         1'          XL              F              XR          K ROOT(1)
         2 ROOT(2)    ROOT(3)    ROOT(4)    ROOT(5)')
C
C         ..... COMMENCE INTERVAL HALVING TO LOCATE FIRST ROOT .....
C
  103     X2=(XL+XR)/2.
          CALL EQUAT1(XL,F1)
          NN=NN+1
          CALL EQUAT1(XR,F3)
          NN=NN+1
          DO 300 J=1,100
          CALL EQUAT1(X2,F2)
          NN=NN+1
          ROOTS(1)=X2
C
C         ..... WRITE CONVERGENCE MONITOR IF REQUIRED .....
C
          IF(I-1)70,71,70
   71     WRITE(3,51)XL,F2,XR ,K,(ROOTS(KK),KK=1,5)
   51     FORMAT(1X,3E16.7,I5,5F11.3)
   70     IF(F2)200,201,202
```

195

```
  200 K1=-1
      GO TO 203
  202 K1=1
  203 IF(F1)204,211,205
  204 K1=K1-1
      GO TO 206
  205 K1=K1+1
  206 IF(K1)207,208,207
  207 XL=X2
      F1=F2
  209 X2=(XL+XR)/2.
      GO TO 210
  208 XR=X2
      ROOTS(1)=X2
      F3=F2
      GO TO 209
  210 IF((XR-XL)-(XRIGHT-XLEFT)*FF)220,220,300
  300 CONTINUE
  201 XX=X2
      XL=X2
      XR=X2
      GO TO 220
  211 XX=XL
      XR=XL
      GO TO 220
  220 FFF=(XR-XL)/(XRIGHT-XLEFT)
C
C     ..... COMPLETE CONVERGENCE MONITOR IF REQUIRED, RETURN .....
C
   52 IF(I-1)54,92,54
   92 WRITE(3,53)XLEFT,XRIGHT,X2,XL,XR,FF,FFF,K,L,NN
   53 FORMAT(/,
     1' INITIAL LOWER LIMIT OF INTERVAL OF UNCERTAINTY........',E15.7,/,
     2' INITIAL UPPER LIMIT OF INTERVAL OF UNCERTAINTY........',E15.7,/,
     3' ABSCISSA OF ZERO PLACE OF EQUAT1 .....................',E15.7,/,
     4' FINAL LOWER LIMIT ON INTERVAL OF UNCERTAINTY .........',E15.7,/,
     5' FINAL UPPER LIMIT ON INTERVAL OF UNCERTAINTY .........',E15.7,/,
     6/,
     7' FRACTIONAL REDUCTION OF INTERVAL SPECIFIED ...........',F15.7,/,
     8' FRACTIONAL REDUCTION OF INTERVAL OBTAINED ............',F15.7,/,
     9' NUMBER OF ROOTS IN INITIAL INTERVAL ..................',I15,/,
     1' ERROR SIGNAL .........................................',I15,/,
     2' NUMBER OF FUNCTION EVALUATIONS EXPENDED IN SEARCH.....',I15)
   54 XX=X2
      IF(K-1)55,55,56
   56 ROOT=ROOTS(2)
      RETURN
   55 ROOT=X2
      RETURN
      END
```

SUBROUTINE YASORT

```
      SUBROUTINE YASORT(N,X,Y)
      DIMENSION X(100),Y(100)
      NN=0
      K=N-1
    5 DO 100 I=1,K
      IF(Y(I+1)-Y(I))1,1,2
    2 SAVEX=X(I)
      SAVEY=Y(I)
      X(I)=X(I+1)
      Y(I)=Y(I+1)
      X(I+1)=SAVEX
      Y(I+1)=SAVEY
      NN=NN+1
```

```
      1 CONTINUE
    100 CONTINUE
        IF(NN)4,4,3
      3 NN=0
        GO TO 5
      4 RETURN
        END
```

SUBROUTINE PENAL

```
        SUBROUTINE PENAL(N,GOOD,X,Y)
        DIMENSION GOOD(9),X(9)
        Y=0.
        DO 100 I=1,N
        Y=Y+(GOOD(I)-X(I))*(GOOD(I)-X(I))
    100 CONTINUE
        Y=-Y
        RETURN
        END
```

appendix

4

REFERENCES

USE OF COMPUTERS IN ENGINEERING EDUCATION

1. Katz, D.L. and E.I. Organick, *Use of Computers in Engineering Education,* First Annual Report, Project on Computers in Engineering Education, Ann Arbor, Mich.: University of Michigan (August 1960), 596 pp.

2. Katz, D.L., E.I. Organick, S.O. Navarro, and B. Carnahan, *Use of Computers in Engineering Education,* Second Annual Report, Project on Computers in Engineering Education, Ann Arbor, Mich.: University of Michigan (December 1961), 302 pp.

3. Katz, D.L., B. Carnahan, E.I. Organick, and S.O. Navarro, *Use of Computers in Engineering Education,* Final Report, Project on Computers in Engineering Education, Ann Arbor, Mich.: University of Michigan (January 1963), 800 pp.

4. ECAC-ECRC Information Systems Committee, "Computers in Engineering Education," *J. Eng. Ed.,* Vol. 56, No. 8 (1966), p. 319.

5. Mischke, Charles R., *Preparing the Undergraduate for Computer-Aided Design,* Proceedings of the Conference on the Impact of Computers on Education in Engineering Design, University of Illinois at Chicago Circle (21–23 April 1966).

6. Katz, D.L. and B. Carnahan, "The Place of Computers in Engineering Education," *J. Eng. Educ.,* Vol. 56, No. 8 (1966), p. 293.

SIMULATION

7. Chorafas, Dimitris N., *Systems and Simulation,* New York: Academic Press (1965).

8. Conway, R.W., "Some Tactical Problems in Digital Simulation," *Management Science,* Vol. 10, No. 1 (1963), pp. 47–61.

9. Conway, R.W., B.M. Johnson, and W.L. Maxwell, "Some Problems in Digital Simulation," *Management Science,* Vol. 6, No. 1 (1959), pp. 92–110.

10. Ehrenfeld, S. and S. Ben-Tuvia, "The Efficiency of Statistical Simulation Procedures," *Technometrics*, Vol. 4, No. 2 (1962), pp. 257–275.

11. Forrester, J.W., *Industrial Dynamics*, Cambridge, Mass.: MIT Press (1961).

12. Hammersley, J.M. and D.C. Handscomb, *Monte Carlo Methods*, New York: John Wiley & Sons, Inc. (1964).

13. Harling, John, "Simulation Techniques in Operations Research—A Review," *Operations Research*, Vol. 6 (1958), pp. 307–319.

14. Hauser, N., N.N. Barish, and S. Ehrenfeld, "Design Problems in a Process Control Simulation," *The Journal of Industrial Engineering*, Vol. 17, No. 2 (1966), pp. 79–86.

15. McMillan, C. and R.F. Gonzales, *Systems Analysis—A Computer Approach to Decision Models*, Homewood, Ill.: Richard D. Irwin, Inc. (1965).

16. Meyer, H.A., ed., *Symposium on Monte Carlo Methods*, New York: John Wiley & Sons, Inc. (1956).

17. Shreider, Y.A., ed., *Method of Statistical Testing (Monte Carlo Method)*, New York: Elsevier (1964).

18. Tocher, K.D., *The Art of Simulation*, Princeton, N.J.: D. Van Nostrand Company (1963).

19. Freeman, D.E., "Programming Languages Ease Digital Simulation," *Control Eng.*, Vol. 11, No. 11 (1964), pp. 103–106.

20. Gordon, G., "A General Purpose Systems Simulator," *IBM Systems Journal*, Vol. 1, No. 1 (1962), pp. 18–32.

21. Herscovitch, H. and T.H. Schneider, "An Expanded General Purpose Simulator," *IBM Systems Journal*, Vol. 4, No. 3 (1965), pp. 174–183.

22. Markowitz, H.M., B. Hausner, and H.W. Karr, *SIMSCRIPT: A Simulation Programming Language*, Englewood Cliffs, N.J.: Prentice-Hall, Inc. (1963).

23. *Control and Simulation Language*, Introductory and Reference Manuals, London: Esso Petroleum Co. Ltd., IBM United Kingdom.

24. Brennen, R.D. and R.N. Linebarger, "A Survey of Digital Simulator Programs," *Simulation*, Vol. 3, No. 6 (1964).

25. Brennen, R.D. and R.N. Linebarger, "An Evaluation of Digital Analog Simulator Languages," *IFIP Proceedings*, Vol. 2 (1965).

26. Clancey, John J. and Mark S. Fineberg, "Digital Simulation Languages: A Critique and a Guide," *AFIPS Conference Proceedings*, Vol. 27, Part I (1965), pp. 23–36.

27. Harnett, R.T., et al., *MIDAS Programming Guide*, AD430892, Wright-Patterson Air Force Base (1964).

28. Shannon, Paul T., et al., "Computer Simulation of a Sulfuric Acid Plant," *Chem. Eng. Progr.*, Vol. 62 (1966), pp. 49–59.

29. "Ethyl Chloride—Shell Development Process," *Petroleum Refiner*, Vol. 40, No. 1 (1961), p. 241.

30. Naylor, T.H., J.L. Balintfy, D.S. Burdick, and K. Chu, *Computer Simulation Techniques*, New York: John Wiley & Sons, Inc. (1966).

31. Tocher, K.D., "Review of Simulation Languages," *Operations Research Quarterly* (1965).

32. *Bibliography on Simulation*, IBM Publication No. 320-0924-0, Poughkeepsie, N.Y.

33. Welch, H.J., *The Use of Computers in Civil Engineering Education*, Ann Arbor, Mich.: College of Engineering, University of Michigan (1963).

34. Miller, C. L., *COGO, Department of Civil Engineering Report*, Cambridge, Mass., Massachusetts Institute of Technology (1961).

35. Gordon, G., "A General Purpose Systems Simulation Program," *Proceedings of the Eastern Joint Computer Conference*, Washington, D.C.: Macmillan Company (1961).

36. Hart, D.E. and B. Hargreaves, "DYANA-A Computer Program for the Automatic Analysis of Dynamic Systems," *Proc. NEC*, Vol. 16 (1960), pp. 308–315.

37. Fenves, S.J., R.D. Logcher, S.P. Mauch, and K.F. Reinschmidt, *STRESS-A User's Manual*, Cambridge, Mass.: MIT Press (1964).

38. Farber, D.J., R.E. Griswold, and I.P. Polonsky, "Snobol, A String Manipulation Language," *Journ. of the ACM*, Vol. 11, No. 2 (January 1964), pp. 21–30.

39. The Research Laboratory of Electronics and the Computation Center, *An Introduction to COMIT Programming*, Massachussetts Institute of Technology (1961).

40. Newell, A., ed., *Information Processing Language-V Manual*, Englewood Cliffs, N.J.: Prentice-Hall, Inc. (1961).

OPTIMIZATION : TERMINOLOGY

41. Hadley, G., *Linear Algebra*, Reading, Mass: Addison-Wesley Publishing Co., Inc. (1961), Ch. 6.

42. Hancock, H., *Theory of Maxima and Minima*, Boston: Ginn and Company (1917) (Dover, 1960).

43. Wilde, Douglass J., *Optimum Seeking Methods*, Englewood Cliffs, N.J.: Prentice-Hall, Inc. (1964), Ch. 3.

44. Zoutendijk, G., *Methods of Feasible Directions*, New York: Elsevier Publishing Company (1960), Part I.

OPTIMIZATION : FUNCTION EXTREMUM WITHOUT CONSTRAINTS

45. Brooks, Samuel H., "A Discussion of Random Methods for Seeking Maxima," *Operations Research*, Vol. 6, No. 2 (March 1958), pp. 244–251.

46. Brooks, Samuel H., "A Comparison of Maximum Seeking Methods," *Operations Research*, Vol. 2, No. 4 (July 1959), pp. 430–457.

47. Cauchy, A.L., "Méthode générale pour la resolution des systèmes d'équations simultanées," *C.R. Acad. Sci. Paris*, Vol. 25 (1847), pp. 536–538.

48. Crockett, J.B. and H. Chernoff, "Gradient Method of Maximization," *Pacific J. Math.*, Vol. 5 (1955), pp. 33–50.

49. Curry, H.B., "The Method of Steepest Descent for Nonlinear Minimization Problems," *Quart. Appl. Math.*, Vol. 2, No. 3 (1944), pp. 258–261.

50. Davidon, William C., "Variable Metric Method for Minimization," Argonne National Laboratory, ANL-5990 Rev. (November 1959).

51. Hooke, Robert and T.A. Jeeves, "Comment on Brooks' Discussion of Random Methods," *Operations Research*, Vol. 6 (1958), pp. 881–882.

52. Hooke, Robert and T.A. Jeeves, "Direct Search Solution of Numerical and Statistical Problems," *J. Assoc. Comp. Mach.*, Vol. 8, No. 2 (April 1962), pp. 212–229.

53. Johnson, S.M., "Optimal Search for a Maximum is Fibonaccian," The RAND Corp., P-856 (1956).

54. Kiefer, J., "Sequential Minimax Search for a Maximum," *Proc. Amer. Math. Soc.*, Vol. 4 (1953), pp. 502–506.

55. Krolak, P. and L. Cooper, "An Extension of Fibonaccian Search to Several Variables," *Comm. ACM*, Vol. 6, No. 10 (October 1963), pp. 639–641.

56. Shah, B.V., R.J. Buehler, and O. Kempthorne, "Some Algorithms for Minimizing a Function of Several Variables," *J. SIAM*, Vol. 12, No. 1 (March 1964), pp. 74–92.

57. Wilde, Douglass J., *Optimum Seeking Methods*, Englewood Cliffs, N.J.: Prentice-Hall, Inc. (1964).

58. Westervelt, Frank, "Analysis and Synthesis of Engineering Systems by Digital Computer Programming," ASME Paper No. 62-WA-214, New York.

OPTIMIZATION: LINEAR PROGRAMMING

59. Dantzig, George B., *Linear Programming and Extensions*, Princeton, N.J.: Princeton University Press (1963).

60. Gass, Saul I., *Linear Programming: Methods and Applications*, 2nd Ed., New York: McGraw-Hill Book Company (1964).

61. Hadley, G., *Linear Programming*, Reading, Mass.: Addison-Wesley Publishing Co., Inc. (1962).

62. Riley, Vera and Saul I. Gass, *Bibliography on Linear Programming and Related Techniques*, Baltimore: Johns Hopkins Press (1958).

OPTIMIZATION: DYNAMIC PROGRAMMING

63. Aris, Rutherford, *Discrete Dynamic Programming*, New York: Blaisdell (1964).

64. Bellman, Richard E., "The Theory of Dynamic Programming," Ch. 11 in E.F. Beckenbach, ed., *Modern Mathematics for the Engineer*, New York: McGraw-Hill Book Company (1956).

65. Bellman, Richard E. and Stuart E. Dreyfus, *Applied Dynamic Programming*, Princeton, N.J.: Princeton University Press (1962).

66. Bellman, Richard E. and Rebecca Karush, "Dynamic Programming: A Bibliography of Theory and Application," The RAND Corporation, RM-3051-PR (February 1964).

67. Dreyfus, S.E., "Introduction to Dynamic Programming," The RAND Corporation, P-1369 (4 June 1958).

OPTIMIZATION: NONLINEAR PROGRAMMING

Surveys

68. Dorn, W.S., "Nonlinear Programming—A Survey," *Management Science*, Vol. 9 (1963), pp. 171–208.

69. Kelley, Henry J., "Method of Gradients," Ch. 6 in G. Leitmann, ed., *Optimization Techniques with Applications to Aerospace Systems*, New York: Academic Press (1962).

70. Spang, H.A., III, "A Review of Minimization Techniques for Nonlinear Functions," *SIAM Review*, Vol. 4 (1962), pp. 343–365.

71. Wolfe, Philip, "Recent Developments in Nonlinear Programming," in Alt and Rubinoff, eds., *Advances in Computers*, III, New York: Academic Press (1962).

72. Wolfe, Philip, "The Present Status of Nonlinear Programming," in Graves and Wolfe, eds., *Recent Advances in Mathematical Programming*, New York: McGraw-Hill Book Company (1963).

73. Wolfe, Philip, "Methods of Nonlinear Programming," in Graves and Wolfe, eds., *Recent Advances in Mathematical Programming*, New York: McGraw-Hill Book Company (1963).

Methods

74. Arrow, Kenneth L. and Leonid Hurwicz, "Reduction of Constrained Maxima to Saddle-Point Problems," *Proceedings of the Third Berkeley Symposium on Mathematical Statistics and Probability*, Berkeley and Los Angeles: University of California Press (1950).

75. Arrow, Kenneth L. and Leonid Hurwicz, "Gradient Methods for Constrained Maxima," *Operations Research*, Vol. 5 (1957), pp. 258–265.

76. Arrow, Kenneth L., Leonid Hurwicz, and H. Uzawa, *Studies in Linear and Nonlinear Programming*, Stanford: Cal.: Stanford University Press (1960).

77. Brown, R.R., "A Generalized Computer Procedure for the Design of Optimum Systems, Part I and Part II," *AIEE Transactions, Comm. and Elect.*, Vol. 78, Part I (1959), pp. 285–293.

78. Carroll, Charles W., "The Created Response Technique for Optimizing Nonlinear Restrained Systems," *Operations Research*, Vol. 9 (1961), pp. 169–184.

79. Dennis, Jack B., *Mathematical Programming and Electrical Networks*, Cambridge, Mass.: MIT Press (1959).

80. Dorn, W.S., "On Lagrange Multipliers and Inequalities," *Operations Research*, No. 9 (1961), pp. 95–104.

81. Forsythe, George E., "Computing Constrained Minima with Lagrange Multipliers," *J. SIAM*, Vol. 3 (1955), pp. 173–178.

82. Griffith, R.E. and R.A. Stewart, "A Nonlinear Programming Technique for the Optimization of Continuous Processing Systems," *Management Science*, Vol. 7, pp. 379–392 (1961).

83. Hadley, G., *Nonlinear and Dynamic Programming*, Reading, Mass.: Addison-Wesley Publishing Co., Inc. (1964).

84. Fritz, John, "Extremum Problems with Inequalities as Subsidiary Conditions," in *Studies and Essays* (Courant Anniversary Volume), New York: Interscience Publishers, Inc. (1948).

85. Kelley, J.E., Jr., "The Cutting Plane Method for Solving Convex Programs," *J. SIAM*, Vol. 8 (1960), pp. 703–712.

86. Klingman, W.R. and D.M. Himmelblau, "Nonlinear Programming with the Aid of a Multiple-Gradient Summation Technique," *Jour. of the ACM*, Vol. 11, No. 4 (October 1964), pp. 400–415.

87. Kuhn, H.W. and A.W. Tucker, "Nonlinear Programming," in J. Neyman, ed., *Proceedings of the Second Berkeley Symposium on Mathematical Statistics and Probability*, Berkeley and Los Angeles: University of California Press (1951).

88. Rosen, J.B., "The Gradient Projection Method for Nonlinear Programming: Part I, Linear Constraints," *J. SIAM*, Vol. 8 (1960), pp. 181–217.

89. Rosen, J.B., "The Gradient Projection Method for Nonlinear Programming: Part II, Nonlinear Constraints," *J. SIAM*, Vol. 9 (1961), pp. 514–532.

90. Rosenbrock, H.H., "Automatic Method for Finding the Greatest or Least Value of a Function," *The Computer Journal*, Vol. 3, No. 3 (1960), pp. 175–184.

91. Tucker, A.W., "Linear and Nonlinear Programming," *Operations Research*, Vol. 5 (1957), pp. 244–257.

92. Wilde, Douglass J., "Differential Calculus in Nonlinear Programming," *Operations Research*, Vol. 10 (1962), pp. 764–773.

93. Wilson, R.B., *A Simplicial Algorithm for Concave Programming*, Doctoral Dissertation, Graduate School of Business Administration, Harvard University (1963).

94. Wolfe, Philip, "Accelerating the Cutting Plane Method for Nonlinear Programming," *J. SIAM*, Vol. 9 (1961), pp. 481–488.

95. Wolfe, Philip, "Some Simplex-Like Nonlinear Programming Procedures," *Operations Research*, Vol. 10 (1962), pp. 438–447.

96. Zoutendijk, G., *Methods of Feasible Directions*, New York: Elsevier (1960).

OPTIMIZATION: MACROSCOPIC STRATEGIES

97. Aris, R., G.L. Nemhauser, and D.J. Wilde, "Optimization of Multistage Cyclic and Branching Systems by Serial Procedures," *A. I. Ch. E. Journal*, Vol. 10, No. 11 (November 1964), pp. 913ff.

98. Jackson, R., "Some Algebraic Properties of Optimization Problems in Complex Chemical Plants," *Chem. Eng. Sci.*, Vol. 19, No. 1 (January 1964), pp. 19–31.

99. Mitten, L. and G. Nemhauser, "Multistage Optimization," *Chem. Eng. Progr.*, Vol. 59, No. 1 (January 1963), pp. 52ff.

100. Rudd, D.F., "The Logical Structure of Design Equations," Unpublished Notes, Madison, Wisconsin: University of Wisconsin, Department of Chemical Engineering.

101. Rudd, D.F., "Sensitivity and the Analysis of Large Processing Systems," Unpublished Notes, Madison, Wisconsin: University of Wisconsin, Department of Chemical Engineering.

102. Rudd, D.F. and Luis P. Echeverria, "Economic Sensitivity and Decomposition in Process Design," Unpublished Notes, Madison, Wisconsin: University of Wisconsin, Department of Chemical Engineering.

103. Rudd, D.F. and C.C. Watson, *Strategy in Process Engineering*, in Preparation.

104. Steward, Donald V., "On an Approach to Techniques for the Analysis of the Structure of Large Systems of Equations," *SIAM Review*, Vol. 4, No. 4 (October 1962), pp. 321–342.

105. Wilde, D.J., "Strategies for Optimizing Macrosystems," *Chem. Eng. Progr.*, Vol. 61, No. 3 (March 1965), pp. 86–93.

NUMERICAL METHODS

106. Hildebrand, F.B., *Introduction to Numerical Analysis*, New York: McGraw-Hill Book Company (1956).

107. Todd, J., ed., *A Survey of Numerical Analysis*, New York: McGraw-Hill Book Company (1962).

108. Carnahan, B., H.A. Luther, and J.O. Wilkes, *Applied Numerical Methods* (preliminary edition), New York: John Wiley & Sons, Inc. (1964).

109. Southworth, R.W., *Digital Computation and Numerical Methods*, New York: McGraw-Hill Book Company (1965).

110. McCormick, J.M. and M.G. Salvadori, *Numerical Methods in FORTRAN*, Englewood Cliffs, N.J.: Prentice-Hall, Inc. (1964).

111. Ralston, A., *A First Course in Numerical Analysis*, New York: McGraw-Hill Book Company (1965).

112. Conte, S.D., *Elementary Numerical Analysis*, New York; McGraw-Hill Book Company (1965).

113. Hamming, R.W., *Numerical Methods for Scientists and Engineers*, New York: McGraw-Hill Book Company (1962).

114. Kuo, S.S., *Numerical Methods and Computers*, Reading, Mass: Addison-Wesley Publishing Co., Inc. (1965).

115. Hagwood, J., *Numerical Methods in ALGOL*, New York: McGraw-Hill Book Company (1965).

116. McCracken, D.D. and W.S. Dorn, *Numerical Methods and FORTRAN Programming*, New York: John Wiley & Sons, Inc. (1964).

117. Barish, N.N., *Economic Analysis for Engineering and Managerial Decision Making*, New York: McGraw-Hill Book Company (1962).

118. Baumol, William J., *Economic Theory and Operations Analysis*, Englewood Cliffs, N.J.: Prentice-Hall, Inc. (1965).

119. Bullinger, Clarence E., *Engineering Economy*, New York: McGraw-Hill Book Company (1958).

120. DeGarmo, E.P., *Engineering Economy* (3rd ed.), New York: The Macmillan Company (1960).

121. Grant, E.L. and W.G. Ireson, *Principles of Engineering Economy*, New York: Ronald Press (1960).

122. Manne, Alan S., *Economic Analysis for Business Decisions*, New York: McGraw-Hill Book Company (1961).

123. Morris, William T., *The Analysis of Management Decisions*, Homewood, Ill.: Richard D. Irwin (1964).

124. Roscoe, Edwin S., *Project Economy*, Homewood, Ill.: Richard D. Irwin (1960).

125. Schweyer, Herbert E., *Analytical Models for Managerial and Engineering Economics*, New York: Reinhold Publishing Corporation (1964).

126. Taylor, George A., *Managerial and Engineering Economy: Economic Decision Making*, Princeton, N.J.: D. Van Nostrand Company (1964).

127. Thuesen, H.G. and W.J. Fabrycky, *Engineering Economy*, Englewood Cliffs, N.J.: Prentice-Hall, Inc. (1964).

MAN-COMPUTER INTERACTION

128. Sutherland, I.E., "SKETCHPAD, A Man-Machine Graphical Communication System," *AFIPS Conference Proceedings*, Vol. 23, Spring Joint Computer Conference, Spartan Books and Cleaver Hume Press (1963), p. 329.

129. Johnson, T.E., "SKETCHPAD III, A Computer Program for Drawing in Three Dimensions," *AFIPS Conference Proceedings*, Vol. 23, Spring Joint Computer Conference, Spartan Books and Cleaver Hume Press (1963), p. 347.

130. "The GM DAC-I System—Design Augmented by Computers," *General Motors Report-430*, General Motors Corporation (October 1964).

131. Corbato, F.J., "An Experimental Time-Sharing System," *Proceedings of the Spring Joint Computer Conference*, Baltimore, Maryland: Spartan Books, Inc. (1962).

132. Corbato, F.J., "The Compatible Time-Sharing System: A Programmer's Guide," Cambridge, Mass.: MIT Press (1963).

133. Fano, R.F., "The MAC System: A Progress Report," A paper presented at the Symposium on Computer Augmentation of Human Reasoning, Washington, D.C. (16 June 1964). Preceedings to be published by the Office of Naval Research.

134. Schwartz, J.I., E.G. Coffman, and Clark Weissman, "A General-Purpose Time-Sharing System," *Proceedings of the Spring Joint Computer Conference*, Baltimore, Maryland: Spartan Books, Inc. (1964).

135. *BASIC*, Hanover, New Hampshire: Dartmouth College Computation Center (June 1965).

136. Rosenberg, A., "Time-Sharing: A Static Report," *Datamation*, Vol. 12, No. 2 (1966), pp. 66–77.

137. Parkhill, D.F., *The Challenge of the Computer Utility*, Reading, Mass.: Addison-Wesley Publishing Co., Inc. (1966).

INDEX

Qualitative parameters, 37

Random-failure interval, 27
Rapid transit car, 32
Ratio, gear, 34, 102
References, 199
  engineering economics, 206
  man-computer interaction, 206
  numerical methods, 205
  optimization, 201-204
  problem-oriented languages, 201
  simulation, 199
  use of computers in engineering education, 199
Region, feasible, 13
Regional constraint, 12
Reliability, 26
  complex arrangement, 29
  elements in parallel, 28
  elements in series, 27
Ridge, 81
Risk, 24
ROOT1, 109, 176, 193
Rules:
  formating, 40
  inertia reflection, 128

Safety factor (*see* Design factor)
Sample mean (*see* Population mean)
Search, 55
  area elimination, 73
  dichotomous, 64
  exhaustive, 58
  golden section, 64
  gradient, 74, 79
  grid, 89
  interval-halving, 59
  multidimensional, 67
  pattern, 87
  sequential, 58
  sequential linear, 71
  simultaneous, 56, 58
Self-documenting decks, 41
Sequencing decks, 46

Sequential search, 58
Sequential linear search, 71
Shish-kebab inertia equivalent, 129
Simple parameters, 16
Simultaneous search, 56, 58
Speed, balancing, 32
Standard deviation, 18
Structural error, 137
Subroutine capability, 8, 47
Subroutine documentation, 50, 53
Subroutine testing, 49
Subroutines, 47
Suitable alternatives, 14
Surface:
  bimodal, 80
  merit, 13, 36, 38
  penalty, 16, 118
Synthesis, three-point, 136

Tactical figure of merit function, 14
Tax, 22
Tentative decision, 4, 6, 7
Testing, subroutine, 49
Theorem:
  Bienayme-Chebyshev, 19
  Camp-Meidell, 19
Time, 31
TMOTOR subroutine, 109
Trade-off function, 34, 36
Train:
  gear, 126
  rapid transit, 31, 102

Uncertainty, 24
Uncertainty interval, 56
Unconditional GO TO statement, 7
Unimodal function, 56
Utility function, 11

Variance, 18

Wear-out interval, 27